The
World's Fighting Planes

Fourth and completely revised edition

WILLIAM GREEN

ILLUSTRATED BY
P. ENDSLEIGH CASTLE
& DENNIS I. PUNNETT

DOUBLEDAY AND COMPANY, INC.
GARDEN CITY, NEW YORK

DOUBLEDAY EDITION 1965

MADE AND PRINTED IN GREAT BRITAIN

INTRODUCTION

A little more than five years ago the last edition of *The World's Fighting Planes* appeared, and a glance at the following pages will suffice to disclose to the reader the extent of progress in the development of combat aircraft during the half-decade that has since elapsed. This edition describes and illustrates many aircraft that five years ago would have been considered by the layman almost Wellsian in both appearance and performance, and typical of the contrasts to be found are the variable-geometry General Dynamics F-111, evolved to fulfil a vast array of tasks, and the piston-engined Douglas Skyraider which dates back to the Second World War and whose fantastic versatility the F-111 bids fair to rival in the years ahead.

The problem of continuing or discontinuing the development and production of combat aircraft and what types—if any—should be developed has become ever more complex in recent years, and dependence upon such factors as military advantage, accuracy of delivery, survival, reliability, cost, time scale, enemy capability, and, not least, public opinion, render a solution ever more difficult. Most believe, however, that there will be a continuing requirement for new and improved manned warplanes, and in this edition of *The World's Fighting Planes* a serious attempt is made to present not only those combat aircraft in service or about to enter service, but also, where possible, those under development for the 'seventies and 'eighties, such as the SAAB-37 Viggen, the VFW 1262 and the Ling-Temco-Vought A-7.

Strongly apparent is the ever-increasing diversity and extent of effort in multi-purpose fighter development, frequently embodying S.T.O.L. and even V.T.O.L. capabilities, whereas new bombers are few, although there are such notable exceptions as the TSR-2. A perusal of the pages devoted to the Soviet Union will reveal that technological advances in combat aircraft design are by no means the prerogative of what has now become known as "the West", however, although there is no substantive evidence indicating that Russian designers are devoting any more effort to the development of manned bombing systems than are their western counterparts.

Previously *The World's Fighting Planes* has included training, transport and liaison aircraft and helicopters, but in preparing this new edition it has been found necessary to be more selective, and it is thus devoted to aircraft which, in the generally accepted sense, are true *fighting* planes, the only exceptions being strategic reconnaissance aircraft, such as Lockheed's notorious U-2. Nevertheless, in order to present as complete as possible a picture of the development of the combat aircraft included, details are provided of their non-combat (e.g., training, early warning, tanker) variants. A number of lesser types, some still operational with the world's smaller air forces, have been omitted in order that the maximum coverage may be given to the newer and more important developments, and every effort has been made to provide quantitative information concerning the aircraft described, placing each type in current perspective by detailing its present operational status and listing its service users.

It is necessary in this introduction to make two further points. Firstly, while photographs and tone general arrangement drawings are used for the most part, the latter, it is felt, revealing more effectively the character of an aircraft, line drawings are used to provide visual comparison between variants of the same basic aircraft, and to illustrate obsolescent aircraft in process of being phased out of first-line service, the lesser important types, and new types currently under development or construction but yet to fly. Secondly, the specifications for aircraft of the Soviet Union are, where official details have not been revealed, based on assessments made from all available information, photographic evidence and, where applicable, information given by the Soviet authorities to the F.A.I. in claiming new international records, and these should be considered as approximations for the general guidance of the reader.

In conclusion, the author is particularly anxious to acknowledge his indebtedness to Roy M. Braybrook and Hal Andrews for their advice and assistance, and to Peter Endsleigh Castle and Dennis Punnett for the tremendous effort that they have expended in ensuring that the drawings included in this edition attained the highest possible standard of accuracy.

November 1964   WILLIAM GREEN

ACKNOWLEDGEMENTS

The sources of some of the photographs appearing in this volume are as follows (the numerals in parentheses following the page numbers indicate the position of the photographs on the page, reading from top to bottom): Air Presse, Page 22 (3); Aircent, Page 23 (3 & 4); W. Balogh, Page 135 (1), 138 (3); Serge P. Blandin, Page 8 (3), 18 (2, 3 & 4), 22 (1 & 4), 23 (2), 25 (3 & 4), 167 (2), 207 (2); Butler-Green, Page 14 (2), 88 (2), 95 (3); Flight Refuelling, Page 101 (2 & 3); Flugwelt, Page 77 (1); Flight International, Page 20 (1); H. Havelaar, Page 190 (2); R. E. Hourigan, Page 5 (2); Gerhard Joos, Page 8 (1 & 2), 34 (1), 35 (2 & 3), 211 (2), 212 (1 & 2); Lehtikuva Oy, Page 55 (1 & 2); Pierre Leyvastre, Page 140 (1); Howard Levy, Page 156 (2); Neil A. Macdougall, Page 156 (1), 165 (1), 183 (1); T. Matsuzaki, Page 128 (1), 130 (1); David W. Menard, Page 135 (2), 189 (1); Robert C. Mikesh, Page 128 (2), 149 (1), 165 (2), 177 (1 & 2), 184 (1, 2, 3 & 4); Frank B. Mormillo, Page 172 (2), 173 (1); M. Olmstead, Page 128 (4), 158 (1), 203 (1); S. P. Peltz, Page 207 (1); E. Ritaranta, Page 48 (2), 115 (1); Hanfried Schliephake, Page 205 (1); Glenn E. Smith Jr., Page 178 (2); South African Air Force, Page 20 (2); R. E. A. Taylor, Page 17 (2); E. Sekigawa, Page 138 (1 & 2), 148 (1), 149 (2), 160 (1), 168 (2), 179 (1), 182 (1), 192 (1 & 2), 201 (1), 208 (1); Michel Tiziou, Page 12 (2); U.S. Navy, Page 62 (2), 64 (1 & 2), 65 (2 & 3), 141 (1), 142 (2), 153 (1), 154 (1), 155 (1 & 2), 158 (3), 162 (4); Peter M. Warren, Page 86 (1 & 2), 99 (1); Gordon S. Williams, Page 143 (1), 146 (1), 147 (1), 148 (2), 160 (3), 166 (1 & 2), 187 (1).

CONTENTS

COMMONWEALTH CA-27 SABRE

Few in the West would question the statement that the Sabre was the outstanding combat aircraft of its generation. This accolade is not bestowed lightly, for it is no exaggeration to claim that the lack of an interceptor fighter of the Sabre's calibre in the early 'fifties could have been calamitous to United Nations forces in Korea. Still one of the most widely-used of single-seat fighters, the Sabre was manufactured in a variety of versions and in several countries, and it has been generally conceded that the best of the numerous variations on the Sabre theme was that evolved in Australia as the CA-27.

Although replacement of the CA-27 Sabre by the Mirage IIIO began during 1964, the first R.A.A.F. squadron to commence conversion being No. 75 which formerly operated Sabres alongside No. 76 Squadron as No. 81 Wing, the earlier fighter will remain in first-line operational service until 1966-67, and, in addition to No. 76 Squadron, currently equips Nos. 3 and 77 Squadrons which form No. 78 Wing at Butterworth, Malaya, and No. 78 Squadron which, during 1964, was on detachment at Ubon, Thailand.

The decision to acquire a manufacturing licence for the North American Sabre was reached by the Australian government in October 1951, six months after an Australian mission had visited NAA to investigate the possibility of adapting the fighter to meet R.A.A.F. requirements. These included demands for additional power and larger calibre armament, and the most important changes introduced by the Australian model were the replacement of the General Electric J47-GE-27 turbojet by the Rolls-Royce Avon, and the provision of twin 30-mm. Aden cannon in place of the sextet of 0.5-in. guns. These changes dictated some radical alterations to the Sabre's fuselage, for the Avon demanded a larger air intake and, weighing 400 lb. less than the American engine, had to be positioned further aft to maintain c.g. location. In order to avoid major changes to the cockpit arrangement, the extra intake was obtained by slicing the forward fuselage horizontally, inserting a 3.5-in. splice, and lowering the bottom line. As the aft-mounted engine could no longer be supported entirely by the original forward

fuselage, this had to be lengthened and the rear fuselage shortened accordingly, the latter being redesigned to support the jet pipe so that neither tailplane inertia loads nor tail unit flight loads were transferred to the engine. Some structural redesign was necessitated by the choice of Aden cannon, and only some forty per cent of the original fuselage structure remained when the Australian prototype, designated CA-26 (A94-101), flew on August 3, 1953.

Additional changes embodied by the initial production model, the CA-27 Sabre Mk. 30, included some revision of the cockpit, propylnitrate engine starting and an increase in fuel capacity, and the first of these, powered by a C.A.C.-assembled Avon R.A.7 designated Avon 20, flew on July 13, 1954, and was delivered to the R.A.A.F. a month later, on August 19, 1954. Twenty-two Sabre Mk. 30s (A94-901 to A94-922)

(Above, right) Sabre Mk. 32s of No. 3 Squadron, the first R.A.A.F. unit to operate the Commonwealth-built Sabre, and (below) a Sabre Mk. 32 (A94-947) flown by the "Red Diamonds" aerobatic team of No. 76 Squadron.

were produced, these being equipped with wing slats, and No. 3 Squadron received its first aircraft on March 1, 1956. The twenty-third production aircraft (A94-923) had the slats removed and introduced the so-called "6-3" wing leading edge, this being the first Sabre Mk. 31. Twenty-one aircraft of this type were built (during 1957-58 most Mk. 30s were brought up to Mk. 31 standards), the seventeenth and twenty-first being modified to include 70 Imp. gal. of fuel in the wing leading edges, raising internal capacity to 422 Imp. gal. Internal capacity could be augmented on the Mk. 31 by a pair of 100 or 166.5 Imp. gal. drop tanks.

The definitive production model, the Mk. 32, had the C.A.C.-built Avon 26 engine and four underwing pylons, the latter reducing leading edge fuel capacity to 60 Imp. gal. Sixty-eight Sabres of this model were built to bring total production by Commonwealth Aircraft to 112 machines.

CA-27 SABRE MK.32 SPECIFICATION

Power Plant: *One C.A.C.-built Rolls-Royce Avon 26 turbojet rated at 7,500 lb.s.t.*
Armament: *Two 30-mm. Aden cannon and two AIM-9 Sidewinder infra-red homing missiles or two 500-lb. bombs plus two 100 Imp. gal. drop tanks.*
Performance: *Max. speed, 700 m.p.h. at sea level (Mach 0.92), 672 m.p.h. at 10,000 ft., 607 m.p.h. at 38,000 ft.; average cruise, 550 m.p.h.; initial climb rate, 12,000 ft./min.; service ceiling, 55,000 ft.; combat radius, 290 mls., (with two 100 Imp. gal. drop tanks and two AAMs), 400 mls.; max. range (with two 166.5 Imp. gal. drop tanks), 1,150 mls.*
Weights: *Empty, 12,120 lb.; loaded (clean), 15,990 lb., max. (two 100 Imp. gal. drop tanks and two 500-lb. bombs), 18,650 lb.*
Dimensions: *Span, 37 ft. 1¼ in.; length, 37 ft. 6 in.; height, 14 ft. 4¾ in.; wing area, 302.26 sq. ft.*

COMMONWEALTH CA-29 MIRAGE

In 1960, the Australian government began to consider several aircraft types as potential replacements for the R.A.A.F.'s CA-27 Sabres, and in June of that year an Australian mission evaluated the Mirage IIIA-01. Subsequently, G.A.M.Dassault converted a "preseries" Mirage IIIA to take a Rolls-Royce Avon Mk. 67 turbojet in place of the standard Atar, and as the Mirage IIIO, which flew for the first time on February 13, 1961, this aircraft was examined by a further Australian mission alongside the normal Atar-powered version. The Avon 67 offered 12,530 lb.s.t. dry and 16,000 lb. with afterburning, weighed approximately 640 lb. more than the French engine but possessed a lower specific fuel consumption. The Mirage IIIO featured slightly larger air intakes (five per cent) and modified shock cone travel, and the Avon engine offered several advantages over the Atar, particularly at low altitudes. It also raised the fighter's gun-firing ceiling by some 10,000 ft., but the Australian mission evinced preference for the Atar and, before the end of 1961, the Australian government had ordered an initial batch of thirty Atar-powered Mirages for licensed construction in Australia, followed by orders for a further thirty, plus options on forty more. The options were taken up late in 1963, bringing total R.A.A.F. orders to one hundred machines.

The Australian model, which, like the "one-off" Avon-powered aircraft, is designated Mirage IIIO by the parent company, is essentially similar to the Mirage IIIE tactical strike aircraft of the Armée de l'Air (see page 22) with the Atar 09 C3 turbojet and CSF

Cyrano II fire control equipment, and will carry for the intercept rôle MATRA R.530 infra-red or radar-homing missiles. The Australian Department of Supply factories are prime contractors for the production of the Mirage, the Commonwealth Aircraft Corporation, which has applied the designation CA-29 to the type, being responsible for the manufacture of complete wing assemblies, including ailerons, the tail surfaces and tail cone, as well as for the manufacture or assembly of many other smaller components, and for the production of the Atar 09 turbojet.

The first two definitive Mirage IIIO fighters for the R.A.A.F. were built and assembled by the parent company, and after R.A.A.F. technicians had completed conversion courses with the Armée de l'Air's 2e Escadre de Chasse, the first of these (A3-1) was officially handed over to the R.A.A.F. at Villaroche on April 9, 1963, and completed navigation and fire control equipment tests at Melun-Villaroche and Cazeaux before being dismantled for air-freighting to Australia. The third and fourth Mirage IIIOs (A3-3 and -4) were shipped from France to Australia as fully-equipped major assemblies, and the first of these was flown for the first time at the Australian Department of Supply's airfield at Avalon, near Melbourne, on November 16, 1963. The next four aircraft (A3-5 to -8) were shipped in similar component form without systems and wiring installed, two more (A3-9 and -10) were shipped as last-stage sub-assemblies, and the eleventh aircraft (A3-11) was the first to be built from French-manufactured primary parts, with the sixteenth (A3-16) incorporating the first Australian-built primary parts. Commonwealth Aircraft's production of the Atar 09 was scheduled to attain eighty-five per cent of its component parts with the thirty-second engine.

Mirage training is being undertaken by No. 2 Fighter Operational Conversion Unit at Williamtown, and the first R.A.A.F. squadron to re-equip with this type is No. 75, also at Williamtown, which is scheduled to be followed by No. 76 Squadron. Fifty Mirage IIIOs are scheduled to be in R.A.A.F. service by November 1965. External stores loads of the Mirage IIIO are generally similar to those of the Mirage IIIE (see page 22) and performance is similar to that of the Mirage IIIC (see page 21).

The fourth Mirage IIIO (A3-4), the second aircraft delivered in the form of fully-equipped major assemblies.

CANADAIR CL-13 SABRE

Although the Sabre was conceived nearly twenty years ago, this remarkable fighter still provides the backbone of the interceptor and fighter-bomber equipment of many nations, and Canadian-built versions currently serve with several NATO air arms, as well as the air forces of Colombia, South Africa and Yugoslavia.

The Canadian government decided to manufacture the Sabre under licence in 1949, and in August of that year placed an order for one hundred machines with Canadair Limited. Initially, it was planned to manufacture the F-86A, and the first aircraft of this type to be built by Canadair received the designation CL-13 Sabre Mk. 1, and bearing the R.C.A.F. serial number 19101, flew on August 9, 1950. Only the one example of the Sabre Mk. 1 was completed, subsequent production machines being built to F-86E standards as Sabre Mk. 2s, the first of these (19102) flying in October 1950, a total of 350 (19102-99 and 19201-452) subsequently being delivered. The Sabre Mk. 2 was powered by the 5,200 lb.s.t. General Electric J47-GE-13 turbojet, and sixty aircraft of this type were supplied to the U.S.A.F. as F-86E-6-Can Sabres, while the 100th production airframe (19200) was selected to test the Canadian-designed Orenda turbojet, and, with a 6,000 lb.s.t. Orenda 3, became the sole example of the Sabre Mk. 3.

With the 353rd aircraft off the assembly line (19453), Canadair introduced a number of modifications to the cabin air conditioning, compass, pressurization controls, and canopy release, designating this version Sabre Mk. 4. It was originally planned that the Sabre Mk. 4 would employ the Orenda 3 turbojet but, in fact, the J47-GE-13 was retained, and

438 examples of this model (19453-890) were produced. During the early 'fifties, R.A.F. Fighter Command had evinced anxiety over its lack of swept-wing transonic fighters, and early in 1953 it had been decided to acquire Canadair Sabres, MDAP funds assisting in providing the R.A.F. with 430 aircraft. The first of these were Mk. 2s which began to reach the U.K. in October 1952, but the bulk of the Sabres delivered to the R.A.F. were Mk. 4s which re-equipped Nos. 3, 4, 20, 26, 67, 71, 93, 112, 130, and 234 Squadrons with the 2nd Tactical Air Force in Germany, and Nos. 66 and 92 Squadrons with Fighter Command.

The Canadair Sabre was finally withdrawn from R.A.F. service by June 1956, and in the following year 180 ex-R.A.F. Sabre Mk. 4s were delivered to the Italian Air Force, serving with the IVa Aerobrigata Intercettori Diurni which began to re-equip with the F-104G Starfighter during 1963, and the IIa Aerobrigata which forms a part of NATO's 5th ATAF. A further 121 ex-R.A.F. Sabre Mk. 4s were eventually delivered to the Yugoslav Air Force, and currently remain active with that service.

As later versions of the Canadair Sabre became available to the R.C.A.F., most of the Mk. 2s and 4s were fitted with extended wing leading edges and, from July 1954, 104 were delivered to the Royal Hellenic Air Force as F-86E(M) Sabres, and 105 were supplied to the Turkish Air Force, these still furnishing the backbone of the intercept capability of these air arms.

CL-13A SABRE MK. 5: By 1953, Orenda Engines had evolved a special version of their turbojet for Sabre installation—the 6,355 lb.s.t. Orenda 10. With this

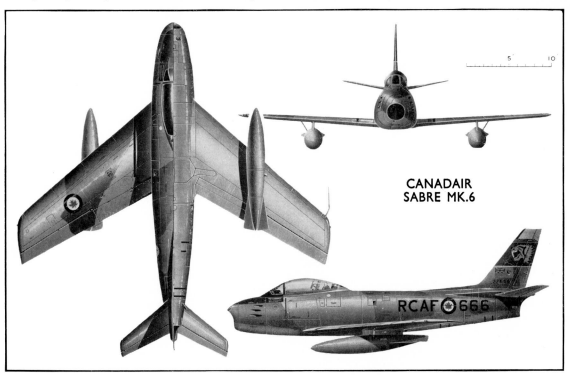

CANADAIR
SABRE MK.6

(Above and immediately below left) Canadair Sabre Mk. 6s of Waffenschule 10, the operational training wing for fighter pilots at Oldenburg, and (bottom left) a Canadair-built F-86E(M) of the Royal Hellenic A.F.'s aerobatic team.

power plant, and extended "6-3" wing leading edge and wing fences of the F-86F-30-NA, the 791st Canadair-built aircraft (23001) emerged as the first CL-13A Sabre Mk. 5, this aircraft flying for the first time on July 30, 1953. The Orenda engine was slightly larger in diameter than the J47-GE-13, necessitating the enlarging of the frame openings over the engine bay, the provision of different pick-up points, and some minor local structural changes.

Empty weight was increased from 11,100 lb. to 11,365 lb., and loaded weight (clean) was raised from 14,640 lb. to 15,120 lb., but the Sabre Mk. 5 could attain an altitude of 40,000 ft. in half the time taken by the Mk. 2, this height being reached in nine minutes, while the "6-3" leading edge enabled 1.5 g to be pulled at Mach 0.92 at 30,000 ft. before buffeting appeared, although it raised stalling speed and produced a yaw-and-roll effect before the stall which necessitated a faster landing approach.

Three hundred and seventy Sabre Mk. 5s (23001-370) were manufactured for the R.C.A.F., seventy-five of these later being presented to the Federal German Luftwaffe and used for training purposes.

CL-13B SABRE MK. 6: On November 2, 1954, the first example of the very much improved Sabre Mk. 6 (23371) was completed, this differing from its predecessor principally in having the 7,275 lb.s.t. two-stage Orenda 14 turbojet which resulted in a major improvement in the fighter's climb rate and altitude

performance. Empty and loaded weights were reduced from those of the Mk. 5, and early production Mk. 6s had the extended wing leading edges and wing fences introduced by the Mk. 5, although the majority of aircraft subsequently built reinstated the automatic leading-edge slats, these being modified to combine their low-speed handling benefits with the high-speed advantages offered by the "6-3" leading edge.

A total of 382 Sabre Mk. 6s (23371-752) was produced for the R.C.A.F., this type re-equipping all squadrons of the No. 1 Air Division from 1955 until finally supplanted by the CF-104 Starfighter in 1963. Six Sabre Mk. 6s were delivered to the Colombian Air Force in 1956, and these were followed by thirty-four aircraft for the South African Air Force. The S.A.A.F. Sabre Mk. 6s equipped Nos. 1 and 2 Squadrons until 1964, when the latter re-equipped with Mirage IIICZ. The last 225 Sabre Mk. 6s were built for the Federal German Luftwaffe, and currently serve with that service's Jagdgeschwader 71, 72 and 73, the German machines bringing total Sabre Mk. 6 production to 655, the last being completed on October 9, 1958. The Sabre Mk. 6 has now been withdrawn from first-line R.C.A.F. service, although some aircraft are employed by the Sabre Transition Unit at Chatham, New Brunswick, to provide pilots with experience in aircraft of high subsonic performance and in low-level tactics before they proceed to the No. 6 (Strike and Reconnaissance) O.T.U. at Cold Lake, Alberta.

CL-13B SABRE MK.6 SPECIFICATION

Power Plant: *One Orenda Engines Orenda 14 turbojet rated at 7,275 lb.s.t.*
Armament: *Six 0.5-in. Colt-Browning machine guns and provision for various underwing offensive loads (e.g., two 100-lb., 500-lb., or 1,000-lb. bombs, 750-lb. napalm tanks, 500-lb. fragmentation clusters, or sixteen 5-in. rocket projectiles).*
Performance: *(At 14,044 lb.) Max. speed, 710 m.p.h. at sea level (Mach 0.933), 680 m.p.h. at 10,000 ft. (Mach 0.92), 620 m.p.h. at 36,000 ft. (Mach 0.94); initial climb rate, 11,800 ft./min.; time to 40,000 ft., 6 min.; tactical radius (clean), 363 mls.; max. range (with two 166.5 Imp. gal. drop tanks), 1,495 mls.*
Weights: *Empty, 11,143 lb.; normal loaded, 16,426 lb.; max., 17,611 lb.*
Dimensions: *Span, 37 ft. 1 in.; length, 37 ft. 6 in.; height, 14 ft. 7 in.; wing area, 304 sq. ft.*

CANADAIR CL-28 ARGUS

A unique hybrid in that it employs the wings, tail surfaces, flight controls and undercarriage of a British transport aircraft, the Britannia, married to a fuselage of Canadian design and American engines, the Canadair CL-28 Argus maritime reconnaissance aircraft is operated by Nos. 404 and 405 Squadrons of the R.C.A.F. Maritime Air Command from Greenwood, Nova Scotia, and by No. 541 Squadron from Summerside, Prince Edward Island.

One of the most effective anti-submarine aircraft for mid-ocean operations yet produced, the Argus, which is designated CP-107 by the R.C.A.F., was flown for the first time on March 28, 1957, the first machine (20710) and the following twelve aircraft (20711 to 20722 inclusive) being Mk. 1s, and the final twenty production machines being Mk. 2s, the last of these being completed on July 13, 1960. The principal differences between the Mks. 1 and 2 are to be found in differing disposition of the navigational and communications radio, and the tactical electronic equipment, the redesigned and smaller "chin" radome of the later aircraft which reduces aerodynamic drag and results in a substantial weight saving, and the ECM antennae above the fuselage of the Mk. 2.

The Argus carries a crew of fifteen—three pilots, three navigators, two flight engineers and seven electronic equipment operators—and has a maximum fuel capacity of 6,688 Imp. gal. which may be supplemented by a 500 Imp. gal. weapons bay tank. Apart from its

The eighth production Argus Mk. 1 (20718) with the original bulged "chin" radome.

primary rôle of searching out and killing submerged and surfaced hostile craft, the Argus performs the mine-laying, long-range convoy escort, maritime search and rescue, and anti-shipping strike tasks, and a correspondingly wide variety of electronic equipment is therefore installed. Each of the two weapons bays in the centre fuselage has a length of 18 ft. 6 in. and a 4,000 lb. weapons capacity, and this internal load of offensive stores, which embraces the full range of conventional anti-submarine weapons, may be supplemented by a further 3,800 lb. on each of two underwing pylons. No defensive armament is carried, and the precise nature of the Argus's offensive armament has not been revealed, but may be assumed to include all the standard NATO maritime armament, ranging from the electric acoustic torpedoes of the LK. 4 or Mk. 43 Brush type to the normal 385-lb. American-type depth charge.

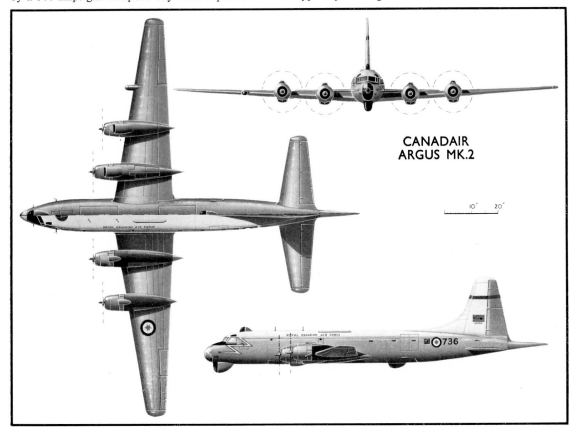

CANADAIR
ARGUS MK.2

10′ 20′

(*Above*) *The third production Argus Mk. 2 (20725). The Argus currently equips three squadrons of the R.C.A.F.'s Maritime Air Command.* (*Below left*) *A comparison of the search radomes of the Argus Mks. 1 (background) and 2 (foreground).*

CL-28 ARGUS MK.2 SPECIFICATION

Power Plants: *Four Wright Turbo Compound R-3350 (TC18EA1) Type 981 radial air-cooled engines each rated at 3,400 h.p. and 3,700 h.p. for take-off with water injection.*

Armament: *Up to 8,000 lb. of conventional depth charges, bombs (ballistic or photoflash), or active and passive homing torpedoes internally, and up to 7,600 lb. of ASMs or other offensive weapons on underwing pylons.*

Performance: *Max. speed, 315 m.p.h. at 20,000 ft., 288 m.p.h. at sea level; cruise (max. at sea level), 230 m.p.h.; typical mission profile (cruising to and from patrol area at 223 m.p.h. at 5,000 ft.), patrol for 12 hr. at 190 m.p.h. below 1,000 ft. at range of 830 mls. with allowance for 575-ml. diversion, 8 hr. at range of 1,210 mls., 4 hr. at range of 1,590 mls.; normal cruise endurance, 24 hr.; max. range, 5,900 mls.; initial climb rate, 1,700 ft./min.*

Weights: *Empty, 81,000 lb.; normal loaded, 148,000 lb.*

Dimensions: *Span, 142 ft. 3½ in.; length, 128 ft. 3 in.; height, 36 ft. 8½ in.; wing area, 2,075 sq. ft.*

CANADAIR CL-90 STARFIGHTER

Selected as a CL-13B Sabre replacement by the Canadian government in mid-1959, the CL-90 is a Canadair-built version of the F-104G Starfighter (see page 180) modified specifically to meet R.C.A.F. requirements. Designated CF-104 by the R.C.A.F., this single-seat strike and reconnaissance fighter currently equips the No. 1 Air Division in Europe. This consists of No. 1 Wing (Nos. 439 and 441 Squadrons) based at Marville, France, and employed in the photo-reconnaissance rôle but eventually to be modified to permit their operation with conventional weapons, No. 3 Wing (comprising Nos. 427, 430 and 434 Squadrons) based at Zweibrucken, Germany, and No. 4 Wing (Nos. 421, 422 and 444 Squadrons) based at Baden-Solingen, Germany, the German-based units having

nuclear capability, each aircraft being allocated a standard NATO one-megaton store.

The selection of the Starfighter was announced on July 2, 1959, and a month later, on August 14th. it was stated that Canadair Limited would manufacture airframes for two hundred aircraft of this type, the power plants being built by Orenda Engines Limited. Allocated the designation CL-90 by the Canadian manufacturer, the Starfighter was originally to have been known as the CF-111 in service, but R.C.A.F. nomenclature for the aircraft was quickly changed to CF-104 for obvious reasons.

Whereas the F-104G is a multi-mission aircraft capable of undertaking intercept missions as well as the strike and reconnaissance rôles, its NASARR (North

American Search and Ranging Radar) F15A-41B equipment being optimised in both air-to-air and air-to-ground modes, the CF-104 has NASARR R-24A optimised in the air-to-ground mode. The F-104G's 20-mm. M61 Vulcan rotary cannon is not installed in the CF-104, rendering unnecessary the lead angle computer, only a simple fixed-reticle sight being fitted. The space occupied in the F-104G by the M-61, its ammunition and ejector case compartments, is employed in the CF-104 for aluminium fuel tanks which raise total internal capacity by 101.5 Imp. gal. The undercarriage of the CF-104 has larger tyres and longer-stroke liquid springs, and provision is made for the mounting of a Vicom photo-reconnaissance pod on the fuselage centre-line. Weighing less than 300 lb., the Vicom pod houses four 70-mm. Vinten cameras.

An F-104A-15-LO Starfighter (56-0770) was modified to serve as a prototype for the CF-104, and (re-numbered 12700) flew for the first time on September 1, 1960. This aircraft was modified to CF-104 standards only in respect of fire control and flight control system equipment, and did not possess the strengthened airframe of the true F-104G series. The first production CF-104 (12701) was completed on March 28, 1961, and after being airlifted to Palmdale, California—where the first two aircraft off the Montreal production line were performance-proved by Lockheed—flew on May 26th. The first CF-104s to fly at Montreal were the third and fourth production machines (12703 and 12704) which both flew on August 14, 1961, these being powered by the Orenda J79-OEL-7 which has a military rating of 10,000 lb.s.t. dry, and full and minimum after-burning thrusts of 15,800 and 12,300 lb.

The first CF-104s were delivered to No. 6 (Strike and Reconnaissance) O.T.U. at Cold Lake, Alberta, and the first squadron, No. 427, was formed in December 1962, the 200th and last CF-104 (12900) being completed on September 4, 1963 and delivered on January 10, 1964. The performance and dimensions of the CF-104 are generally similar to those of the F-104G (see page 182), but weights are as follows: empty, 13,909 lb.; loaded (clean), 21,005 lb.; max., 28,891 lb.

Part of the agreement between Lockheed and the Canadian government concerning Starfighter manufacture under licence in Canada included the production by Canadair of wings, tail assemblies and rear fuselage sections for sixty-six F-104G Starfighters ordered from the parent company for the Federal German Luftwaffe, the first set of these components being shipped by Canadair to Burbank on June 29, 1960. Subsequently, Canadair received orders for the manufacture of 140 F-104Gs for supply under the MAP to Denmark, Greece, Norway and Turkey, and the first of these (62-2302) flew on July 30, 1963, deliveries to the NATO forces commencing before the end of the year. Originally, both Denmark and Norway were each scheduled to receive twenty-nine F-104Gs to re-equip two squadrons, but the R.Nor.A.F. decided to equip only one squadron, No. 331, with the F-104G, this fulfilling the photo-reconnaissance rôle. Greece and Turkey were scheduled to receive thirty-six and thirty-eight Canadair-built F-104Gs respectively.

CF-104D STARFIGHTER: At the same time the Canadian government placed the order for 200 CF-104s, an order was placed with Lockheed for fourteen tandem two-seat Starfighters which, originally designated CF-113, were delivered to the R.C.A.F. under the designation CF-104D, the first of these flying on June 14, 1961. The original order was supplemented by an order for a further eight machines of this type on October 26, 1961, and yet a further sixteen were ordered on November 5, 1963, bringing the total number of CF-104D Starfighters delivered to the R.C.A.F. to thirty-eight aircraft. The CF-104D is essentially similar to the TF-104G, apart from equipment, and R.C.A.F. pilot training on this type began at Cold Lake in 1962.

(Below) The sixty-eighth production CF-104 (12767) with practise tactical store on centreline pylon, and (above right) a CF-104D (12635) at No. 6 (Strike and Reconnaissance) O.T.U. at Cold Lake, Alberta.

BREGUET 1050 ALIZÉ

The Alizé (above and below) currently equips three Flottilles of the Aéronavale and one Indian Navy squadron.

The Breguet 1050 Alizé (Tradewind) three-seat shipboard anti-submarine aircraft is currently operated by the French Navy's Flottilles 4F, 6F, and 9F, and serves aboard the carriers *Clémenceau* and *Foch*. The Alize is also operated by the Indian Navy's No. 310 Squadron aboard the carrier *Vikrant*.

Combining the hunter and killer rôles in a single aircraft, the Alizé was evolved from the experimental Breguet 960 Vultur shipboard strike aircraft, the first prototype of which was flown on August 3, 1951. The second prototype Vultur served as an aerodynamic test vehicle for the Alizé, the first true prototype of which flew on October 6, 1956, this being followed by second and third prototypes on December 21, 1956 and April 19, 1957 respectively. The prototypes differed one from another in minor respects, and the second, the Br. 1050-02, was used for preliminary landing trials aboard the carrier *Arromanches*. The Br. 1050-03 was later fitted with the production-type Dart R.Da.21 turboprop in place of the R.Da.20, and the later engine was installed in the two "pre-series" aircraft, the Br. 1050-04 and -05, the first of which flew on June 22, 1957.

The first of seventy-five production Alizé anti-submarine aircraft for the French Navy flew on March 26, 1959, and the delivery of twelve aircraft to the Indian Navy began on January 7, 1961. Capable of undertaking low-altitude patrols of more than 3.5 hours duration, and anti-shipping strike tasks, the Alizé has a total internal fuel capacity of 462 Imp. gal., alternative auxiliary tanks in the weapons bay increasing this to 567 Imp. gal. or 633 Imp. gal., for ferry purposes.

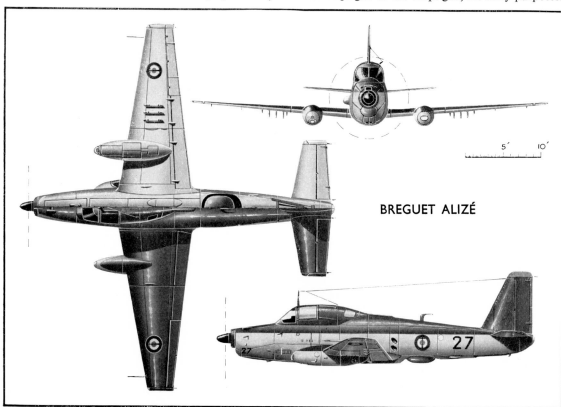

5'   10'

BREGUET ALIZÉ

The pilot is seated to port with one radar operator to starboard and the other to the rear, CSF search radar is housed in a retractable ventral radome, and omni-directional sonobuoys are accommodated in storage bays in the forward sections of the mainwheel housings.

BR.1050 ALIZÉ SPECIFICATION

Power Plant: One Rolls-Royce Dart R.Da.21 turboprop rated at 1,950 s.h.p. for take-off.

Armament: Three 353-lb. depth charges or one electric acoustic torpedo in weapons bay, plus two 353-lb. or 386-lb. depth charges and six 0.5-in. rockets or two Nord 5210 (SS.11M) wire-guided ASMs underwing.

Performance: Max. speed, 285 m.p.h. at sea level, 290 m.p.h. at 3,000 ft., 292 m.p.h. at 10,000 ft.; normal patrol speed, 144 m.p.h. at 1,500 ft.; endurance (with standard internal tankage and radome extended at 144 m.p.h.), 5 hr. 12 min. at 1,500 ft., 5 hr. 16 min. at

10,000 ft., 5 hr. 10 min. at 15,000 ft.; max. endurance (radome extended at 15,000 ft.) with 105 Imp. gal. auxiliary fuel, 6 hr. 55 min., with 270 Imp. gal. auxiliary fuel, 7 hr. 40 min.; max. ferry range (radome retracted and 270 Imp. gal. auxiliary fuel), 1,785 mls.; initial climb (at 18,100 lb. with undercarriage extended), 1,380 ft./min.; service ceiling (at 17,650 lb.), 20,500 ft.

Weights: Empty equipped, 12,566 lb.; normal loaded 18,100 lb.

Dimensions: Span. 51 ft. 2 in.; width folded, 22 ft. 11 in.; length, 45 ft. 6 in.; height, 15 ft. 7 in.; wing area 387.5 sq. ft.

(Above) The Breguet 1150–03 Atlantic prototype which flew on February 25, 1963. Initial contracts call for forty production Atlantics to be shared equally between the Federal German and French navies.

BREGUET 1150 ATLANTIC

The result of a specification for a maritime reconnaissance aircraft to replace the Lockheed P-2 Neptune drawn up under the auspices of the NATO Armaments Committee, the Br. 1150 Atlantic is scheduled to enter service with the French Aéronautique Navale and the Federal German Marinefliegertruppe during 1965-66, and is expected to be adopted by the armed services of other NATO countries.

Selected from twenty-five design studies submitted by aircraft manufacturers of seven nationalities, the Atlantic is being manufactured by a consortium of French, German, Belgian and Dutch companies, with the parent company acting as team leader and responsible for the final assembly of the aircraft, the programme being managed by an organisation known as SECBAT (Société Européenne pour la Construction du Breguet Atlantic). The choice of the Atlantic was announced on October 21, 1958, the detailed specification for the prototypes was approved in June 1959, and on October 21, 1961, the first proto-

type, the Br. 1150-01, made its initial flight. The second prototype, the Br. 1150-02, flew for the first time on February 23, 1962, but was totally destroyed two months later, on April 19th., and the Br. 1150-03, which embodied a 3.28 ft. increase in forward fuselage length, flew on February 25, 1963. The fourth Atlantic, which is considered as a pre-production aircraft, joined the test programme on September 10, 1964, by which time production tooling had been completed and orders placed for twenty machines for the Aéronautique Navale and twenty for the Kriegsmarine. Orders for additional quantities for both of these services were anticipated late in 1964 when discussions were taking place concerning the possible purchase of the Atlantic for R.A.F. Coastal Command.

The Atlantic, in its initial production form, carries twelve crew members, seven of which are accommodated in a central operations compartment. The main weapons bay is 29.52 ft. in length and is located in the

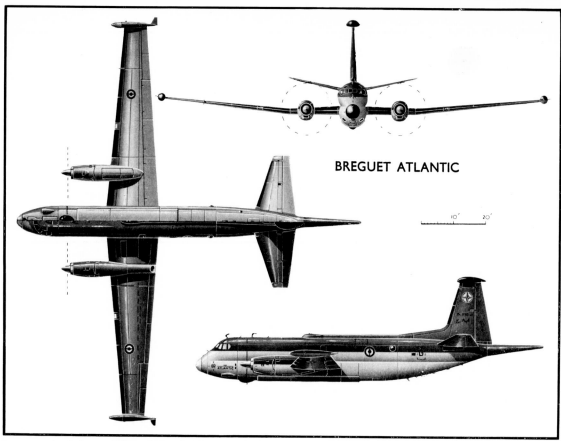

BREGUET ATLANTIC

unpressurized lower lobe of the fuselage, and this accommodates all NATO standard bombs, mines, depth charges and homing torpedoes, underwing pylons carrying ASMs or HVARs. Forward of the

(Above and below) The third prototype Atlantic, the Br. 1150-03, with radome extended and weapons bay doors open.

weapons bay and aft of the nosewheel well is a retractable radome housing CSF search radar, and the American A.S.W. systems are essentially similar to those of the P-2 Neptune.

Several developments of the basic Atlantic design have been projected, including the Mk.1A with an increased overload weight, and the Mk. 2, the latter designation covering a series of studies for a more advanced version, including one equipped with underwing auxiliary jet pods to increase dash speed and transit range.

BR.1150 ATLANTIC SPECIFICATION

Power Plants: *Two Hispano-Suiza-built Rolls-Royce Tyne R.Ty.20 Mk.21 turboprops each rated at 6,105 e.h.p. for take-off.*

Armament: *All NATO standard bombs, 386-lb. U.S. or French depth charges, and active or passive homing torpedoes in ventral weapons bay, and HVARs or ASMs on underwing pylons.*

Performance: *Max. speed, 382 m.p.h. at 20,000–25,000 ft.; patrol speed for max. endurance, 195–200 m.p.h. at 1,000–5,000 ft.; typical mission profile (cruising to and from patrol area at 310 m.p.h.), patrol for 12 hr. at 195 m.p.h. below 1,000 ft. at range of 620 mls. with allowances for diversion; max. cruise endurance, 18 hr.; max. range, 5,760 mls. at 320 m.p.h. at 25,000 ft.; service ceiling, 33,000 ft.*

Weights: *Max. loaded, 93,696 lb.*

Dimensions: *Span, 119 ft. 1¼ in.; length, 104 ft. 1½ in.; height, 27 ft. 1¾ in.; wing area, 1,291.67 sq. ft.*

G.A.M.DASSAULT ETENDARD IVM

Evolved from a private venture contestant in the NATO competition for a lightweight strike fighter eventually won by the Fiat G.91, the Etendard IVM shipboard aircraft undertakes strike and interception missions at low and medium altitudes, and is currently embarked aboard the carriers *Clémenceau* and *Foch*, equipping four Aéronavale flottilles, 11F, 14F, 15F and 17F. The Etendard IVM officially entered service with the Aéronavale on January 18, 1962, ninety machines having been ordered, of which twenty-one have been completed as Etendard IVP reconnaissance aircraft.

Three different fighter prototypes, all dubbed Etendard, were built and flown by G.A.M. Dassault during 1955-57, and prior to the début of the definitive Etendard IVM (the 'M' suffix indicating 'Marine'), all possessing a generally similar aerodynamic configuration. The Etendard II was designed to meet an Armée de l'Air requirement for a small strike fighter powered by a pair of Turboméca Gabizo turbojets each rated at 2,420 lb.s.t. and 3,330 lb.s.t. with afterburning. This type, which flew for the first time on July 23, 1956, suffered from the inadequate development of its Gabizo engines, and was abandoned after a

relatively brief test period. The Etendard IV, powered by a SNECMA Atar 101E-3, was produced as a private venture, its development being engendered by the NATO tactical strike fighter specification which, in fact, called for the installation of the Bristol Siddeley Orpheus, and the third machine, the Etendard VI, did employ this engine and, flying for the first time on March 16, 1957, was specifically intended to fulfil the NATO requirement. The Etendard VI was abandoned as a result of the success of the Fiat entry in the contest, and the company subsequently concentrated on development of the Atar-powered Etendard IV as a company-funded project.

The Etendard IV-01 was flown for the first time on July 24, 1956, and displayed outstanding qualities. Design emphasis had been placed on production simplicity and ease of maintenance, and the Aéronavale foresaw the possibility of adapting the aircraft for use from the new carriers then under construction, ordering a semi-navalised prototype and six fully-navalised pre-production machines under the designation Etendard IVM. The prototype, the Etendard IVM-01, flew for the first time on May 21, 1958, the pre-production aircraft following during 1959-60.

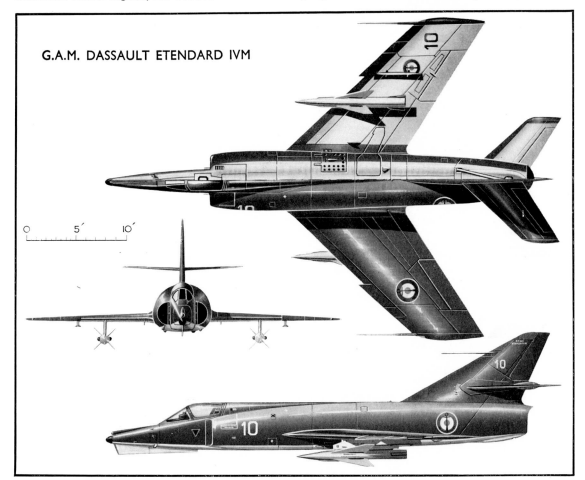

G.A.M. DASSAULT ETENDARD IVM

An Etendard IVP equipped with "buddy" pack refuelling an Etendard IVM. Unlike the IVM, the IVP has a fixed refuelling probe, and carries five OMERA cameras, three of these being installed in the nose.

Modifications incorporated in the aircraft to give it "sea legs" included the provision of folding wingtips, launching attachments and arrester hook, a strengthened undercarriage with long-travel shock absorbers and high-pressure tyres, an extendible nosewheel leg to increase take-off incidence, and increases in wing and rudder areas.

The first pre-production aircraft, the Etendard IVM-02, completed initial carrier qualifications aboard the *Clémenceau* between September 19 and 24, 1960, and this aircraft, like four later pre-production machines, was powered by the SNECMA Atar 08 which was to

(Above) The fifth pre-production Etendard (IVM-06) with air brakes extended, and (below) a standard Etendard IVM.

be adopted as standard for the production model, but the Etendard IVM-03, also known as the Etendard IVB, which flew for the first time on December 2, 1959, was fitted with an 11,200 lb.s.t. Avon 51 (200 series) and adapted for flap blowing, permitting it to use the 103-ft. catapult of smaller carriers. This was also the first Etendard to feature a fin-type antenna beneath the nose for the Nord AS.20 ASM. The final pre-production aircraft was designated Etendard IVP-07, and first flown on November 19, 1960, served as a prototype for the tactical reconnaissance version which carries five OMERA cameras, three of these being mounted in the modified nose and a twin vertical installation being situated in the bay normally housing the twin 30-mm. DEFA cannon. The Etendard IVP also features a flight refuelling probe mounted immediately above the nose fairing in place of the normal Aïda 7 radar, and is equipped for "buddy" tanker duties.

The first production Etendard IVM flew in July 1961, and first deliveries were made to Flottille 15F which served as the operational conversion unit, Flottille 11F being the second unit to re-equip, Flottilles 14F and 17F replacing their veteran F4U-7 Corsairs with the Etendard during 1964. A SAAB Type BT9F toss bomb computer is provided, and the Aïda 7 radar provides detection, telemetry and weapon homing. Integral tanks in the fuselage and wings house a total of 715 Imp. gal., comprising twenty-three per cent of the disposable volume of the aircraft, and these may be supplemented by two 132 Imp. gal. underwing tanks.

ETENDARD IVM SPECIFICATION

Power Plant: *One SNECMA Atar 08B turbojet rated at 9,700 lb.s.t.*

Armament: *Two 30-mm. DEFA cannon and two Nord AS.30 command guidance ASMs or two 1,000-lb. and two 500-lb. bombs or (intercept mission) two infra-red homing AIM-9 Sidewinder AAMs.*

Performance: *Max. speed, 673 m.p.h. at 36,090 ft. (Mach 1.02), 683 m.p.h. at sea level (Mach 0.9); limiting Mach number, 1.4; initial climb rate, 19,685 ft./min.; time to 39,370 ft., 4.45 min.; service ceiling, 50,850 ft.; tactical radius at sea level (clean), 186 mls.; with two 132 Imp. gal. auxiliary tanks at 36,000 ft., 500 mls.; endurance (for ferrying), 3 hr. 45 min. at 510 m.p.h.*

Weights: *Empty, 12,786 lb.; max. catapult weight, 19,840 lb.; max. overload, 22,486 lb.*

Dimensions: *Span, 31 ft. 6 in.; length, 47 ft. 1 in.; height, 12 ft. 7½ in.; wing area, 306 sq. ft.*

G.A.M.DASSAULT MYSTÈRE IVA

Although now obsolescent, the Mystère IVA currently remains in service with the Armée de l'Air's 7e Escadre attached to the 1er CATac, and the 8e Escadre, formed in 1964 as a component of the Défense Aérienne, with three squadrons of the Israeli Defence Force/Air Force, and with units of the Indian Air Force, a total of 421 examples of this interceptor having been built when production terminated late in 1958, 110 being delivered to India, sixty to Israel, and the remainder to the Armée de l'Air. Apart from its operational use with the four escadrons of the 7e and 8e Escadres, the Mystère IVA serves the Armée de l'Air in the advanced training rôle at Cazaux, Dijon, Mont de Marsan, Nancy, and Tours.

Bearing little more than a general aerodynamic resemblance to its immediate predecessor, the Mystère IIC, the 150 production examples of which saw only limited service with the Armée de l'Air, the Mystère IVA features a more robust, oval-section

The Mystère IVA is currently operated by two Armée de l'Air Escadres and (below) by the Indian Air Force.

MYSTÈRE IVA SPECIFICATION

Power Plant: One Hispano-Suiza Verdon 350 turbojet rated at 7,710 lb.s.t.
Armament: Two 30-mm. DEFA cannon with 150 r.p.g. plus two 1,000-lb. or four 500-lb. bombs, or two G.A.M.D. JL-50 pods each containing thirty-six 37-mm. rockets.
Performance: Max. speed, 696 m.p.h. at sea level (Mach 0.913), 615 m.p.h. at 39,370 ft. (Mach 0.94); long-range cruise, 510 m.p.h.; initial climb rate, 8,860 ft./min.; service ceiling, 45,000 ft.; range (clean), 570 mls., (with two 106 Imp. gal. drop tanks), 820 mls.; ferry range (four 106 Imp. gal. drop tanks), 1,050 mls.
Weights: Empty, 12,950 lb.; loaded (clean), 16,530 lb.; max. overload, 20,050 lb.
Dimensions: Span 36 ft. 5¾ in.; length, 42 ft. 1¼ in.; height, 15 ft. 1 in.; wing area, 344.5 sq. ft.

fuselage, a wing of increased sweep-back and reduced thickness/chord ratio, and a more powerful turbojet. The Mystère IVA-01 flew for the first time on September 28, 1952, and in the following April an off-shore procurement order was placed for 225 interceptors of this type, this later being supplemented by an order for a further 100 machines. The first fifty Mystère IVA fighters manufactured for the Armée de l'Air were powered by the 6,280 lb.s.t. Hispano-Suiza Tay 250A turbojet, and the type entered service in 1955 with the 12e Escadre at Cambrai-Epinoy, but all subsequent Mystère IVAs received the more powerful Verdon 350.

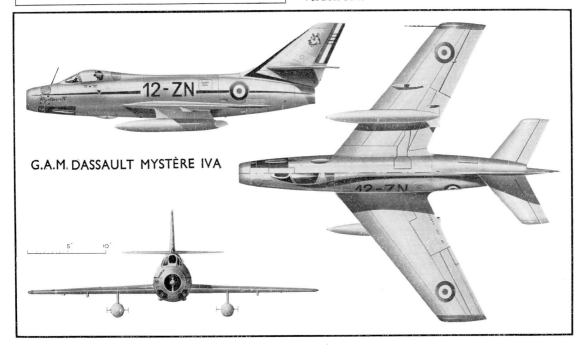

G.A.M. DASSAULT MYSTÈRE IVA

G.A.M.DASSAULT SUPER-MYSTÈRE B.2

The first aircraft capable of reaching supersonic speeds in level flight to attain production status in

(Above) Super-Mystère B.2s of the Armée de l'Air's 10ᵉ Escadre which, based at Creil, comprises Escadrons 1/10 "Valois" and 2/10 "Seine" as part of the Défense Aérienne.

(Above) A Super-Mystère B.2 of the 12ᵉ Escadre which is based at Cambrai and consists of Escadrons 1/12 "Cambraisis" and 2/12 "Cornouaille".

Western Europe, the Super-Mystère B.2 equips the Armée de l'Air's 5ᵉ, 10ᵉ and 12ᵉ Escadres forming part of the Commandement 'Air' des Forces de Défense Aérienne, and also equips one squadron of the Israeli Defence Force/Air Force. One hundred and eighty Super-Mystère B.2s had been completed when production terminated in 1959, twenty-four of these having been delivered to Israel.

The first prototype, the Super-Mystère B.1, flew on March 2, 1955 powered by a Rolls-Royce Avon R.A. 7R turbojet, and the first of five Atar-powered pre-production Super-Mystère B.2s followed on May 15, 1956. The first production Super-Mystère B.2 flew on February 26, 1957, entering service during the course of that year with the 10ᵉ Escadre de Chasse. A further development, the Super-Mystère B.4 with a SNECMA Atar 09 engine, was flown òn February 9, 1958, this variant attaining Mach 1.4 in level flight at 36,090 ft., but only two examples of the B.4 were completed. The primary rôle of the Super-Mystère B.2 is that of day interceptor, but a variety of underwing stores can be lifted for the fighter-bomber rôle.

SUPER-MYSTÈRE B.2 SPECIFICATION

Power Plant: *One SNECMA Atar 101G rated at 7,495 lb.s.t. or 9,920 lb.s.t. with afterburning.*
Armament: *Two 30-mm. DEFA cannon and thirty-five 68-mm. SNEB Type 22 rockets in internally-housed MATRA launcher, plus twelve HVARs, two MATRA M.116E launchers each housing nineteen 68-mm. SNEB rockets, two 1,000-lb. bombs, or two napalm tanks.*
Performance: *Max. speed, 743 m.p.h. at 38,000–41,000 ft. (Mach 1.125), 686 m.p.h. at sea level (Mach 0.9); max. cruise, 620 m.p.h. at 40,000 ft. (Mach 0.94); normal range cruise, 560 m.p.h. at 36,000 ft.; time to 40,000 ft., 5 min.; initial climb rate, 17,500 ft./min.; ceiling, 55,750 ft.; normal endurance, 1 hr. 5 min.; range (clean), 540 mls. at 36,000 ft., (with two 180 Imp. gal. drop tanks), 730 mls.*
Weights: *Empty, 15,400 lb.; normal loaded, 19,840 lb. max. overload, 22,046 lb.*
Dimensions: *Span, 34 ft. 5¾ in.; length, 46 ft. 1¼ in. height, 14 ft. 10¾ in.; wing area, 377 sq. ft.*

(Above, left) A Super-Mystère B.2 of the Israeli Defence Force/Air Force, and (below) a Super-Mystère B.2 of the 5ᵉ Escadre which, based at Orange as part of the Défense Aérienne, comprises Escadrons 1/5 "Vendée" and 2/5 "Ile-de-France."

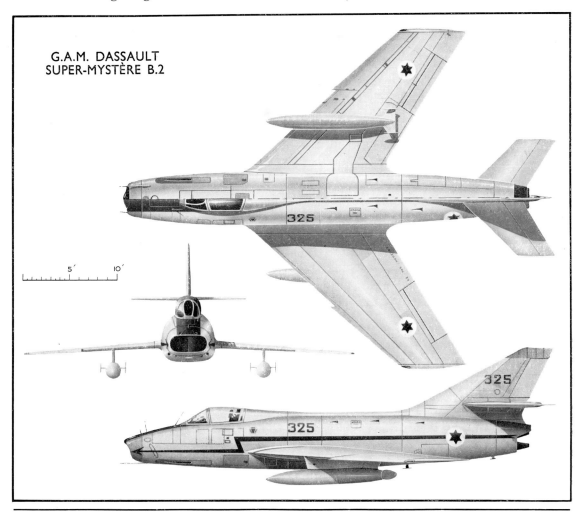

G.A.M. DASSAULT
SUPER-MYSTÈRE B.2

5'   10'

G.A.M. DASSAULT MIRAGE III

One of the most successful European military aircraft of its generation, the Mirage III has been adopted by the air arms of Australia, Israel, South Africa, and Switzerland, as well as by the Armée de l'Air. Equally adaptable for the low-level ground attack or high-altitude intercept roles, the Mirage began life as an attempt to produce the smallest practicable all-weather interceptor capable of attaining an altitude of 60,000 feet in six minutes and fulfilling an Armée de l'Air specification. The first model, the MD.550 Mirage I which flew on June 25, 1955, was intended essentially to prove the practicability of the tailless delta configuration, and was powered by two 1,640 lb.s.t. Bristol Siddeley Viper turbojets. Weighing only 7,341 lb. empty and 11,177 lb. loaded, the Mirage I attained Mach 1.15 in a shallow dive, but with afterburners boosting the thrust of each Viper to 2,160 lb., and the turbojets supplemented by a 3,310 lb. thrust SEPR 66 rocket motor burning a self-igniting mixture of fura-line and nitric acid, Mach 1.3 was attained in level flight on December 17, 1956.

The Mirage I was, of course, too small to carry an effective military load, and a scaled-up version, the Mirage II powered by a pair of Turboméca Gabizo engines each offering 2,420 lb.s.t. and 3,330 lb. with afterburning, was proposed. However, the lightweight engines of this version lacked the power necessary to attain a Mach 2.0 performance, and as data had become available on the transonic drag reducing area rule, later to be supplemented by information acquired by the British aircraft industry with the Fairey FD.2 research aircraft of basically similar configuration to the Mirage, the Mirage II was abandoned in favour of the more ambitious Mirage III. Considerably larger than the Mirage I and some thirty per cent heavier, the Mirage III retained the five per cent thickness/chord ratio with a leading-edge sweep of 60°, but the choice of a single SNECMA Atar 101G.1 turbojet offering an afterburning thrust of 8,818 lb. necessitated an entirely new fuselage profile. Provision for combat equipment was made from the outset, and the Mirage III-001 flew for the first time on November 17, 1956, attaining Mach 1.6 in a dive on January 30, 1957. Higher speeds were not possible with the non-variable air intakes with which the Mirage III-001 was originally fitted. Therefore manually-operated half-cones

(Above) A Mirage IIIC (No. 28) of Escadron 1/2 "Cicogne" carrying a single MATRA R.511 semi-active radar-homing missile on the centreline pylon and equipped with a SEPR 844 rocket motor.

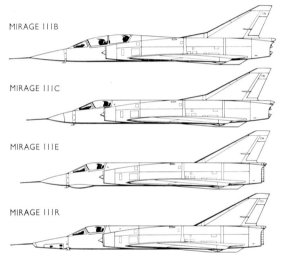

MIRAGE IIIB

MIRAGE IIIC

MIRAGE IIIE

MIRAGE IIIR

(Below) Mirage IIICZ fighters of the South African Air Force's No. 2 Squadron.

or shock-wedges were introduced in the intake mouths, and with the installation of the Atar 101G.2 turbojet rated at 7,650 lb.s.t. and 9,700 lb. with afterburning, maximum level speed was raised from Mach 1.52 to Mach 1.65, a speed of Mach 1.8 (1,188 m.p.h.) later being attained with the aid of a SEPR 66 rocket.

The Mirage III was, in its initial form, intended solely for the intercept rôle, and a demand for wider versatility resulted in the multi-purpose Mirage IIIA, a "pre-series" of ten examples of which was ordered, each aircraft subsequently being allocated specific development tasks (e.g., handling, powerplant, weapons, electronics, etc.). The Mirage IIIA differed from its immediate predecessor in a number of respects. Wing area was increased from 312.153 sq. ft. to 365.973 sq. ft., and the thickness/chord ratio was reduced from five to four-and-a-half per cent at the root tapering to three-and-a-half per cent at the tip. Later the leading-edge was provided with conical camber and an axial "notch". The fuselage was lengthened to accommodate the Atar 09—a supersonic engine with additional compressor and turbine stages to those of the Atar 101G—rated at 9,370 lb.s.t. and 13,230 lb. with afterburning, and provision was made for a detachable SEPR 841 rocket pack offering 1,500 lb. thrust for 160 seconds or 3,000 lb. thrust for 80 seconds.

The first "pre-series" aircraft, the Mirage IIIA-01, flew on May 12, 1958, and in six months, on October 24th, the aircraft attained Mach 2.0 in level flight without the rocket motor mounted, the SEPR 841 being first tested on the Mirage IIIA-02. The Mirage IIIA-05 was the first aircraft to be completed to full production standard, this being effectively a prototype for the initial production model, the Mirage IIIC, which was superficially indistinguishable from the "pre-series" aircraft.

MIRAGE IIIC: The first production version of the Mirage, the IIIC, ninety-five examples of which were ordered for and have been delivered to the Armée de l'Air, was first flown on October 9, 1960, and currently serves with the four squadrons of the 2e and 13e Escadres de Chasse which operate with the ler CATac. The Mirage IIIC is powered by the Atar 09 B3 turbojet, and a SEPR 844 rocket motor (offering a thrust of

MIRAGE IIIC SPECIFICATION

Power Plant: *One SNECMA Atar 09 B3 turbojet rated at 9,370 lb.s.t. or 13,230 lb. with full afterburning (and an optional SEPR 844 rocket motor offering 3,372 lb. at sea level and 3,703 lb. at 52,500 ft. for 80 sec.).*

Armament: *Two 30-mm. DEFA 5-52 cannon with 125 r.p.g. (when optional rocket motor is not fitted) for low-altitude penetration or long-range strike, plus two 1,000-lb. bombs or two G.A.M.D. JL-50 pods each containing thirty-six 37-mm. rockets, two JL-100 pods each containing sixteen 37-mm. rockets and 132 Imp. gal. of fuel, or two JL-200 pods each with thirty-six rockets and 198 Imp. gal. of fuel on underwing pylons. For the intercept rôle semi-active radar-homing MATRA R.511 or R.530 and infra-red homing AIM-9 Sidewinder missiles may be carried, a typical intercept armament comprising one R.511 and two Sidewinders.*

Performance: *Maximum attainable speed, 1,386 m.p.h. at 40,000 ft (Mach 2.1); maximum stabilised speed, 1,188 m.p.h. (Mach 1.8); climb (intercept) to 60,000 ft. with AAMs and SEPR 844 rocket, 6 min. 10 sec., to 50,000 ft. without SEPR 844, 6 min. 55 sec.; normal service ceiling, 59,000 ft.; tactical radius (clean), 180 mls. at 36,000 ft. at 594 m.p.h. (Mach 0.9), (with two 285 Imp. gal. drop tanks), 403 mls. at 1,000 ft. at 460–690 m.p.h.; typical long-range strike mission time (with a 1,000-lb. nuclear store, two 30-mm. cannon and two 176 Imp. gal. drop tanks), 2 hr. 10 min.*

Weights: *Empty, 13,570 lb.; loaded (clean), 17,550 lb., (with SEPR 844 and AAMs), 19,700 lb., (with 1,000-lb. store, twin 30-mm. cannon and two Imp. gal. tanks), 27,777 lb.*

Dimensions: *Span, 26 ft. 11½ in.; length, 45 ft. 5¼ in.; height, 13 ft. 9⅓ in.; wing area, 365.973 sq. ft.*

3,372 lb. at sea level and 3,703 lb. at 52,500 ft.) may be mounted in place of the auxiliary fuselage fuel tank, the twin 30-mm. DEFA 5-52 cannon pack being supplanted by a tank for the TX2 (the non-corrosive secondary rocket fuel), the nitric acid being housed in the rocket pack itself. The Mirage IIIC is employed by the Armée de l'Air primarily in the all-weather intercept rôle, although it is, in fact, a multi-purpose aircraft. The principal electronic equipment is the Cyrano I*bis* fire control system which provides search, lock-on and ranging modes, and is capable of guiding the semi-active radar-homing MATRA R.511 or R.530 missile. A typical intercept armament comprises two infra-red homing AIM-9 Sidewinders and a MATRA R.511.

Seventy-two aircraft basically similar to the Mirage IIIC but without rocket motor and missile armament have been supplied to the Israeli government under the designation Mirage IIICJ, and sixteen aircraft have been delivered to the South African Air Force

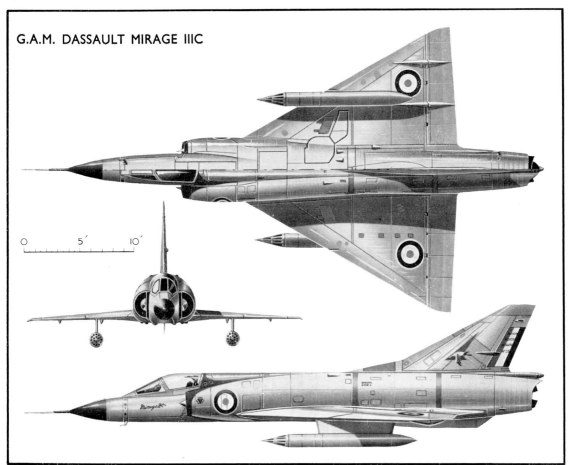

G.A.M. DASSAULT MIRAGE IIIC

(Above) Mirage IIIC No. 38 of Escadron 1/2 "Cicogne", and (below) the second G.A.M.D.-built Mirage IIIS (J-2302).

(Above) Mirage IIIC No. 33 of the 13e Escadre which consists of Escadrons 1/13 "Artois" and 2/13 "Alpes". (Below) Mirage IIIC No. 49 of Escadron 3/2 "Alsace".

as Mirage IIICZs to re-equip that service's No. 2 Squadron. The Mirage IIICZ is intended primarily for the low-level strike rôle with Nord AS.20 command-guidance air-to-surface missiles. A further derivative of the basic IIIC is the Mirage IIIS for Switzerland. The Mirage IIIS is being manufactured under licence in Switzerland by the Fabrique Fédérale d'Avions, the Atar 09 C3 turbojet which is being installed in the Swiss model being produced by Sulzer A.G. The CSF Cyrano fire control and R.511 missiles have been replaced in the Mirage IIIS by Hughes TARAN Mk.1S fire control radar and a Hughes HM-55 or an HM-58 Falcon air-to-air missile, and a strengthened undercarriage is provided. Two pattern aircraft have been delivered to Switzerland by the parent company, but the first Mirage IIIS fighters to be completely built in Switzerland will not commence flight trials until 1965, re-equipment of Swiss Air Force units beginning in 1966. Original plans called for the manufacture of eighty Mirage IIIS fighters, but late in 1964 cost escalation had resulted in a decision to cut this quantity to thirty-six machines.

MIRAGE IIIB: A tandem two-seat pilot training version of the basic design evolved in parallel with the Mirage IIIC is the Mirage IIIB, the prototype of which flew for the first time on October 21, 1959. Twenty-six production examples have been delivered to the Armée de l'Air, the first of these flying on July 19, 1962, and the initial aircraft were allocated to the 2e Escadre and the Centre d'Experimentation Aérien Militaire. As supplied to the Armée de l'Air, the Mirage IIIB carries no radar or armament, and at 17,460 lb., all-up weight is lower than that of the Mirage IIIC, but a fire control system and two 30-mm. DEFA cannon may be installed so that the combat potential is similar to that of the single-seater. The Mirage IIIB has a forward fuselage extension of 23.6 in., increasing overall length to 45 ft. 9½ in., and re-located equipment for a second cockpit in tandem. Performance is almost identical to that of the Mirage IIIC, and two examples have been supplied to Switzerland as the Mirage IIIBS, and three to South Africa as the Mirage IIIBZ.

MIRAGE IIIE: The production successor to the Mirage IIIC, the Mirage IIIE is intended primarily for the tactical nuclear strike rôle, and the prototype flew for the first time on April 5, 1961, two further prototypes being completed, and the first production example flying on January 14, 1964, 130 aircraft of this type having been ordered for the Armée de l'Air. Intended to supplant the F-84F Thunderstreak in service with the six squadrons of the 1er, 4e and 9e Escadres operating with the 1er CATac, the Mirage IIIE is externally distinguishable from the IIIC by an 11.8-inch increase in the length of the front fuselage (increasing overall length to 46 ft. 2⅛ in.) which brings the cockpit further forward of the intakes, and the fairing beneath the nose housing the Marconi Doppler navigation radar. Equipment includes TACAN, and CSF Cyrano II*bis* fire control supplants the Cyrano I*bis* of the Mirage IIIC. In order to provide clearance when retracted for a large central store or fuel tank, the main undercarriage legs are raked forward, and the power plant is the Atar 09 C3 with steel compressor and improved afterburner, offering 9,436 lb.s.t. and 13,625 lb. with afterburning.

The two central stores pylons have a total capacity of 2,000 lb., and apart from its special weapons capability, the Mirage IIIE carries the standard armament of two 30-mm. DEFA 5-52 cannon with 125 r.p.g. in place of the interception computer. Various alternative external stores loads up to a maximum of 8,800 lb. may be carried, and although provision is made for the installation of the SEPR 844 rocket pack, a 121 Imp. gal. auxiliary fuel tank normally occupies the space that would be taken by the rocket (the IIIC having a 72.6 Imp. gal. tank in this position). With a maximum loaded weight of the order of 27,760 lb., the Mirage IIIE has the highest gross weight of any of the series. This version of the Mirage has been selected by the Australian government for licence manufacture in Australia for the R.A.A.F. as the Mirage IIIO (see page 6).

MIRAGE IIIR: Intended to supplant the RF-84F Thunderflash with the Armée de l'Air's 33e Escadre de Reconnaissance Tactique, the Mirage IIIR low- and medium-altitude tactical reconnaissance aircraft

(Above) The fourth production Mirage IIIE, the first production example of which flew on January 14, 1964. The Mirage IIIE tactical strike fighter will enter service with Armée de l'Air units during the course of 1965.

has been evolved from the Mirage IIIE, and possesses a similar power plant and essentially similar airframe to those of the tactical strike model. Two prototypes, the Mirage IIIR-01 and -02, were converted from "pre-series" IIIAs, the first flying on October 31, 1961, and the first production Mirage IIIR flew on February 1, 1963, fifty aircraft of this type having been ordered. Two escadrons of the 33ᵉ Escadre operating with the 1er CATac have re-equipped with the Mirage IIIR, the first of these being Escadron 3/33 "Moselle" which began re-equipping in 1963, followed by Escadron 2/33 "Savoie" in 1964. The third component of the 33ᵉ Escadre, 1/33 "Belfort", continues to operate the RF-84F for reconnaissance pilot training.

The space occupied by the Cyrano II fire control radar in the Mirage IIIE houses a set of OMERA cameras in the IIIR. Equipment for day and night photo-reconnaissance includes up to five OMERA 31 cameras, a photo-electric cell for night photography, a CSF radio altimeter which automatically adjusts the camera repetition rate in relation to altitude, and a removable flare launcher. For armed reconnaissance missions there is a removable mounting with two 30-mm. DEFA 5-52 cannon and ammunition in the forward fuselage bay. Similar underwing loads to those of the Mirage IIIE may be carried, and the pilot is provided with a SFOM reflector sight and a CSF Low Altitude Bombing System (LABS). Eighteen

essentially similar aircraft are to be manufactured under licence in Switzerland under the designation Mirage IIIRS.

(Above) A tandem two-seat Mirage IIIB of Escadron 3/2 "Alsace" based at Dijon Longvic with the 2ᵉ Escadre.

(Below and above, right) A Mirage IIIR of Escadron 3/33 "Moselle", one of the three components of the 33ᵉ Escadre, the others being Escadron 1/33 "Belfort" with RF-84F Thunderflashes, and Escadron 2/33 "Savoie" with Mirage IIIRs.

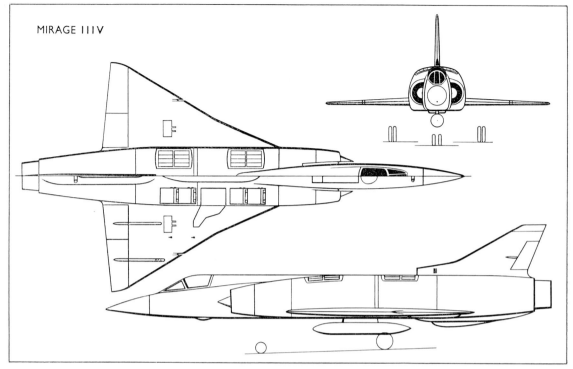

MIRAGE IIIV

Forerunner of the Mirage IIIV V/STOL strike and reconnaissance fighter, the Balzac V-001 employs much of the airframe of the original Mirage III-001 and is, to all intents and purposes, a scaled-down test-bed for the fighter. The Balzac was seriously damaged in an accident on January 10, 1964, but was rebuilt and was expected to resume its flight test programme late in the same year.

MIRAGE IIIV: Based broadly on the design of the current production Mirage IIIE, the Mirage IIIV is a short- and vertical-take-off-and-landing strike and reconnaissance fighter, two prototypes of which, the Mirage IIIV-01 and -02, were ordered in 1961. To provide advance data on the characteristics of the Mirage IIIV, the airframe of the original Mirage III-001 was adapted as the basis for a half-scale research prototype designated Balzac. This employs the original wing and certain fuselage components, the Atar 101G.1 turbojet being replaced by a 4,400 lb.s.t. Bristol Siddeley Orpheus B.Or.3 with suitably smaller air intakes, and eight 2,160 lb.s.t. Rolls-Royce RB.108 Stage 1A lift engines being installed in the fuselage, with retractable intake grills and fairing doors for these above and below the fuselage. Having a loaded weight of 15,432 lb., the Balzac effected its first free

hovering flight on October 13, 1962, the first full transition following on March 18, 1963. Late in 1963, adjustable 45° jet deflectors were provided for the lift engines, but on January 10, 1964, the Balzac was seriously damaged in a crash resulting from a critical divergent lateral oscillation during a hovering descent. The aircraft was subsequently reconstructed and was scheduled to resume trials late in 1964.

The Mirage IIIV-01's flight trials were delayed largely as a result of propulsion engine problems, and initial tests were conducted with a SNECMA-modified Pratt and Whitney JTF10 subsonic turbofan redesignated TF-104 and developing 10,500 lb.s.t. dry, this power plant having been first flight tested on June 4, 1964 in the Mirage IIIT test-bed. The TF-104 was scheduled to be replaced during February 1965, after the completion of initial flight trials, by the SNECMA TF-106, a supersonic derivative of the same turbofan possessing a dry rating of 11,680 lb.s.t., or 19,845 lb. with fully modulated afterburning. Development difficulties with the TF-106 led to the decision, early in 1964, to install in the Mirage IIIV-02 the Pratt and Whitney TF-30 turbofan (JTF10A-20) which, designated TF-306 in France, had earlier been selected to power the General Dynamics F-111 and SAAB-37 Viggen.

The Mirage IIIV-01 has eight vertically-mounted 4,400 lb.s.t. Rolls-Royce RB.162-2 lift engines, although these may be expected to be replaced at an early development stage by 5,500 lb.s.t. RB.162-31s, and approximate loaded weight for vertical take-off is 29,000 lb. Although both prototypes of the Mirage IIIV are single-seaters, it is anticipated that the definitive production model which is expected to enter service with the Armée de l'Air in 1967–68 will be of two-seat configuration.

G.A.M.DASSAULT MIRAGE IVA

Scheduled to attain operational status with the Mirage IVA early in 1965, the 91ᵉ Escadre is the first first-line unit of the Commandement des Forces Aériennes Stratégique—France's Strategic Air Command—to receive this supersonic bomber destined to equip the so-called "force de dissuasion". Despite its name and a close aerodynamic resemblance to the smaller Mirage III, the Mirage IVA is, in fact, an entirely new type, and has been designed for an unrefuelled radius of action at altitude of the order of a thousand miles, including Mach 1.7 dash, although it will normally operate with the KC-135F tankers of the 90ᵉ Escadre of the Commandement du Transport Aérien Militaire. Fifty Mirage IVA bombers have been ordered, approximately half this quantity being scheduled for completion by the end of 1964, with the remainder by mid-1965 when thirty-six are scheduled to have attained operational status.

Carrying two crew members seated in tandem Martin-Baker ground-level ejector seats, the Mirage IVA employs a similar 60° delta layout to that of the Mirage III, but the larger overall dimensions of the bomber have dictated the use of more advanced design and structural techniques. Design development was initiated in 1957, and the first prototype, the Mirage IV-01, was flown for the first time on June 17, 1959, powered by two Atar 09 B turbojets each offering 13,230 lb.s.t. with afterburning. A speed of Mach 1.9 was attained in level flight with this aircraft during the following month. Various modifications were subsequently introduced, an aerodynamic replica of the free-falling nuclear weapon was added, this being semi-recessed beneath the fuselage, and in its new configuration, the Mirage IV-01 achieved Mach 2.0 during its thirty-third flight, following this with a stabilized cruise of Mach 1.85 at 59,000 ft. The aerodynamic effect of the addition of two 550 Imp. gal. underwing fuel tanks was examined.

The Mirage IV-01 was eventually destroyed in an accident on February 13, 1963, after being delivered to the Armée de l'Air for pilot training and having logged 400 flying hours, but in the meantime, three preproduction aircraft had been ordered, the first of these, the Mirage IVA-02, having flown on October 12, 1961, the IVA-03 and -04 following on June 1, 1962 and January 23, 1963 respectively. Powered by Atar 09 C engines, the Mirage IVA-02 possessed slightly larger

overall dimensions than those of the prototype, and embodied considerable redesign, including a new, deeper forward fuselage, new vertical tail surfaces of revised contour, and a new, repositioned undercarriage. The third pre-production aircraft, the Mirage IVA-04, was the first machine to be powered by the definitive Atar 09 K turbojet, and was fully representative of the production model, incorporating the complete bombing-navigation system and flight refuelling equipment. The first pre-production aircraft was used for bombing trials and development at Colomb-Béchar, and the second was employed for flight refuelling trials and the development of the navigation system.

(*Below*) *Top to bottom: The Mirage IV-01, the Mirage IVA-02, the Mirage IVA-03, and the Mirage IVA-04.*

(*Below*) *The first production Mirage IVA which flew for the first time on December 7, 1963. Scheduled to attain operational status with the Armée de l'Air early in 1965, the Mirage IVA will equip the 91ᵉ Escadre.*

A production Mirage IVA fitted with a dummy of the 50-kiloton free-falling nuclear weapon.

The first production Mirage IVA was flown on December 7, 1963, and eight had been delivered by October 1964 when preparations for the service introduction of the type had begun, operational status being planned for the first Mirage IVA unit by early 1965. In service, the Mirage IVA will carry extensive electronic countermeasures equipment and will be equipped with a 50-kiloton free-falling weapon which can be detonated by chronometric fuse at high altitude or by radar at low altitude, and embodies a thermostatically-controlled refrigeration unit. Speed performance of the Mirage IVA is the same with or without the bomb installed. For tactical missions, the Mirage IVA will, from 1970, carry the new television-guided missile with conventional warhead to be developed jointly by MATRA and Hawker Siddeley. The total internal fuel capacity of the Mirage IVA is 3,080 Imp. gal., and this may be supplemented by two 550 Imp. gal. jettisonable auxiliary tanks. Flight refuelling equipment of the probe and drogue type is provided for use with the Boeing KC-135F. The Mirage IVA can operate from normal NATO 2,625-yd. runways, and provision is made for the attachment of twelve JATO rockets. Four Mirage IVAs with weapons on board are to be maintained in the air on alert status around the clock, these being part of the force of thirty-two aircraft to be kept at a constant state of readiness. The Mirage IVAs will form four-plane flights, and those not airborne will be maintained on two categories of alert—four-minute runway alert and longer-term availability. The air component of France's Force Nucléaire Stratégique will account for 20% of the fuel and 44% of the spares costs of the entire Armée de l'Air.

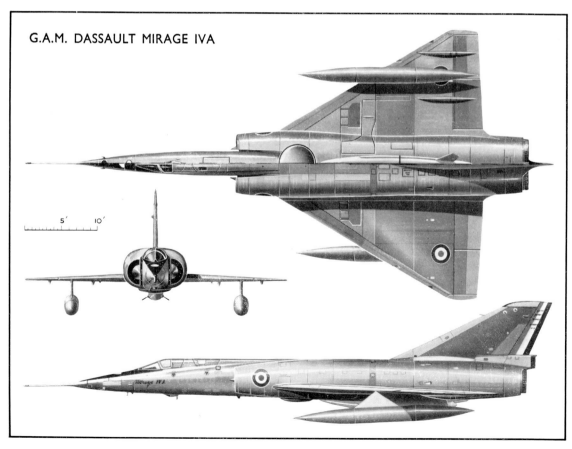

G.A.M. DASSAULT MIRAGE IVA

MIRAGE IVA SPECIFICATION

Power Plants: *Two SNECMA Atar 09 K turbojets each rated at 10,362 lb.s.t. or 15,432 lb.s.t. with full afterburning.*
Armament: *One 50-kiloton free-falling weapon semi-recessed beneath fuselage.*
Performance: *Max. speed, 1,454 m.p.h. at 40,000 ft. (Mach 2.2); max. stabilized speed, 1,122 m.p.h. at 60,000 ft. (Mach 1.7); limiting Mach number, 2.3;*

tactical radius (to target at supersonic speed and return at Mach 0.9), 770 mls.; maximum unrefuelled range (with two 550 Imp. gal. underwing tanks), 2,485 mls. at 595 m.p.h. (Mach 0.9) at 40,000 ft.; climb to 36,090 ft., 4 min. 15 sec.; ceiling, 65,600 ft.
Weights: *Empty, 31,967 lb.; Normal loaded, 69,666 lb.*
Dimensions: *Span, 38 ft. 10¼ in.; length, 76 ft. 11¼ in.; height, 17 ft. 8½ in.; wing area, 839.584 sq. ft.*

The Vautour IIA did not enter service with the Armée de l'Air but was delivered to the Israeli Defence Force/Air Force, and one of twenty-five aircraft supplied to that service and currently equipping two squadrons is illustrated above.

SUD-AVIATION SO-4050 VAUTOUR II

Designed to fulfil the rôles of all-weather interceptor fighter, close support aircraft and level bomber, the Vautour is now obsolescent, but still serves in its two-seat night and all-weather interceptor rôle with the Armée de l'Air's 30ᵉ Escadre Tout-Temps, and in its level bomber form with the 92ᵉ Escadre, although in the latter unit it is now expected to be phased out in favour of the Mirage IVA. The tactical attack version never entered Armée de l'Air service, but the majority of the examples of this model built were supplied to Israel and currently equips two squadrons of that country's air arm.

The first of three prototypes of the Vautour was flown on October 16, 1952 powered by 5,280 lb.s.t. Atar 101B turbojets. This aircraft was later re-engined with the 6,170 lb.s.t. Atar 101C which also powered the second prototype, while the third had two 8,000 lb.s.t. Sapphire A.S.Sa.6 engines. The first of six pre-production Vautours, the SO-4050-04, flew on March 18, 1955, and apart from the SO-4050-05 which had 9,260 lb.s.t. Rolls-Royce Avons, all pre-production machines received the 6,615 lb.s.t. Atar 101D-1 turbojet. One hundred and sixty Vautours were originally ordered for the Armée de l'Air, but this order was subsequently cut by twenty machines, and the remaining 140 aircraft were delivered in the following versions:

VAUTOUR IIN: Produced in larger numbers than other versions of the Vautour, the IIN tandem two-seat night and all-weather interceptor was originally the most heavily armed aircraft in its category, and seventy machines were built, the last of these being delivered in 1959. The crew are seated over the forward armament bay which houses four 30-mm. DEFA 5-52 cannon with 100 r.p.g., and immediately aft of the

cannon installation are two MATRA Type 104A rocket packs housing a total of 232 68-mm. SNEB rockets. By mid-1964, when fifty-three Vautour fighters remained in service, mostly with the 30ᵉ Escadre Tout-Temps, the primary armament comprised four MATRA R.511 semi-passive homing AAMs mounted on pylons beneath the wings, and a slab-type tailplane had been fitted to most aircraft, the designation being changed from IIN to II.1N.

During 1964, a shortage of supersonic interceptors resulted in an investigation of the possibility of extensively modifying the existing Vautour II.1Ns to up-date their operational capability. The existing aircraft can exceed Mach 1.0 slightly in a shallow dive, and proposed changes to endow the aircraft with level

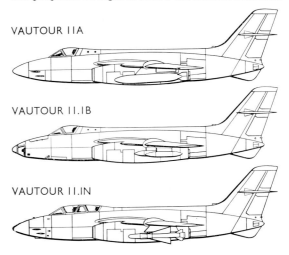

VAUTOUR IIA

VAUTOUR II.1B

VAUTOUR II.1N

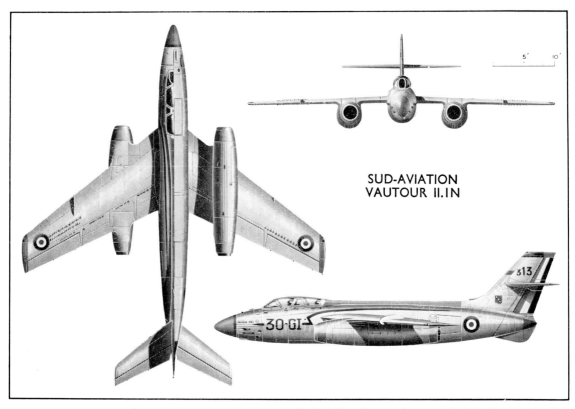

SUD-AVIATION
VAUTOUR II.1N

(Above) A Vautour IIB of the 92e Escadre which is expected to re-equip with the Mirage IVA during 1965. Thirty-one of the forty production Vautour IIB bombers remained in service in mid-1964.

flight supersonic capabilities included the introduction of new wing leading edges, the provision of bulged equipment packs on the fuselage sides to give a measure of area ruling, and the installation of more powerful engines. In the event, this scheme was not proceeded with.

VAUTOUR IIB: The level bombing version of the basic aircraft, the Vautour IIB, which, until the introduction of the Mirage IVA, provided the operational nucleus of the Commandement des Forces Aériennes Stratégique, and was in process of being phased out late in 1964, differs from the Vautour IIN primarily in the forward fuselage which features a glazed nose compartment housing the bombardier. A similar internal weapons bay is provided, and this can accommodate three 1,000-lb. bombs, six 750-lb. or 500-lb. bombs, or nine 200-lb. bombs. The internal weapons load may be supplemented by four 1,000-lb., 750-lb., or 500-lb. bombs on underwing stations. No cannon armament is fitted.

One prototype and one pre-production example of

the level bomber version preceded the first production Vautour IIB which flew on July 31, 1957, and forty aircraft of this type were delivered to the Armée de l'Air, thirty-one of these remaining in service in mid-1964. The application of a slab-type tailplane had by that time resulted in a change in designation from IIB to II.1B.

VAUTOUR IIA: A single-seater, the Vautour IIA tactical attack aircraft carries the same cannon armament as the Vautour IIN and the same bomb load as the Vautour IIB. The first production example flew on April 30, 1956, being preceded by a prototype and two pre-production aircraft, and thirty aircraft were built, of which twenty-five were supplied to Israel for service with the Israeli Defence Force/Air Force.

The following specification relates specifically to the Vautour II.1N interceptor but is generally applicable to the other versions of this aircraft.

VAUTOUR II.1N SPECIFICATION

Power Plants: *Two SNECMA Atar 101E-3 turbojets each rated at 7,720 lb.s.t.*
Armament: *Four 30-mm. DEFA 5-52 cannon with 100 r.p.g., four MATRA R.511 AAMs and 232 68-mm. SNEB rockets.*
Performance: *Max. speed, 686 m.p.h. at sea level (Mach 0.9), 590 m.p.h. at 40,000 ft.; initial climb rate (at 33,069 lb.), 11,820 ft./min.; service ceiling, 49,000 ft.; time to 39,370 ft., 7 min.; tactical radius, 750 mls.; ferry range, 3,700 mls.*
Weights: *Empty, 23,150 lb.; normal loaded, 33,069 lb.; max. loaded, 45,635 lb.*
Dimensions: *Span, 49 ft. 6½ in.; length, 51 ft. 1 in.; height, 14 ft. 1¾ in.; wing area, 484.376 sq. ft.*

VFW 1262

Winner of the VAK (Vertical-Aufklärungs-und-Kampfeinsitzer) 191 contest held in 1964 to select a VTOL successor to the Fiat G.91R lightweight and reconnaissance aircraft for service in both the Luftwaffe and the Italian Air Force during the 'seventies, the VFW 1262 is to be developed jointly by the Vereinigte Flugtechnische Werke GmbH (VFW) in Germany and Fiat in Italy, current plans providing for prototypes or pre-production models to fly by 1969 at the latest.

Four designs were evaluated in the VAK 191 contest, these being the Hawker Siddeley Kestrel (VAK 191A), the VFW 1262 (VAK 191B), the EWR 340 (VAK 191C), and the Fiat G.95/4 (VAK 191D), and the winning design, the VFW 1262, combines the vectored thrust and composite power plant concepts, a single lift engine being placed fore and aft of the main engine which will provide thrust for both lift and forward propulsion. The selected lift engines are 5,500 lb.s.t. Rolls-Royce RB.162-31s, and the principal power plant will be the Rolls-Royce/MAN RB.193 with thrust deflection via swivelling nozzles. The RB.193 will offer a maximum thrust of approximately 12,000 lb., and work on this power plant in the U.K. is being shared 2:1 between Rolls-Royce and Bristol Siddeley. The lift engines will be provided with doors to deflect their thrust rearwards during ground running immediately prior to take-off to reduce ground erosion, and it is possible that, in lightly loaded condition, forward flight may be sustained on the lift engines alone in the event of the principal engine failing in cruise.

The small size of the principal engine will allow the provision of an internal weapons bay, presumably equipped with a rotary weapons door, and the extremely small and flapless wings, combined with the horizontal ground attitude, suggest that short take-off techniques will not be used. The requirement to which

Currently in the detailed design phase, the VFW 1262 lightweight VTOL strike and reconnaissance aircraft, illustrated in model form above, will combine a vectored-thrust Rolls-Royce RB.193 for both lift and forward propulsion with two direct lift RB.162-31 engines.

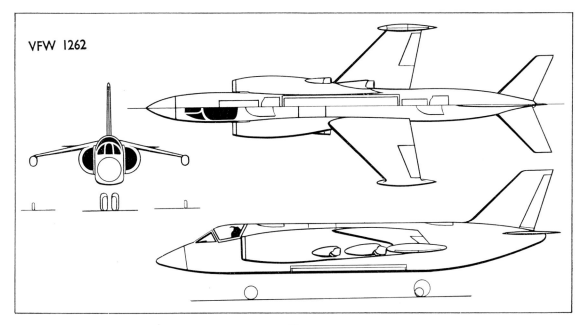

VFW 1262

the VFW 1262 has been designed called for high subsonic performance with a target approach speed over a 250-mile low-level range of Mach 0.92.

Estimated gross weight for vertical take-off is currently of the order of 17,000 lb., overall dimensions including a span of 18 ft. 0 in., and a length of 47 ft. 1 in.

The VFW 1262, winner of the VAK 191 contest, is expected to be developed jointly by Federal Germany and Italy as a replacement for the Fiat G.91R in the strike and reconnaissance rôles.

EWR-SÜD VJ 101D

Despite its designation, the VJ 101D V/STOL strike and reconnaissance fighter which is currently being developed by the Entwicklungsring-Süd as a potential successor to the F-104G Starfighter bears no relationship to the VJ 101C V/STOL research aircraft. Two prototypes of the VJ 101D were ordered by the Federal German Defence Ministry in December 1962, although no time scale has been indicated for the completion and testing of these aircraft, and at the time of closing for press detail design had still to be finalised, and the future of the programme was by no means certain.

As currently projected, the VJ 101D will be powered by two 6,850 lb.s.t. RB.153-61 turbofan engines developed jointly by Rolls-Royce and MAN-Turbo-

motoren GmbH, reheat jet pipes boosting the thrust of each engine to some 11,600 lb. for level flight. These power plants are to be fitted with switch-in deflectors which will enable the entire dry thrust to be used for lift, in which it will be augmented by five pure-lift Rolls-Royce RB.162-31 engines which, each developing 5,500 lb.s.t., will be mounted in line along the centre fuselage, providing a total lift force of 41,200 lb., and indicating a gross weight of the order of 35,000 lb. for VTOL operation. The switch-in thrust deflectors developed by MAN-Turbomotoren divert thrust for VTOL through two pipes on the inner sides of the engines which emerge in tandem on the aircraft centre-line. The deflectors may be swivelled 15° aft to aid transition.

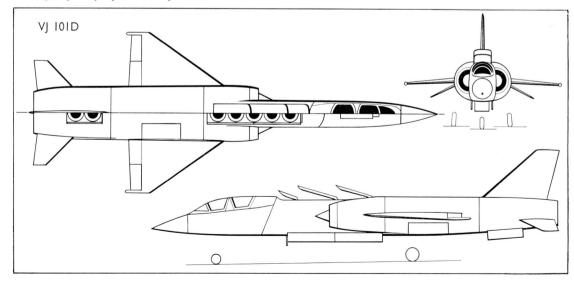

VJ 101D

HAL HF-24 MARUT

The Marut (Wind Spirit) is the first Indian jet combat aircraft of indigenous design to attain production. Development was initiated by Hindustan Aircraft Limited (HAL) in 1956, the design team at that time comprising eighteen German engineers led by Professor Kurt Tank, three Indian senior design engineers and twenty-two other Indian design personnel. A full-scale wooden glider model was built for free-flight trials, this being flown for the first time on March 21, 1959, and assembly of the first of two HF-24 Marut prototypes (BR-462) began in April 1960, taxying trials commencing eleven months later, in February 1961, by which time HAL had received orders for eighteen pre-production and forty-four production Marut fighters. Initiation of the flight test programme was delayed as a result of a runway accident, but the first flight finally took place on June 17, 1961, the *official* first flight following on June 24th in the presence of the then Defence Minister, Shri Krishna Menon.

The Marut was designed to meet a specification drawn up by the Indian Air Force which called for a multi-mission aircraft possessing high supersonic performance, and from the outset the Marut was designed with a view to the ultimate installation of a pair of Bristol Siddeley Orpheus B.Or.12 turbojets each offering a dry thrust of 6,740 lb. and 8,170 lb. with afterburning. In the event, development of this version of the Orpheus was discontinued, and the Indian government is being offered the basic Orpheus engine married to the high-pressure inner spool of the Pegasus, and offering a similar performance to that of the abandoned Orpheus B.Or.12. In the meantime, it had been decided to produce an interim version of the aircraft, the Marut Mk.1 with non-afterburning Orpheus 703 engines pending the availability of suitable power plants for the definitive Marut Mk.2.

In October 1962 the second prototype Marut (BR-463) joined the test programme, followed in March 1963 by the first pre-production Marut Mk.1 (BD-828) which, like the prototypes, was fitted with imported Orpheus 703 engines of 4,850 lb.s.t. In the meantime, HAL's Engine Division, which had received an initial order for 135 licence-built Orpheus 703 engines, had begun development of an afterburning system, and it was decided to install a pair of afterburning Orpheus turbojets in the second pre-production airframe (BD-829) as the prototype Marut Mk.1A. The HAL-developed afterburner currently boosts thrust by some sixteen per cent (to 5,630 lb.), but it is anticipated that this will be raised to thirty-six per cent, boosting thrust of the Orpheus 703 to approximately 6,600 lb., and enabling the Marut to attain level speeds of the order of Mach 1.2 (790 m.p.h. above 36,000 ft.). The improved afterburners are being installed in the fourth and fifth pre-production aircraft which, serving as prototypes of the Marut Mk.1A, were scheduled to join the test programme early in 1965.

In the meantime, in August 1963, the Indian Defence Ministry placed an order with HAL for a further 152 aircraft, bringing total orders for the Marut to 214 machines which, including the pre-production aircraft, comprised eighty Mk.1s with the non-afterburning Orpheus and 134 Mks.1A and 1B with the afterburning Orpheus. However, the Marut is considered as potentially a Mach 2.0 aircraft, and in order to exploit the full potential of the basic design an appreciably more powerful afterburning turbojet is

(Below and above, right) The third pre-production Marut Mk. 1 (BD-830) with the various weapons and offensive stores that it will carry in service. The first operational Marut Mk. 1 squadron is scheduled to be equipped by January 1966.

HF-24 MARUT MK.1

(Above and below) The first prototype HF-24 Marut (BR-462) which flew for the first time on June 17, 1961.

required for the Mark 2 version currently considered to be the definitive model. The Soviet Union has offered the RD-9F turbojet (essentially similar to the engine installed in the late production MiG-19), but although extensive tests were conducted with this power plant, the Russians were not prepared to develop the RD-9F beyond its present Mach 1.4 compressor stress limit, and negotiations between the Indian and Soviet governments concerning this engine were terminated at the beginning of 1964. Various other power plants have been considered, including the previously mentioned Orpheus derivative, the Brandner-designed E-300 turbojet which is being flight tested in a Marut airframe prior to installation in the HA-300 (see page 77), the Rolls-Royce RB.153, the Pratt and Whitney J52, and the General Electric GE1/JO-1, but no decision had been taken at the time of closing for press.

The time scale for the initial eighteen pre-production and forty-four production Marut fighters originally called for the delivery of the fifth to the tenth pre-production machines (BD-832 to BD-837) to the Indian Air Force's Air Trials Unit during the summer of 1964, a second six to the Handling Flight during the winter of 1964-65, with first squadron deliveries in mid-1965, but this programme would seem to have

slipped despite the *formal* handing-over of four Maruts (the first prototype and the first three pre-production aircraft which are, in fact, to be retained by HAL for development purposes) to the Indian Air Force on May 10, 1964.

The first Indian Air Force squadron with sixteen Marut Mk.1 fighters is scheduled to be equipped by January 1966, and the second squadron of sixteen aircraft—to be fitted with Ferranti Airpass (Airborne Interception Radar and Pilot's Attack Sight System)—will be equipped by September 1966.

The Marut is a multi-mission aircraft capable of fulfilling the intercept, strike and reconnaissance rôles. For the intercept rôle, the Mks.1 and 1A carry four 30-mm. Aden cannon which will eventually be supplemented by four Atoll infra-red homing missiles. Up to 4,000 lb. of ordnance may be carried externally, and although basically a single-seater, the Marut has room for a second cockpit in tandem (Mk.1B), and provision has been made in the design for dual controls. In the prototypes the space immediately aft of the pilot is occupied by test instrumentation, but in the service single-seat versions this may be occupied by a missile launcher with four vertical rows of twelve spin-stabilised rockets, a camera pack, weapons system electronics or additional fuel.

MARUT MK.1 SPECIFICATION

Power Plants: *Two HAL-built Bristol Siddeley Orpheus 703 turbojets each rated at 4,850 lb.s.t.*
Armament: *(Internal) Four 30-mm. Aden cannon with 125 r.p.g. or forty-eight spin-stabilised rockets, and (externally) four 1,000-lb. general purpose bombs, four MATRA rocket pods each containing nineteen 3-in. rockets, sixteen 60-lb. HVARs, or four Atoll infra-red homing AAMs.*
Performance: *Approx. max. speed, 630 m.p.h. at 40,000 ft. (Mach 0.95), 705 m.p.h. at sea level (Mach 0.925); time to 40,000 ft., 7 min.; service ceiling, 46,000 ft.; approx. combat radius (internal fuel), 380–420 mls. at 560 m.p.h. at 36,000 ft. (Mach 0.85).*
Weights: *Loaded, 18,740 lb.; max. overload, 24,250 lb.*
Dimensions: *Span, 29 ft. 6⅓ in.; length, 51 ft. 7⅓ in.; height, 13 ft. 1½ in.; approx. wing area, 295 sq. ft.*

FIAT G.91

The G.91 lightweight reconnaissance and strike fighter was the successful contender for orders in a NATO contest announced in December 1953. An initial contract for three prototypes and twenty-seven pre-production machines was placed on June 3, 1955, and little more than a year later, on August 9, 1956, the first prototype, powered by a 4,050 lb.s.t. Orpheus B.Or.1 turbojet, was flown. The loss of this prototype during the early stages of the flight test programme resulted in some delay, and the second prototype, which flew in July 1957, featured some redesign and employed the 4,850 lb.s.t. Orpheus B.Or.3 turbojet. The first pre-production G.91 was flown on February 20, 1958, and in August of that year the 103º Gruppo Caccia Tattici Leggeri was formed at Pratica di Mare for the operational evaluation of the aircraft, and the training of NATO pilots in the ground attack rôle.

There was some delay before quantity production orders were placed and, in the event, only Italy and Germany were to adopt the type, the principal versions of which are the G.91R single-seat reconnaissance and strike fighter and G.91T tandem two-seat advanced trainer.

G.91R: The G.91R is basically similar to the pre-production G.91 but features a redesigned fuselage nose housing three Vinten cameras for forward and lateral oblique photography. The initial model, the G.91R.1, twenty-five examples of which were ordered for the Italian Air Force, carries an armament of four 0.5-in. Colt-Browning machine guns, and has two underwing stores pylons for two 250-lb. bombs, two napalm tanks,

or various combinations of 2.75-in., 3-in. or 5-in. HVARs. A further twenty-five aircraft, essentially similar to the initial model but designated G.91R.1A and having modified navigational equipment, were supplied to the Italian Air Force, and currently serve with the 14° and 103° Gruppi Caccia Tattici Leggeri.

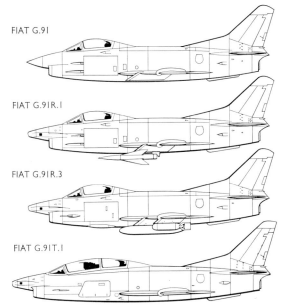

FIAT G.91

FIAT G.91R.1

FIAT G.91R.3

FIAT G.91T.1

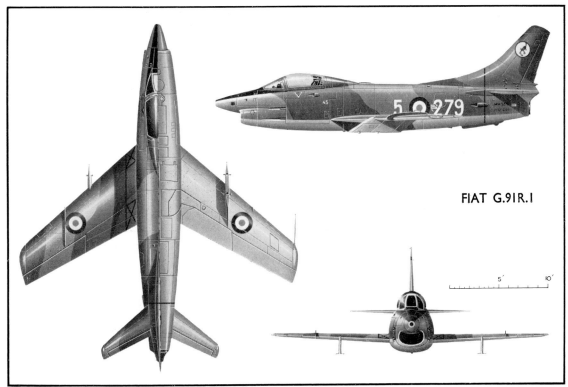

FIAT G.91R.1

A tandem two-seat Fiat G.91T.3 trainer of Waffenschule 50. The G.91T.3 of the Luftwaffe differs from the G.91T.1 of the Italian Air Force (see opposite) in equipment, and is some 200 lb. heavier.

The variant ordered for the Luftwaffe, the G.91R.3, differs from the G.91R.1 and 1A in having an armament of two 30-mm. DEFA cannon, the provision of four underwing pylons, and various equipment changes, including the installation of Bendix Doppler and Computing Devices of Canada Position and Homing Indicator. Seventy-four aircraft manufactured by the parent company were supplied to the Luftwaffe, and the first unit to operate the G.91R.3, Aufklarungsgeschwader 53 (Aufkl.G53), was commissioned on May 5, 1962. In the meantime, licence manufacture of the G.91R.3 in Germany had been initiated by a consortium of Dornier, Messerschmitt and Heinkel, the first German-built aircraft flying from the Oberpfaffenhofen airfield on July 20, 1961, a total of 240 machines eventually being ordered. The second Luftwaffe unit to equip with the G.91R.3 was Aufkl.G.54.

The G.91R.4 carries the same gun armament as the G.91R.1 but features similar equipment to that of the G.91R.3 and has four underwing stores pylons. Twenty-five examples of this version were originally to have been supplied to each of the Greek and Turkish air forces but, in the event, they passed into the Luftwaffe inventory. The G.91R.5 was a proposed version with increased range for Norway, and the G.91R.6 is an improved version for the Italian Air Force, twenty-five of which were ordered in 1964. The G.91R.6 features a reinforced undercarriage with modified wheels and tubeless tyres, enlarged air brakes, and will be equipped with Doppler and a Position and Homing Indicator not previously installed in Italian Air Force G.91s. Internal fuel capacity is increased from 352 to 372 Imp. gal., a pitch damper is introduced, the electrical and air conditioning systems are boosted, provision is made for JATO rockets, and the underwing pylons are capable of lifting heavier loads and are supplemented by additional wing strongpoints.

G.91T: A tandem two-seat training development of the single-seat G.91R, the G.91T may also be used as a tactical fighter, and the first of two prototypes flew on May 31, 1960. Two versions have since been manufactured in quantity, the first of these being the G.91T.1 for the Italian Air Force, sixty-six examples of which have been ordered, and the second being the G.91T.3 for the Luftwaffe, forty-four examples having been delivered to that service.

(Below) Fiat G.91R.1A reconnaissance and strike fighters of the Italian Air Force's 51st Stormo. Two Gruppi Caccia Tattici Leggeri of the Italian Air Force are currently operating the G.91R.1 and 1A.

The Italian Air Force has ordered a total of sixty-six G.91T.1 tandem two-seat trainers (above). Operational missions may be undertaken by the G.91T which has a built-in armament of two 0.5-in. guns and carries various underwing loads.

The G.91T.1 and T.3 differ in equipment, the latter being some 200 lb. heavier, but both carry a pair of 0.5-in. Colt-Browning machine guns, and can lift two 500-lb. bombs, sixty-two 2-in. rockets, thirty-eight 2.75-in. rockets, or two Nord AS.20 or AS.30L missiles on their two underwing pylons. According to equipment, empty weight ranges from 7,240 to 7,405 lb., and loaded weight from 11,800 to 11,995 lb. A projected advanced systems training version with NASARR in the nose, the gun bays occupied by electronic equipment, and similar instrument positioning to that of the F-104G Starfighter is designated G.91T.4, and further projected derivatives employing the lengthened fuselage of the G.91T include the G.91.BS/1 single-seat and BS/2 two-seat battlefield surveillance aircraft, and the twin-jet G.91Y single-seat long-range strike and reconnaissance aircraft and G.91YT two-seat trainer. Both 'Y' models are intended to have side-by-side mounted General Electric J85 turbojets in place of the single Orpheus.

G.91 PAN: Sixteen of the twenty-seven pre-production G.91 strike fighters which served with the 103° Gruppo until supplanted by the G.91R were in process of conversion to G.91 PAN configuration during 1964. The G.91 PAN is a special version for the Pattuglia Acrobatica Nazionali (National Aerobatic Team) in which all armament has been removed and replaced by ballast, pitch dampers (similar to those of the G.91R.6) have been fitted, the G.91 and G.91R.1 having only yaw dampers, and special smoke tanks are mounted beneath the wings.

Several other experimental versions of the basic aircraft have been tested, including the G.91A, a pre-production aircraft modified to have automatic leading-edge slats and integral wing tanks, an increase

(Above) G.91R.4s of Waffenschule 50, the operational training wing responsible for the training of Luftwaffe reconnaissance pilots.

A G.91R.3 of Aufklarungsgeschwader 53 at Leipheim.

in wing span and gross area to 29 ft. 6½ in. and 194 sq. ft. respectively, and increased internal fuel capacity, and the G.91N, another pre-production aircraft modified to evaluate various navigational aids, including Rho-Theta and Decca.

G.91R SPECIFICATION

Power Plant: *One Bristol Siddeley Orpheus 80302 turbojet rated at 5,000 lb.s.t.*
Armament: *(G.91R.1) Four 0.5-in. Colt-Browning machine guns with 300 r.p.g., (G.91R.3) two 30-mm. DEFA cannon with 125 r.p.g. and (G.91R.3 and R.6) two 250-lb. or 500-lb. general-purpose bombs, twelve 3-in. or six 5-in. HVARs, two Nord AS.20 or AS.30L ASMs, or two packs of nineteen or thirty-one 2-in. rockets.*
Performance: *Max. speed, 668 m.p.h. at sea level (Mach 0.88), 675 m.p.h. at 5,000 ft. (Mach 0.9), 637*
m.p.h. at 20,000 ft. (Mach 0.91); initial climb rate, 6,000 ft./min.; time to 13,120 ft., 4 min. 30 sec., to 24,246 ft., 6 min. 40 sec.; service ceiling, 43,000 ft.; combat radius (including ten minutes loiter), 196 mls.; range (ferry), 1,150 mls. (352 Imp. gal. internal fuel and two 114 Imp. gal. drop tanks) at 253 m.p.h. at 35,000 ft.
Weights: *Empty, 7,240–7,405 lb.; normal loaded, 11,800–11,995 lb.; max. overload, 12,500 lb.*
Dimensions: *Span, 28 ft. 1 in.; length, 33 ft. 9¼ in.; height, 13 ft. 1½ in.; wing area, 176.7 sq. ft.*

SAAB-29

Currently being phased out of service with the Flygvapnet, or Royal Swedish Air Force, in favour of the SAAB-35, the SAAB-29 provided the backbone of Swedish day fighter defence throughout most of the 'fifties, and when production terminated in April 1956, a total of 656 machines of this type had been delivered. The final interceptor model, the SAAB-29F, is still serving with the Flygvapnet's Flottiljer (Wings) 3, 4 and 9, although it will be replaced during the course of 1965, and with the two Jagdbomberstaffeln of the Austrian Air Force.

The SAAB-29, nicknamed "Tunnan", or "Flying Barrel", was the first swept-wing interceptor fighter of European design to enter production, and the first of three prototypes powered by British-built Ghost 45 turbojets of 4,400 lb.s.t. flew on September 1, 1948, F 13 at Norrköping commencing to re-equip with the initial production model, the SAAB-29A with a Svenska Flygmotor-built version of the Ghost, the RM 2, in May 1951. Designated J 29A in Flygvapnet service, the fighter was limited to Mach 0.86 in level

flight at all altitudes, maximum speed being 640 m.p.h. at 5,000 ft., although, with underwing tanks fitted, limiting speed was 495 m.p.h. Initial climb rate was 7,800 ft./min., service ceiling was 47,500 ft., and empty and normal loaded weights were 9,479 lb. and 13,360 lb. respectively. Rate of roll was high, turning radius small, and the aircraft made an excellent gun platform. Some aileron flutter had been experienced with the prototypes when the wing-mounted air brakes were extended, and on the production model the full-span ailerons, which had provided flap action by droop, were modified, small, simple flaps being introduced, the air brakes being transferred to the fuselage, and irreversible aileron control being provided.

Some two hundred SAAB-29A fighters had been completed when, on March 11, 1953, the prototype SAAB-29B was flown, this embodying some increase in internal fuel capacity and having multi-mission capabilities, entering service both as an interceptor (J 29B) and attack aircraft (A 29B). In the latter rôle the aircraft could supplement its four 20-mm. Hispano cannon with an underwing load of fourteen 14.5-cm. or twenty-four 75-mm. Bofors unguided AAMs with air-to-ground capability, napalm tanks, 220-lb. flash bombs or 550-lb. general-purpose bombs. Evolved in parallel with the SAAB-29B, the SAAB-29C was a reconnaissance version with six automatic cameras in the forward fuselage replacing the cannon bay. First flown on June 3, 1953, this model entered service as the S 29C, all aircraft of this type later being fitted with a "dog tooth" type wing leading edge which raised the critical Mach number slightly and improved transonic characteristics.

The SAAB-29D was the first variant to be fitted with a Swedish-designed afterburner, boosting the 4,750 lb.s.t. of the RM 2 engine to 6,170 lb.s.t., and increasing initial climb rate from 7,800 ft./min. to nearly 12,000 ft./min. Only a small number of SAAB-29Ds were built, and the next variant, the SAAB-29E which first flew on December 3, 1953, was the first to standardise on the "dog tooth" wing leading edge, both this and the afterburner being combined in the definitive production model, the SAAB-29F, which flew as a prototype on March 20, 1954.

A 29B

S 29C

J 29F

A SAAB-29F of No. 1 Jagdbomber-Staffel of the Austrian Air Force. Thirty SAAB-29F fighter-bombers have been delivered to Austria, equipping two staffeln, and fifteen are equipped for the fighter-reconnaissance rôle.

Sidewinder-equipped J 29F fighters of F 3. The J 29Fs of F 4 also carry these missiles.

The SAAB-29F possesses both intercept and attack capability, and those remaining in Flygvapnet service as J 29Fs are equipped to carry a pair of Rb 324 (Sidewinder) infra-red homing missiles. Fifteen ex-Flygvapnet SAAB-29Fs were delivered to Austria in 1961, a similar quantity being supplied during the following year. The second batch of SAAB-29Fs supplied to Austria comprised modified aircraft suitable for the reconnaissance-fighter rôle. These may be fitted with a detachable camera pod which, housing three Vinten cameras, may be installed in place of the portside pair of 20-mm. cannon.

SAAB-29F SPECIFICATION

Power Plant: *One Svenska Flygmotor-built (de Havilland) RM 2B (Ghost 50) turbojet rated at 4,750 lb.s.t. and 6,170 lb.s.t. with afterburning.*

Armament: *Four 20-mm. Hispano cannon and two Rb 324 infra-red homing AAMs or twenty-four 75-mm. Bofors or eight 18-cm. or 15-cm. unguided AAMs with air-to-surface capability, or two 550-lb. bombs.*

Performance: *Max. speed, 658 m.p.h. at 5,000 ft. (Mach 0.86), 560 m.p.h. at 40,000 ft.; cruise, 500 m.p.h. at 36,000 ft. (Mach 0.757); initial climb, 11,810 ft./min.; service ceiling, 50,850 ft.; range (ferry with two 88 Imp. gal. external tanks), 1,678 mls.*
Weights: *Empty, 10,141 lb.; max loaded, 17,637 lb.*
Dimensions: *Span, 36 ft. 1 in.; length, 33 ft. 2½ in.; height, 12 ft. 3½ in.; wing area, 258 sq. ft.*

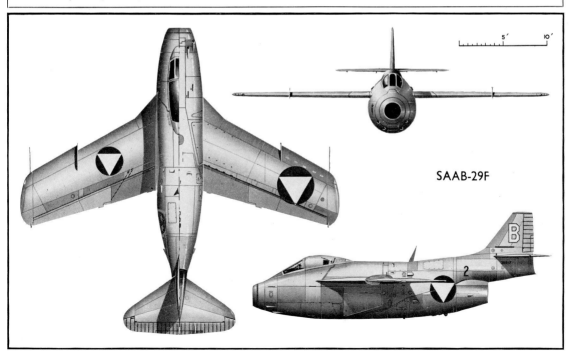

SAAB-29F

SAAB-32 LANSEN

Development of the Lansen (Lance) was initiated in 1948 to meet a Flygvapnet requirement for a two-seat, all-weather attack aircraft, instructions to proceed being transmitted to SAAB in December of that year. It was originally planned to install the indigenous STAL Dovern II turbojet of 7,275 lb.s.t., but the abandonment of development of this power plant resulted in the modification of the Lansen at an early design stage for the Rolls-Royce Avon. Four prototypes of the SAAB-32, as the aircraft was designated, were ordered, the first of these flying on November 3, 1952 with an Avon R.A.7R offering 7,500 lb.s.t. dry and 9,500 lb. with afterburning. During the course of

flight testing, on October 25, 1953, one of the SAAB-32 prototypes exceeded Mach unity in a shallow dive, becoming the first Swedish aircraft of indigenous design to achieve this feat.

Quantity production of the aircraft was initiated in 1953, and as the A 32A Lansen, the type entered service with F 17 early in 1956, subsequently being supplied to the remaining three Flygvapnet attack wings, F 6, F 7 and F 14. The A 32A currently equips all four attack wings, and during the late 'sixties will be progressively phased out in favour of the AJ 37A Viggen, all attack Lansens being retired by 1971–72. At the present time, the primary armament of the A 32A comprises two Rb 304 twenty-five-mile-range ASMs intended primarily for anti-shipping use, and these are to be supplemented by a new SAAB-developed ASM.

SAAB-32B: To meet Flygvapnet requirements for a two-seat night and all-weather interceptor, work on the adaptation of the basic SAAB-32 design to fulfil this rôle began in 1955, the result being the prototype SAAB-32B which flew for the first time on January 7, 1957. Production of the SAAB-32A was completed early in 1958, and the SAAB-32B followed on the assembly line, deliveries commencing in mid-1958, and the type entering service with the Flygvapnet as the J 32B Lansen in the following year, F 1, F 12, and one squadron of F 21 subsequently re-equipping with this type, the last example of which was delivered on May 2, 1960.

Externally, the SAAB-32B differs little from the earlier -32A, but internally extensive redesign has been

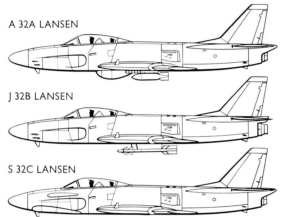

A 32A LANSEN

J 32B LANSEN

S 32C LANSEN

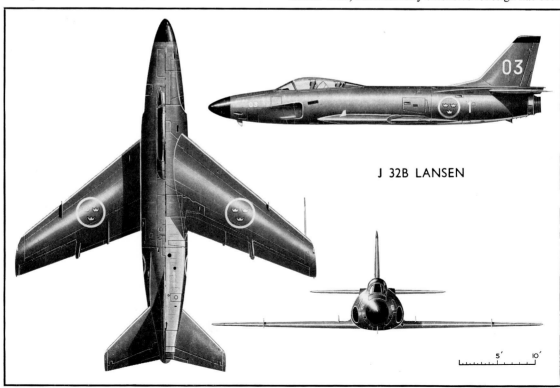

J 32B LANSEN

An A 32A Lansen of F 14 (Hallands Flygflottilj) based at Halmstad as a component of Eskader 1. The A 32A will begin to give place to the AJ 37 Viggen from 1969 and will have been phased out of service by 1972.

undertaken. The most significant change is the adoption of the 200-series Avon engine which, built under licence by Svenska Flygmotor as the RM 6A, employs a Swedish-developed afterburner. The installation of this more powerful engine necessitated the enlarging of the air intakes and internal ducting, and modifications were introduced in the control system to improve handling at transonic speeds. Apart from changes dictated by the new turbojet, weight of fire over that of the earlier version of the Lansen was markedly increased by the installation of four 30-mm. Aden M/55 cannon employed in conjunction with a SAAB S6 all-weather gun sight, a general-purpose type fire control system designed for all-weather lead-pursuit interceptions.

SAAB-32C: A two-seat tactical reconnaissance version of the Lansen similarly powered to the SAAB-32A, the SAAB-32C flew for the first time on March 26, 1957, production deliveries to the Flygvapnet commencing in the following year, and the type currently serves with F 11 as the S 32C. The SAAB-32C differs from the -32A primarily in having a redesigned nose section which can accommodate several alternative camera arrangements, and special aids make possible night photography from a wide range of altitudes. Complete electronic equipment for night navigation and radar reconnaissance is installed, and production of this type was completed in April 1960.

J 32B Lansen all-weather and night fighters of F 1 which, based at Hässlö, Västeras, is a component of Eskader 3.

LANSEN SPECIFICATION

Power Plant: (A 32A) One Svenska Flygmotor-built (Rolls-Royce) RM 5 (Avon 100 Series) turbojet rated at 8,050 lb.s.t. and 9,920 lb.s.t. with afterburning, (J 32B) one RM 6A (Avon 200 Series) turbojet rated at 11,250 lb.s.t. and 15,190 lb.s.t. with afterburning.
Armament: (A 32A) Four 20-mm. Swedish Hispano cannon and four Rb 304 ASMs, twelve 220-lb. flash bombs, four 550-lb. or two 1,100-lb. general-purpose bombs, or twelve 18-cm. or twenty-four 15-cm. or 13.5-cm. HVARs. (J 32B) Four 30-mm. Aden M/55 cannon and four infra-red homing Rb 324 (Sidewinder) AAMs, or four pods each housing nineteen 7.5-cm. or eighteen 13.5-cm. rockets.
Performance: (A 32A) Max. speed, 700 m.p.h. at sea level (Mach 0.92); cruise, 528 m.p.h. at 36,000 ft. (Mach 0.8); initial climb, 11,800 ft./min.; service ceiling, 49,200 ft. (J 32B) Max. speed and cruise as for A 32A; initial climb, 19,700 ft./min.; service ceiling, 52,500 ft.; approx. range (ferry), 2,000 mls.
Approx. Weights: (A 32A) Empty, 16,500 lb.; normal loaded, 22,000 lb.; max., 28,660 lb. (J 32B) Empty, 17,600 lb.; normal loaded, 27,000 lb.; max., 29,800 lb.
Dimensions: Span, 42 ft. 7¼ in.; length (A 32A), 48 ft. 0¾ in. (J 32B), 47 ft. 6¾ in.; height (A32A), 15 ft. 7 in. (J 32B), 15 ft. 3 in.; wing area, 402.57 sq. ft.

SAAB-35 DRAKEN

Destined to provide the mainstay of Sweden's air defence until the mid 'seventies, the Draken (Dragon) is currently one of the most advanced production

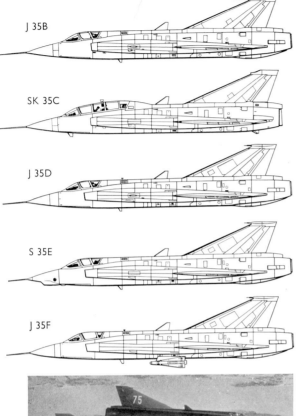

J 35B

SK 35C

J 35D

S 35E

J 35F

European single-seat interceptors, and remains unique among service combat aircraft in employing a wing planform of "double-delta" configuration. Issued in 1949, the specification to which the Draken was designed demanded a single-seat all-weather interceptor capable of operating from relatively small airfields and possessing a Mach range of 1.4 to 1.5. At an early stage, the SAAB design team headed by Erik Bratt conceived the "double-delta" configuration which, comprising two distinct triangles, had the advantage of keeping the thickness ratio low on the inboard sections of the wing housing the main undercarriage members, intake ducting, fuel, equipment and the cannon armament.

In order to obtain flight experience with this radical wing planform, a flying scale model of the projected fighter, the SAAB-210 powered by a 1,050 lb.s.t. Adder A.S.A.1 turbojet, was built and flew for the first time on January 21, 1952, subsequently providing considerable data on the low-speed characteristics of the "double-delta" configuration. Detail design of the fighter, the SAAB-35, was initiated in December 1951, and in August 1953 a contract was awarded for three prototypes and three pre-production aircraft, plus a complete nose section for a two-seat training variant. Powered by an imported Rolls-Royce Avon 200 Series engine, the first SAAB-35 prototype flew on October 25, 1955, going supersonic (without afterburning) for the first time on January 26, 1956. The second and third prototypes joined the test programme in January and March 1956 respectively, attaining level flight speeds of the order of Mach 1.4 before being joined, on February 15, 1958, by the first pre-production aircraft which differed from the prototypes primarily in having a Svenska Flygmotor-built version of the Avon 200, the RM 6B, with a Swedish S.F.A. Model 65 afterburner.

SAAB-35A: The initial production order for the Draken was placed in August 1956, and designated J 35A by the Flygvapnet, the first two aircraft of this type were delivered to F 13 at Norrköping on March 8, 1960, this unit completing its conversion from the J 29 by March 2, 1961. F 16 at Uppsala was the second wing to receive the J 35A, and with its RM 6B turbojet rated at 11,250 lb.s.t. and boosted to some 15,190

(Above left and below) The J 35A Draken, seen here in service with F 13 during 1963, has now been supplanted by the J 35B, earlier aircraft being modified to the later standards or converted as Sk 35C trainers.

J 35B Drakens of the "Acro Delta" aerobatic team of F 18. The J 35B is externally similar to its predecessor, the J 35A, but has a SAAB S 7 collision-course gunsight and fire control system, and modified electronics.

lb.s.t. by the S.F.A. Model 65 afterburner, this aircraft attained a maximum level speed of Mach 1.8. The sixty-third production J 35A featured a modified rear fuselage housing the improved Model 66 afterburner. This increased overall length, including pitot head, from 49 ft. 10¾ in. to 52 ft. 5 in., or, excluding pitot head, from 43 ft. 7 in. to 46 ft. 1¼ in., and was adopted as standard for all subsequent production J 35As and also for the J 35B.

The J 35A carried an armament of two 30-mm. Aden M/55 cannon mounted inboard of the break in the wing leading edge, the gun armament later being supplemented by four Rb 324 (Sidewinder) infra-red homing AAMs. SAAB S 6B infra-red and radar fire control equipment was installed, and internal fuel capacity totalled 493 Imp. gal., although this could be supplemented for ferry purposes by auxiliary tanks in the gun bays and four jettisonable 66 Imp. gal. tanks. Empty weight was 14,528 lb., maximum loaded weight being some 20,000 lb., and in clean condition initial climb rate was of the order of 39,400 ft./min.

By mid-1964, F 13's J 35A Drakens had all been converted to the later J 35B standard or to Sk 35C two-seaters, and the wing itself had re-equipped with the J 35D. F 16 had also relinquished its J 35As in favour of the J 35B, the only remaining J 35As being a few employed by the operational conversion unit at Uppsala.

SAAB-35B: The SAAB-35B Draken, or J 35B, which flew for the first time on November 29, 1959, is essentially similar to the original production -35A and, indeed, many aircraft of this type are conversions of the earlier model, the principal change being the introduction of the SAAB S 7 collision-course gunsight and fire control system, the electronics being designed for integration with the STRIL 60 air defence control system. Alternative external loads include two SAAB rocket launchers each housing nineteen 75-mm. Bofors rockets, these being the J 35B's primary weapons for the collision course intercept mission, four 550-lb. bombs, or nine 220-lb. bombs. The first J 35B

Drakens were delivered to F 16 at Uppsala in 1961, and F 18 at Tullinge began converting to the type during 1962. The J 35B possesses a similar performance to that of the J 35A and carries similar ordnance loads.

SAAB-35C: Serving with the Operational Training Unit at Uppsala under the designation Sk 35C, the

The camera nose of the tactical reconnaissance S 35E.

(Above and below, left) Two aerodynamic prototypes of the J 35F Draken which will carry Rb 327 radar-guided and Rb 328 infra-red homing Falcon AAMs as its principal armament. One 30-mm. Aden cannon will be retained.

SAAB-35C tandem two-seat operational training conversion of the Draken flew for the first time on December 30, 1959. A relatively small number of aircraft of this type have been produced by converting early production J 35A fighters, the original short rear fuselage and Model 65 afterburner being retained. The new front fuselage, in which the instructor is seated slightly above the pupil and is provided with a periscopic sight for landing, has only a marginal effect on performance which is almost identical to that of the J 35A. No armament is carried, and overall dimensions are similar to those of the initial production J 35A.

SAAB-35D: With the current production model of the Draken, the J 35D, the more powerful RM 6C engine—a licence-built version of the Rolls-Royce RB.146 Avon 300 Series—with an S.F.A. Model 67 afterburner raises maximum speed to slightly more than Mach 2.0. The more powerful engine has necessitated some redesign and lengthening of the air intakes, and internal fuel capacity has been raised by 115 Imp. gal. to a total of 608 Imp. gal. Armament remains the same as that of earlier Draken interceptors, but the Lear automatic flight control system is supplanted by the SAAB FH 5 system.

The prototype J 35D, a converted J 35A airframe, was flown on December 27, 1960, and production began in the Autumn of 1962, F 13 at Norrköping completing conversion from the J 35A to the new model early in 1964, the second J 35D wing being F 10 at Angelholm which had begun conversion before the end of the year.

The J 35D is the first production version of the Draken to be equipped with ground-level ejector seats, which are also to be fitted to the J 35B retroactively, and offers a substantial improvement in performance over earlier models (see specification).

SAAB-35E: A tactical reconnaissance version of the -35D with an entirely redesigned camera nose, the SAAB-35E flew for the first time on June 27, 1963, and was expected to enter service with F 11 before the end of 1964. The camera nose slides forward to permit quick access to and extraction of camera magazines, and there are forward-facing, trimetrogen and individual oblique and vertical cameras. The SAAB-35E, which is designated S 35E by the Flygvapnet, is suitable for low, medium or high altitude photo reconnaissance by day or night, and photoflash bombs may be carried for night illumination.

The first Sk 35C (35800) two-seat operational training conversion of the J 35A. The short tailpipe originally featured by the J 35A but later lengthened is retained by the Sk 35C trainer.

SAAB-35F: Currently considered to be the definitive production model of the Draken interceptor, the SAAB-35F is now entering production and is expected to join Flygvapnet operational units during 1965. Scheduled to be built in larger numbers than any other version of the Draken, the SAAB-35F, or J 35F, will be equipped with the SAAB S 7B incorporating a more advanced tracking radar system of higher output, a more sensitive receiver and a well-developed anti-countermeasures system. The collison-course fire control system, used in conjunction with Swedish derivatives of the Hughes Falcon missile, will enable the J 35F to counter low-flying targets from all directions, and it will be capable of firing its missiles at all altitudes, in cloud, day or night, at targets flying substantially faster than sound and using electronic countermeasures.

The J 35F will employ a similar power plant to that of the J 35D, and overall performance will be similar, but primary armament will comprise Rb 327 and Rb 328 missiles, one cannon being deleted. The Rb 327 and 328 are respectively radar-guided and infra-red homing AAMs evolved from the American Hughes Falcon, and four of these missiles will normally be carried. The decision to adopt the Falcon missile was taken in 1959, and by comparison with American-built weapons of this type, the Swedish-built missiles are extensively modified to meet Flygvapnet requirements. The attachment points for other ordnance loads are retained.

Production of the Draken is expected to continue until 1969 when this aircraft will finally be phased out in favour of the JA 37 Viggen.

SAAB-35D DRAKEN SPECIFICATION

Power Plant: One Svenska Flygmotor-built (Rolls-Royce) RM 6C (RB.146 Avon 300 Series) turbojet rated at 13,220 lb.s.t. and (approx.) 17,500 lb.s.t. with after-burning.
Armament: Two 30-mm. Aden M/55 cannon and four Rb 324 (Sidewinder) infra-red homing AAMs, four SAAB launchers each housing nineteen 75-mm. Bofors rockets, four 550-lb. general-purpose bombs, or nine 220-lb. flash bombs.
Performance: Max. speed, 1,320 m.p.h. at 40,000 ft. (Mach 2.0); cruise, 590 m.p.h. at 36,000 ft. (Mach 0.9); initial climb rate (clean), 49,000 ft./min.; time to 50,000 ft., 4.5 min.
Weights: Empty, 16,017 lb.; loaded (clean), 20,400 lb.; max. overload, 22,663 lb.
Dimensions: Span, 30 ft. 10¾ in.; length, 46 ft. 10¼ in., (over probe), 50 ft. 4 in.; height, 12 ft. 8⅓ in.; wing area, 529.8 sq. ft.

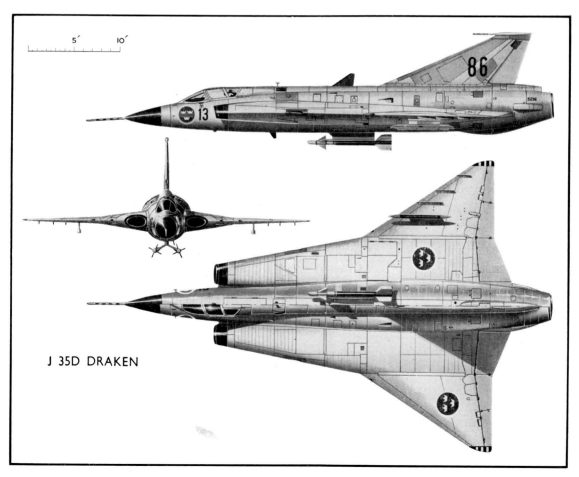

J 35D DRAKEN

SAAB-37 VIGGEN

Scheduled to enter the flight test phase in 1966, the SAAB-37 Viggen (Thunderbolt) has been designed to meet a Flygvapnet specification drawn up in the late 'fifties for a "standardised flying platform" aircraft with short take-off and landing capabilities which, in its various versions, will supplant all current Swedish attack, reconnaissance and interceptor aircraft. Development was initiated during 1958, the aerodynamic design, equipment, etc., were frozen early in 1963, and on April 7, 1964 the Swedish government presented its proposals for Viggen development and production, covering a total of slightly more than eight hundred aircraft. The first deliveries will be made in 1969, and the Viggen will serve with the Flygvapnet throughout the 'seventies.

The wing planform of the Viggen has been optimized for high lift coefficient at low speed and reverses the "double-delta" sweep configuration of its predecessor, the Draken. A dihedralled foreplane or trimming surface is mounted ahead of the wing to trim out the nose-down pitching moment of the large,

high-lift flaps, the effectiveness of this surface being increased by flap blowing. Short landing performance will evidently be achieved by a combination of low touch-down speed and thrust reversal.

The Viggen is to be powered by a single Svenska Flygmotor-built RM 8 turbofan—a licence-built version of the Pratt and Whitney JT8D-22 which will be fitted with an S.F.A.-developed afterburner and a SAAB thrust reverser. This power plant may be expected to have an initial rating of the order of 16,000 lb.s.t., boosted to about 28,000 lb.s.t. by afterburning, but development should result in a military rating of some 18,000 lb.s.t. dry and 31,500 lb.s.t. with afterburning at a fairly early stage in the development life of the Viggen. On this basis, it may be expected that the aircraft will have an all-up weight in the strike rôle of some 35,000 lb. Overall span and length may be expected to be of the order of 33 ft. and 52 ft. respectively.

The first version of the Viggen to be produced will be the AJ 37A attack aircraft with secondary intercept capability which is scheduled to supplant all A 32A Lansens commencing in 1969. The AJ 37's primary weapon will be an up-dated version of the Rb 304 ASM for use against shipping targets, this missile eventually being supplemented by a new, lighter SAAB ASM which will be used against both land and sea targets. Alternative external loads will include general-purpose bombs, HVARs and napalm tanks, and the AJ 37 will have no built-in cannon armament, although it will be possible to carry such weapons in pods. A dual-control version of the Viggen, the Sk 37, is being developed in parallel with the AJ 37 version.

The all-weather interceptor version of the Viggen, the JA 37, which will follow the AJ 37A into Flygvapnet service and begin to supplant the Draken during the early 'seventies, will be completely integrated into the STRIL 60 semi-automatic air defence system, and will have secondary attack capability. The

(Above left and below) Artist's impressions of the SAAB-37 Viggen which is intended to supplant all other combat types in service with the Flygvapnet during the 'seventies.

The models of the Viggen (above) show clearly the unusual canard configuration adopted for this multi-purpose aircraft.

primary armament of this variant will be the radar-guided Rb 327 and infra-red homing Rb 328 AAMs, and interceptor weight is likely to be of the order of 30,000–33,000 lb. Preceding the JA 37 will be the S 37 reconnaissance model which will follow the AJ 37 on the assembly line. The S 37 will employ both camera and non-optical reconnaissance systems, and equip-

ment of all variants of the Viggen will include a SAAB-Honeywell miniaturised digital computer which will perform navigation and position determination tasks, fire control and armament calculations, fuel status monitoring, automatic control of the aircraft, and data exchange with the STRIL 60 ground-based computers.

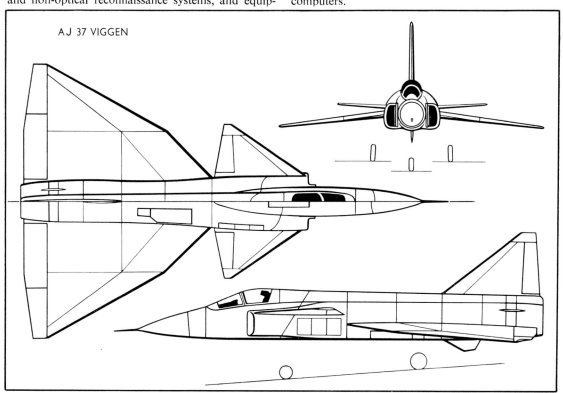

AJ 37 VIGGEN

BERIEV BE-10 (MALLOW)

Whereas the long-range maritime reconnaissance flying boat has now been discarded by most countries, the last western example of this category of aircraft to remain in service being the Martin P-5 Marlin (see pages 186–7), Russia's naval air arm, the Aviatsiya Voenno-Morskovo Flota, or A.V.-M.F., would seem to have been reluctant to rely solely on land-based aircraft for the maritime rôle, carrying the flying boat into the 'sixties with the Be-10.

Currently the only turbojet-driven flying boat in service anywhere in the world, and possibly the last large military water-borne aircraft to be produced, the

Be-10 has been developed by a design bureau headed by the doyen of Russian flying-boat designers, Georgi Mikhailovich Beriev, as a successor to the piston-engined Be-6 (Madge) in service with the A.V.-M.F. Designed to combine reasonable endurance with high subsonic dash capability and limited capacity for operation in open waters, the Be-10 was publicly revealed for the first time during the 1961 Aviation Day fly-past, by which time it had allegedly been in service with the A.V.-M.F. for about a year.

Somewhat less bold in concept than the Martin P6M Seamaster which had flown six years previously and been abandoned by the U.S. Navy in favour of land-based aircraft, the Be-10 has a relatively long and narrow planing bottom to reduce hydrodynamic and aerodynamic drag, and to permit operation in rough waters by cushioning the landing loads. The wing is shoulder-mounted on the tall hull, and the turbojets are located high on its sides. The pronounced anhedral of the wing permits the tip floats to be mounted on relatively short pylons, eliminating the need for retraction gear. Information supplied to the F.A.I. in 1961, when the Be-10 established an impressive series of international records for water-borne aircraft,

The Be-10 has been in service with the A.V.-M.F. for some five years. Twin cannon are mounted in the forward hull.

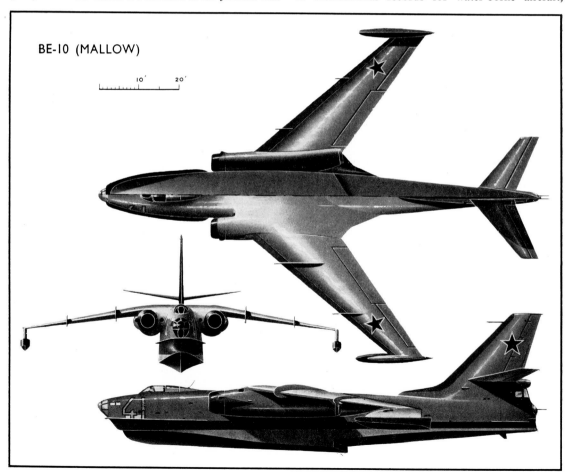

BE-10 (MALLOW)

10′   20′

(Above and at foot of page) The Be-10 is likely to be the last large military flying boat to be built in quantity, and is the only pure jet flying boat to have attained service status.

referred to the turbojets as AL-7PB engines each of 14,330 lb.s.t., and from the size of the air intakes, it would seem likely that these are turbofans rather than pure jets, suggesting that the Soviet Union developed by-pass engines slightly earlier than did the western countries. The engines are located immediately beneath the wing roots and their jet pipes are canted outwards under the trailing-edge fillets so that their jets do not attach to the hull sides.

The capacious hull of the Be-10 provides ample space for a large search radar dish which is presumably located in the forward portion, and defensive armament apparently comprises two fixed, forward-firing 20-mm. or 23-mm. cannon in the nose and two similar weapons in a tail turret over which there is mounted gun-laying radar. The offensive load may be confined to small sub-kiloton depth charges as there is no indication of a rotary weapons door in the hull, the multi-spar-structure wing cannot house stores, and there is no provision in the engine nacelles for weapons bays. There would seem to be insufficient clearance for anti-shipping missiles, such as the Kennel, under-wing, and it is possible, therefore, that stores are mounted on racks which extend from the sides of the hull during an attack.

The F.A.I.-recognised records offer some indication of the performance of the Be-10, these including a 566.69 m.p.h. speed record over a straight course, a 544.2 m.p.h. speed record with an 11,023-lb. payload over a 621-mile closed-circuit course, and altitude records of 49,088 ft. without payload, 46,135 ft. with 11,023 lb., and 39,360 ft. with 33,069 lb. While service ceiling is likely to be somewhat below the record altitudes, the dash performance is probably represented by the speed records. Published photographs have revealed nothing enabling the dimensions and weights of the Be-10 to be gauged accurately, and the following specification, based on deductions from information provided by the F.A.I. and interpretation of photographic evidence, should be considered as provisional.

BE-10 (MALLOW) SPECIFICATION

Power Plants: Two Type AL-7PB turbojets each rated at 14,330 lb.s.t.
Armament: Four 20-mm. or 23-mm. cannon (two fixed forward-firing and two in tail turret) and probably sub-kiloton depth bombs.
Estimated Performance: Max. speed, 560 m.p.h. at 5,000 ft. (Mach 0.75), 500 m.p.h. at 36,000 ft.; range cruise, 350–400 m.p.h.; tactical radius (with nominal load of 4,400 lb.), 1,300 mls.; patrol endurance, 6–8 hr.; service ceiling, 40,000 ft.
Estimated Weights: Empty, 53,000 lb.; normal loaded, 90,000 lb.; max. overload, 100,000 lb.
Estimated Dimensions: Span, 73 ft.; length, 102 ft.; height, 33 ft.; wing area, 1,200 sq. ft.

ILYUSHIN IL-28 (BEAGLE)

Although obsolete, the Il-28 light tactical bomber, evolved by a design bureau headed by Sergei V. Ilyushin and the first jet bomber to attain large-scale service with Russia's V.-V.S (Voenno-Vozdushnye Sily—Military Aviation Forces), still ranks as an important item in the armouries of the air forces of China, Czechoslovakia, East Germany, Hungary,

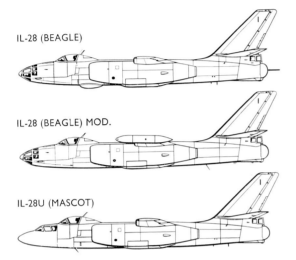

IL-28 (BEAGLE)

IL-28 (BEAGLE) MOD.

IL-28U (MASCOT)

Indonesia, Poland, Rumania, and the United Arab Republic, and is still employed in substantial numbers by the V.-V.S.'s Frontovaya Aviatsiya (Frontal Aviation) and the Aviatsiya Voenno-Morskovo Flota, Russia's shore-based naval air arm.

Produced as a successor to the piston-engined Tupolev Tu-2, the Il-28 was flown as a prototype in 1947 by the well-known Russian test pilot V. K. Kokkinaki, power being provided by two of the Rolls-Royce Nene turbojets imported by the Soviet Union in that year. Entering service with the V.-V.S. in 1949 powered by the first Russian production variant of the Nene, the 4,960 lb.s.t. Klimov RD-45, the Il-28 carried three crew members: pilot, navigator/bombardier and radio operator/rear gunner. The internal bomb load comprised four 1,100-lb. or up to twelve 550-lb. bombs, a small navigational-bombing radar was installed beneath the forward fusalage and defensive armament comprised two fixed forward-firing 20-mm. or 23-mm. cannon in the fuselage nose operated by the pilot, and two similar weapons in a manually-operated tail barbette.

Progressively more powerful versions of the basic Klimov engine were installed in the Il-28, the RD-45 being supplanted at an early production stage by the RD-45FA of 5,952 lb.s.t., and, finally, by the improved VK-1 of 6,040 lb.s.t. during the early 'fifties when deliveries of the bomber to Warsaw Pact countries began.

(*Above*) A modified Il-28 of the Hungarian Air Force with tandem ventral radomes, the second radome possibly housing countermeasures equipment, and (below) the two Il-28s supplied to Finland.

An Il-28 of the German Democratic Republic's Luftstreitkräfte which uses the type for meteorological and training purposes with armament and radar removed.

Several variants of the basic Il-28 are in service, including one featuring tandem ventral radomes, the second radome probably housing countermeasures equipment, a meteorological conversion with the ventral radome deleted, and an operational and pilot training version, the Il-28U (Mascot). Most Il-28-equipped units possess one or two Il-28Us for combat proficiency checks, and although the airframe of this model is essentially similar to that of the basic bombing version, the ventral radome and the nose glazing are deleted, and a second cockpit with a full set of controls for the pupil pilot is mounted ahead and below the standard cockpit. Two examples of the Il-28 have been supplied to the Finnish Air Force by which service they are employed as target tugs. All versions of the Il-28 may be fitted with 200 Imp. gal. auxiliary tanks at the wingtips.

IL-28 (BEAGLE) SPECIFICATION

Power Plants: *Two Klimov VK-1 turbojets each rated at 6,040 lb.s.t.*

Armament: *Two fixed forward-firing 20-mm. or 23-mm. cannon and two 20-mm. or 23-mm. cannon in tail barbette, plus four 1,100-lb. or twelve 550-lb. general-purpose bombs internally.*

Performance: *Max. speed, 580 m.p.h. at 15,000 ft. (Mach 0.81), 530 m.p.h. at 32,800 ft.; cruise, 450 m.p.h. at 32,000–38,000 ft.; service ceiling, 41,000 ft.; tactical radius (with 4,400-lb. bomb load), 685 mls., (with two 200 Imp. gal. wingtip tanks) 850 mls.; range (ferry), 2,200 mls.*

Weights: *Empty, 27,400 lb.; approx. normal loaded, 43,000 lb.*

Dimensions: *Span, 64 ft.; length, 58 ft.; height, 22 ft.; wing area, 538 sq. ft.*

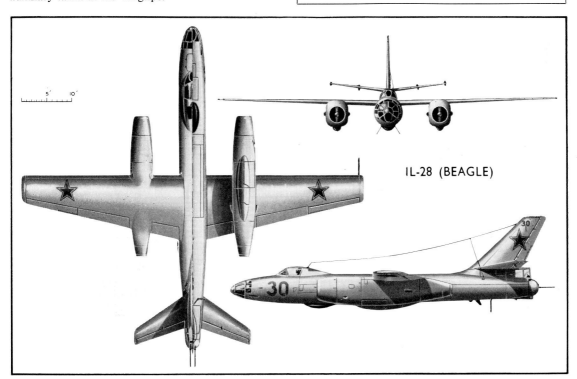

IL-28 (BEAGLE)

MIG-17 (FRESCO)

Probably manufactured in larger numbers than any other individual jet combat type, the MiG-17 is, despite having been long since superseded by more advanced fighters on Russian assembly lines, the most widely used of warplanes of Soviet design. Indeed, this "second generation" Russian jet fighter today bears the insignia of more of the world's air arms than any other warplane.

Essentially an aerodynamically refined development of the MiG-15 retaining the VK-1 turbojet installed in the late production MiG-15bis, the MiG-17 is claimed by Soviet sources to have exceeded Mach 1.0 in level flight with test pilot I.T. Ivashchenko at the controls early in 1952, but this claim would seem to have been based on faulty instrumentation if western experience is any gauge. By comparison with the earlier MiG-15, the MiG-17 introduced a wing of thinner section and greater sweep angle (leading edge sweep ranging from 47° inboard to 43° outboard), the harmful effect of these

(Above and below) Fresco-A fighters of a V.-V.S. aerobatic team taking-off.

changes on low speed stability being minimised by the introduction of a third wing fence. The rear fuselage was extended, increasing the fineness ratio, the design of the air brakes was revised and the span of the tailplane increased.

The MiG-17 entered service as a day interceptor in 1953, and the type remained in production in Soviet factories for the V.-V.S. and for export until the late 'fifties, and still later in Czech, Polish and Chinese plants, and a number of variants were produced and remain in service. To facilitate identification of the principal versions, suffix letters have been applied to the western appellation "Fresco", these being as follows:

FRESCO-A: The initial production version of the MiG-17, dubbed Fresco-A and powered by the non-afterburning Klimov VK-1 centrifugal-type turbojet of 6,040 lb.s.t., carried a similar armament to that of the MiG-15bis, this comprising one 37-mm. N-37 cannon and two 23-mm. NR-23 cannon, the former to starboard and the latter to port, with a lead pursuit optical gyro gunsight. Underwing pylons were provided for two 88 Imp. gal. drop tanks, these supplementing the 360 Imp. gal. capacity internal tanks.

FRESCO-B: Some difficulties were evidently experienced with the narrow air brakes mounted low on the rear fuselage of the initial production version, and therefore enlarged rectangular airbrakes were introduced and mounted on the fuselage sides, aft of the wings, à la Sabre. It may be assumed that another factor motivating this air brake positioning was the development of a short afterburner for the VK-1 engine and the desire to move the hydraulic actuators for the air brakes from the vicinity of the afterburner which was to be utilised by later variants of the MiG-17. It would seem that the repositioned air brakes were not entirely successful, their extension possibly causing a pitching moment, for this version of the MiG-17, the Fresco-B, appeared in only limited numbers, and all subsequent models of the fighter reverted to the rear fuselage-mounted brakes.

(Below) Two early production MiG-17 (Fresco-A) day fighters of the V.-V.S. Powered by the non-afterburning VK-1 turbojet, this version has now been relegated to the training rôle.

(*Above and below, right*) *The Fresco-D limited all-weather and night fighter variant of the MiG-17 in service with the German Democratic Republic's Luftstreitkräfte.*

FRESCO-C: Whereas both the Fresco-A and -B versions of the MiG-17 have long been obsolete, the Fresco-C, the definitive day fighter model, is extremely widely used, and was manufactured under licence in Czechoslovakia as the S-105, in Poland as the LIM-5, and in China, where production was continuing as late as 1962.

The principal change introduced by the Fresco-C was to be found in the power plant. This, the VK-1A, was fitted with a short afterburner, boosting available thrust to 6,990 lb. The tail cone was cut back, exposing the end of the afterburner nozzle, and shorter, deeper air brakes were fitted, the hydraulic actuators being mounted further forward on the rear fuselage centreline. Initially, the built-in armament was similar to that of earlier models, but the slow-firing (400 r.p.m.) 37-mm. weapon was eventually replaced by a third 23-mm. cannon, and underwing loads could include four pods each housing eight 55-mm. unguided rockets, two 210 mm. unguided ASMs or two 550-lb. bombs. Late production Fresco-C fighters were fitted with the improved VK-1FA afterburning engine.

FRESCO-D: A limited night and all-weather fighter derivative of the Fresco-C, the -D features a radar scanner in a central intake bullet and a second radar in an extended upper intake lip for the Scan ODD intercept equipment. The fuselage nose has been lengthened slightly, and in order to make room for

The definitive day fighter version of the MiG-17, the Fresco-C, in service with the Iraqi Air Force. Iraq possesses one squadron of MiG-17s which operates alongside units equipped with the later MiG-19 and MiG-21.

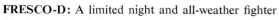

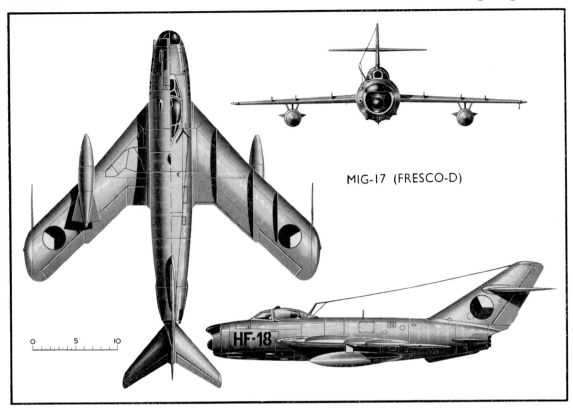

MIG-17 (FRESCO-D)

HF-18

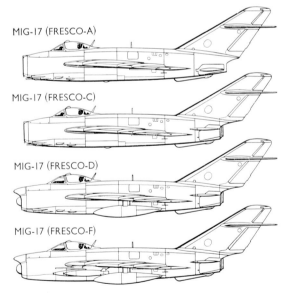

MIG-17 (FRESCO-A)

MIG-17 (FRESCO-C)

MIG-17 (FRESCO-D)

MIG-17 (FRESCO-F)

three 23-mm. cannon, as do also Fresco-Es which differ only in having a non-afterburning VK-1, but during the early 'sixties a missile-armed version of the Fresco-D made its appearance. Referred to by some sources as the Fresco-F, this limited night and all-weather interceptor has all cannon armament removed and four small beam-riding missiles—apparently early versions of the Alkali—on rails under the inboard wing sections, these being carried in addition to a pair of 88 Imp. gal. drop tanks.

The principal service versions of the MiG-17 are the Fresco-C and -D, and the following specification for the former model is generally applicable to the latter.

the pilot's radar scope, the windscreen has been moved forward and the quarter-lights modified accordingly. The radar ranging operates through a horizontal dielectric strip in the intake splitter, the ranging unit being housed in the intake lip, and the A.I. scanner being mounted in the hemispherical radome.

Power is provided by an afterburning VK-1A or -1FA, and most Fresco-Ds carry an armament of

MIG-17 (FRESCO-C) SPECIFICATION

Power Plant: *One Klimov VK-1A or -1FA turbojet rated at 6,040 lb.s.t. and 6,990 lb.s.t. with afterburning.*
Armament: *Three 23-mm. Nudelmann-Rikter NR-23 (VYa) cannon and four pods each housing eight 55-mm. rockets, two 210-mm. unguided ASMs, or two 550-lb. general-purpose bombs.*
Performance: *Max. speed, 627 m.p.h. at 40,000 ft. (Mach 0.95), 700 m.p.h. at sea level (Mach 0.92); time to 40,000 ft., 6.8 min.; service ceiling, 57,500 ft.; combat radius (clean), 320 mls., (with two 88 Imp. gal. drop tanks and two 550-lb. bombs) 360 mls.*
Weights: *Approx. loaded (clean), 13,000 lb., (with two drop tanks) 14,750 lb.*
Dimensions: *Span, 31 ft.; length, 36 ft. 4 in.; height, 11 ft.; wing area, 244 sq ft.*

MIG-19 (FARMER)

The lineal successor to the MiG-17, Artem I. Mikoyan's MiG-19 was the first Russian warplane capable of supersonic speeds in level flight to attain service status, and possesses the distinction of having introduced the air forces of a number of countries to supersonic flight, this type currently serving with the air arms of China, Cuba, Czechoslovakia, East Germany, Indonesia, Iraq, North Korea, Poland, the United Arab Republic and Yugoslavia.

The first prototype MiG-19 allegedly flew for the first time late in 1953, the initial production model, a simply-equipped day fighter with the by then traditional Russian fighter armament of one 37-mm. N-37 and two 23-mm. NR-23 cannon, entering service in 1955. Whereas the cannon armament of the MiG-15 and MiG-17 was housed in a rapidly replaceable pack in the lower portion of the fuselage nose without any risk of gunfire inducing engine surge, the centrifugal-type engines of these fighters being relatively insensitive to inlet flow variations, the introduction of more sensitive axial-flow engines in the MiG-19 necessitated moving the 23-mm. weapons to the wing roots to reduce the effect on the engine airflow. These engines were, in the initial production model, RD-5s offering 4,800 lb.s.t. dry and 6,700 lb.s.t. with afterburning—exceptionally small power plants mounted side-by-side

in the rear fuselage. These engines were fed by a circular, unsophisticated air intake with an area of approximately 3.5 sq. ft. The choice of a paired turbojet installation was probably dictated by a lack of large axial-flow turbojets suitable for fighter installation at the time of the MiG-19's conception. Allocated the code-name "Farmer" in the West, the

An initial production MiG-19 (Farmer-A) day fighter with cutaway elevators and fuselage-mounted 37-mm. cannon.

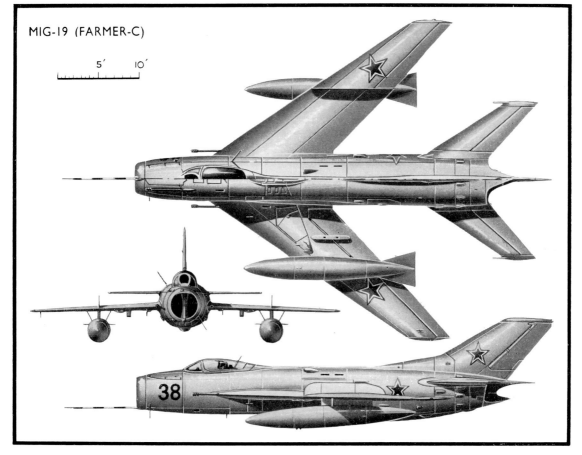

MIG-19 (FARMER-C)

5'   10'

(Above) One of the initial production versions of the MiG-19 limited all-weather fighter with extended fuselage and 23-mm. cannon in the wing roots.

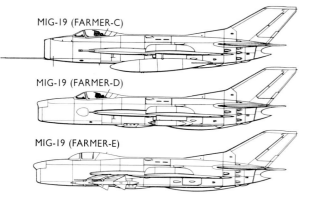

MIG-19 (FARMER-C)

MIG-19 (FARMER-D)

MIG-19 (FARMER-E)

MiG-19 was progressively developed during its production life, the principal variants being as follows:

FARMER-A: The initial production model of the MiG-19, unlike later models, had only the two lateral airbrakes and had conventional elevators which were cut away at their roots. It could be fitted with under-wing pylons for four rocket launcher pods each containing eight 55-mm. rockets, two pods each housing nineteen 55-mm. rockets, two 325-mm. or 220-mm. AAMs or two 210-mm. ASMs, and these could be carried in addition to a pair of 88, 132 or 176 Imp. gal. drop tanks.

FARMER-B: The Farmer-B was the first limited night and all-weather interceptor version of the MiG-19, with two radar antennae in the nose, the conical scan dish being housed in a central radome carried on the intake splitter, the antenna for range measurement being mounted in the enlarged upper lip of the air intake. The gun armament was similar to that of the Farmer-A, but the RD-5 power plants were replaced by RD-9Bs, each offering an afterburning thrust of the order of 7,150 lb.s.t.

FARMER-C: The definitive day fighter development of the basic design, the Farmer-C, had a lead pursuit optical gun sight but introduced a new fast-firing, single-barrel, revolver-type cannon of 30-mm. calibre which was presumably developed as a result of Korean experience. The combined slow-firing weapons of 23- and 37-mm. calibre, due to their very different ballistic drop, could only be arranged to give concentrated fire over a very narrow range bracket, and the new weapon provided a major increase in firepower, one being mounted in the starboard side of the forward fuselage and another being mounted in each wing root. The Farmer-C also introduced an additional air brake

A late production MiG-19 fighter in service with the Czech Air Force. Note ventral air brake introduced on this model and the 30-mm. cannon with muzzle brakes in the wing root and in starboard side of nose.

under the forward fuselage and a slab-type tailplane with anti-flutter weights projecting from the tips.

This version of the MiG-19 is currently the most widely used model, and has been supplied to some ten countries, although it has now been largely replaced in V.-V.S. service by later types such as the MiG-21.

FARMER-D: The limited all-weather Farmer-D was a parallel development to the -C day fighter, embodying the aerodynamic refinements that it introduced, although gun armament was reduced, the fuselage-mounted weapon being deleted. The fuselage nose was lengthened by about 1.8 ft., and a further improvement of the basic engine, the RD-9F, was apparently installed, this power plant also being employed by late production Farmer-C day fighters.

A variant of the Farmer-D, which has been unofficially referred to as the Farmer-E, has a modified cockpit enclosure and all cannon armament deleted, the guns being replaced by four beam-riding Alkali missiles mounted on special pylons inboard of the drop tanks and well forward on the wing in order to clear the inward-retracting undercarriage.

It is uncertain if many MiG-19s have been modified to Farmer-E standard, but the following specification for the Farmer-C version may be considered generally applicable to all models.

MIG-19 (FARMER-C) SPECIFICATION

Power Plants: Two Klimov RD-9F (VK-9) turbojets each rated at approx. 5,500 lb.s.t. and 7,200 lb.s.t. with afterburning.
Armament: Three 30-mm. cannon and four honeycomb pods each housing eight 55-mm. unguided rockets, two pods each housing nineteen 55-mm. rockets plus two Atoll infra-red homing AAMs, or four 210-mm. HVARs.
Performance: Max. speed, 846 m.p.h. at 35,000 ft. (Mach 1.28), 740 m.p.h. at 50,000 ft. (Mach 1.12); initial climb rate, 30,000 ft./min., (with two 176 Imp. gal. tanks and two Atoll AAMs) 17,000 ft./min.; service ceiling (clean), 55,000 ft.; combat radius (clean), 280 mls.
Weights: Loaded (clean), 18,000 lb.; max. overload, 22,500 lb.
Dimensions: Span, 30 ft. 6 in.; length, 41 ft. 6 in., (over probe) 48 ft. 9 in.; height, 13 ft. 6 in.; wing area, 285 sq. ft.

MIG-21 (FISHBED)

The MiG-21 single-seat day point defence interceptor is a simple, relatively light fighter achieving a high performance on a low powered engine by carrying the bare minimum of armament and emphasizing low drag at the cost of some structural problems. Pilots claim that it enjoys exceptional ease of handling and is highly manoeuvrable, and modified versions of the basic aircraft have established several F.A.I.- recognised records, but numbered among the MiG-21's shortcomings is its power plant which lacks any anti-surge device, offers poor throttle response and possesses a short overhaul life. Nevertheless, the MiG-21 marked a noteworthy advance in Soviet interceptor design, and the type has now largely assumed the mantle of its predecessors, the MiG-17 and MiG-19, having been exported to Cuba, Czechoslovakia, Finland, East Germany, Hungary, Indonesia, Iraq, Poland, Rumania, the U.A.R., and Yugoslavia. It is also being manufactured under licence in Czecho-

slovakia and India, and is the principal clear-weather interceptor of the V.-V.S.

Development of the MiG-21 was initiated in the early 'fifties, two prototypes being demonstrated in public over Tushino, Moscow, on June 24, 1956, the type being promptly allocated the western code-name

(Below and above, right) MiG-21 fighters of the Finnish Air Force. The first ten aircraft of this type were supplied to Finland in April 1963, and these have the port 30-mm. cannon faired over, only the starboard weapon being retained.

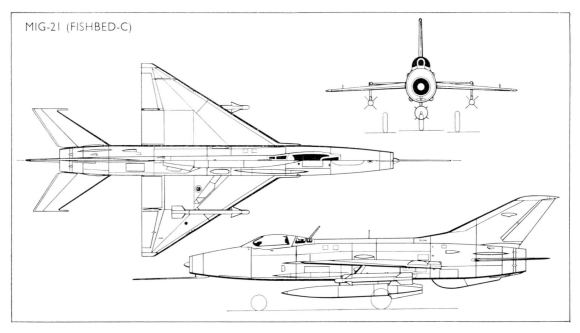

MIG-21 (FISHBED-C)

"Fishbed". At the same time, one example of a variant of the basic design, dubbed "Faceplate", appeared, and although this type was not to attain quantity production status, it revealed an interesting Russian experiment in "limited commonality"—two types with a number of major components in common but differing in certain critical features chosen to suit individual rôles. The small "tailed delta"—a configuration pioneered by the Russians—with a relatively high wing loading is technically one of the most attractive arrangements for a supersonic interceptor, combining low wave drag and structural weight with good supersonic manoeuvrability. However, the delta's poor subsonic lifting capacity seriously limits any secondary ground attack rôle, whereas the straight-forward swept wing, although demanding a heavier structure, offers a marked superiority at subsonic speeds in being able to attain much higher lift coefficients without buffeting. This increased

manoeuvrability provides the flexibility of operation essential in a fighter including ground attack among its tasks.

Thus, while the Fishbed employed a small delta wing, the contemporary Faceplate, which featured an almost identical fuselage and tail assembly, and was intended for the general-purpose rather than the pure intercept rôle, utilized a tapered swept wing of appreciably greater span. In the event, only the former attained quantity production, entering service with the V.-V.S. late in 1959, the Faceplate's production being restricted to a service evaluation quantity.

The suffix letters -A and -B were allocated to prototype and pre-production versions of the Fishbed, and the first day fighter variant of the MiG-21 to appear in quantity is known in the West as the Fishbed-C.
FISHBED-C: The MiG-21 achieved some publicity when, as the Ye-66 and flown by Colonel Georgi Mossolov, it established an absolute speed record of

A standard MiG-21 point-defence interceptor with ventral drop tank and underwing racks for Atoll infra-red AAMs.

Fishbed-D, the all-weather version of the MiG-21 with enlarged engine air intake and A.I. radome producing a double shock.
A fairing aft of the cockpit canopy slightly reduces drag, and no cannon armament is installed.

1,484 m.p.h. on October 31, 1959. With the addition of a 6,615 lb. thrust rocket motor, this same aircraft, labelled Ye-66A, raised the world altitude record to 113,892 ft. on April 28, 1961. However, there is little doubt that the power plants installed in these record-breaking aircraft were substantially boosted over the standard engine installed in the service MiG-21 which has a dry rating of 9,500 lb.s.t. and a normal after-burning thrust of 12,500 lb.

The standard day interceptor version of the MiG-21 has provision for two 30-mm. cannon, but frequently only the starboard weapon is installed, the primary armament consisting of two Atoll infra-red homing AAMs, unsophisticated missiles generally similar to the early Sidewinder and satisfactory for docile targets in clear weather granted a good firing position. A form of radar-ranging is housed in a small intake diffuser cone.

FISHBED-D: An A.I.-equipped all-weather version of the MiG-21, presumably evolved as a stop-gap measure pending the introduction of the very much more potent MiG-23, is known as the Fishbed-D. This differs from the standard day intercept model in having an enlarged engine air intake with an A.I. radome producing a double shock to improve high-speed thrust, and a fairing aft of the canopy, resulting in a reduction in drag and a consequent slight improvement in performance, maximum speed in clean

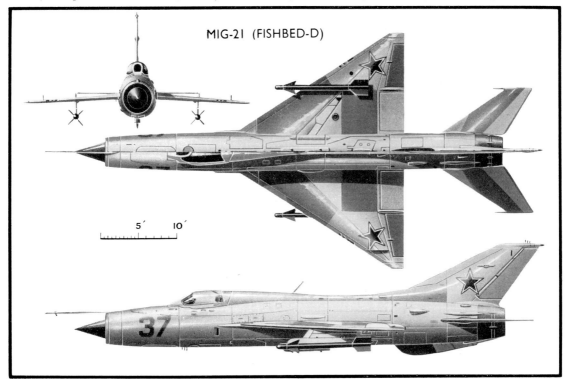

MIG-21 (FISHBED-D)

5′   10′

An early production Fishbed-C with underwing smoke canisters photographed during an air display.

configuration being raised from Mach 2.0 to about Mach 2.2. The cannon armament is deleted, standard armament being a pair of Atoll missiles, but this light armament and the limited tactical radius of the aircraft can hardly be considered to result in an effective all-weather weapon.

There are several further variants of the basic MiG-21 design, including a tandem two-seat advanced

trainer version, and an additional single-seat interceptor model which has been dubbed Fishbed-E. Some 450 MiG-21s are to be manufactured under licence by Hindustan Aeronautics Limited, and early in 1965 the Indian Air Force is scheduled to receive forty-four Russian-built MiG-21s, six having been supplied to that service earlier.

MIG-21 (FISHBED-C) SPECIFICATION

Power Plant: *One unspecified axial-flow turbojet rated at 9,500 lb.s.t. and 12,500 lb.s.t. with afterburning.*
Armament: *One or two 30-mm. cannon plus two Atoll infra-red homing AAMs.*
Performance: *Max. speed (clean), 1,320 m.p.h. at 36,000 ft. (Mach 2.0), (with two Atoll AAMs and one 132 Imp. gal. drop tank), 990 m.p.h. (Mach 1.5); initial climb rate (with two Atoll AAMs), 30,000 ft./min.; combat radius (clean), 375 mls. Range (ferry with one 132 Imp. gal. drop tank), 1,260 mls.*
Weights: *Normal loaded, 17,000 lb.; max. overload, 18,800 lb.*
Dimensions: *Span, 25 ft. 0 in.; length, 47 ft. 0 in.; height, 14 ft. 6 in.; wing area, 250 sq. ft.*

MIG-23 (FLIPPER)

Perhaps the most outstanding of the latest generation of Russian combat aircraft, the MiG-23, or Flipper, is potentially one of the best current short-range, single-seat all-weather interceptors extant, and is presumably intended to form a team in the I.A.-P.V.O. (Istrebitel-nya Aviatsiia Protivovozdushnoi Oborony—Fighter Air Armies of the Air Defence Forces) with surface-launched missiles and the longer-ranging Fiddler.

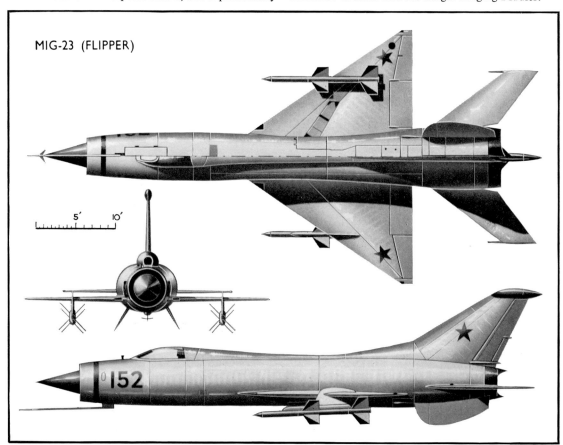

MIG-23 (FLIPPER)

5′   10′

0152

MIG-23 (FLIPPER) SPECIFICATION

Power Plants: *Two unspecified axial-flow turbojets each rated at 9,500 lb.s.t. and 12,500 lb.s.t. with after-burning.*

Armament: *Two Awl two-stage (probably IR-homing) AAMs, or combinations of radar-guided and IR-homing AAMs.*

Performance: *Max. speed (clean), 1,520–1,580 m.p.h. at 40,000 ft. (Mach 2.3–2.4); stabilized speed (with two Awl missiles), 1,190–1,320 m.p.h. (Mach 1.8–2.0); range cruise, 595 m.p.h. (Mach 0.9); initial climb, 35,000–40,000 ft./min.; service ceiling, 60,000 ft.; time to 50,000 ft., 4.5–5 min.; range (ferry), 1,500 mls.*

Weights: *Empty, 24,000 lb.; loaded, 34,000 lb.; max. overload, 38,500 lb.*

Dimensions: *Span, 30 ft. 0 in.; length, 65 ft. 0 in.; height, 17 ft. 0 in.; wing area, 420 sq. ft.*

(Above and below) A MiG-23 with two Awl AAMs underwing.

A straight-forward development of the MiG-21 which it is undoubtedly intended to succeed, and employing a virtually identical wing, the MiG-23 has twice the weight and thrust of its predecessor, and may be distinguished by the fact that the wing is proportionally smaller, is set lower and further aft on the substantially longer fuselage, and the fuselage itself is broader at the rear to accommodate side-by-side mounted turbojets. The MiG-23 does not appear to possess cannon armament, two 15-ft. Awl missiles being mounted beneath the wings, these apparently being two-stage weapons with infra-red guidance. It may be assumed, however, that alternative loads may include a mixture of radar-guided and IR-homing missiles. The large conical diffuser or centrebody in the air intake may be presumed to house an A.I. dish scanner of about 28 in. diameter, providing a range of some thirty miles.

Without external stores, the MiG-23 is presumably restricted in speed to some arbitrary figure such as Mach 2.4 by its aluminium alloy structure. A single drop tank of up to 264 Imp. gal. capacity may be mounted on a centreline pylon which, according to reports, can also take a pack containing a rocket motor and oxidant tank, although there would seem to be little reason for boosting this fighter's climb rate or ceiling.

The specification at the head of the previous column should be considered as provisional.

SUKHOI FISHPOT

Evolved in parallel with the MiG-21 by a design bureau headed by Pavel Osipovich Sukhoi, the Fishpot was designed from the outset for the all-weather intercept rôle, and as with the Mikoyan bureau, Sukhoi adopted the principle of "limited commonality" in that major components of the Fishpot were shared

A Fishpot-B all-weather interceptor with four Alkali beam-riding AAMs and twin ventral drop tanks.

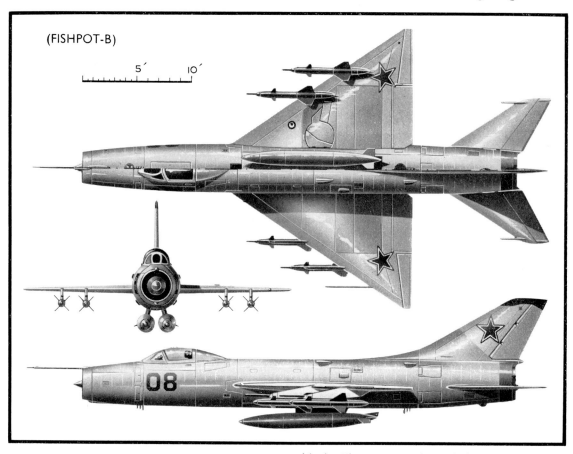

(FISHPOT-B)

5´   10´

(Above and below, and head of opposite page) A Fishpot-B with four Alkali beam-riding AAMs and twin ventral tanks.

with the Fitter, a ground attack fighter developed at the same time. When the Fishpot made its début in prototype form over Tushino in 1956, it was generally assumed in the West that the Sukhoi fighter was in a similar category to the contemporary MiG-21, but, in fact, whereas the Mikoyan aircraft was a small and light clear-weather interceptor, the Fishpot was a relatively large and heavy aircraft which was designed from the outset for the all-weather rôle, its closest western equivalent being the F-102A Delta Dagger.

The prototype Sukhoi all-weather interceptor carried its A.I. radar over a chin-type air intake in a rather similar fashion to the F-86D Sabre, and 30-mm. cannon were mounted in the wing roots, this version being dubbed Fishpot-A. At an early stage in the fighter's flight development, however, a more orthodox circular air intake was adopted, the A.I. being mounted in a central intake cone and the cannon armament being deleted. This version, the Fishpot-B, was in service in some numbers with the V.-V.S. by the early 'sixties.

The armament of the Fishpot-B normally comprises four Alkali AAMs which are apparently employed with an A.I. radar modulated for beam riding, the missiles being carried underwing with two 132 Imp. gal. drop tanks being mounted side by side beneath the fuselage. There would seem to be little doubt that the initial production Fishpot-B is related to the record-breaking aircraft which, referred to as the T-431, established a zoom climb altitude record of

94,657 ft. in 1959. Data released to the F.A.I. indicated an afterburning thrust of 19,840 lb. for the power plant, suggesting an engine of some 14,500 lb.s.t. dry. However, later production Fishpot-B fighters were seen to employ a slightly enlarged air intake, indicating an uprated engine, and when, on September 4, 1962, the T-431 established another short-lived record—maintaining an altitude of 69,456 ft. over a 9–15 ml. course —the afterburning thrust of the turbojet was referred to as 22,046 lb.s.t.

An even more impressive record established by the T-431 was a 500-km. closed-circuit speed of 1,452 m.p.h. (Mach 2.2) set up on September 25, 1962. However, this aircraft is believed to differ from the standard service Fishpot-B in a number of respects, and is probably the developed version of the Sukhoi fighter demonstrated at Tushino in 1961, the nose centre-body being moved forward to produce a two-shock intake, and various aerodynamic improvements being introduced. As seen at Tushino, this variant of the Fishpot carried two missiles similar to those employed by the Firebar.

FISHPOT-B SPECIFICATION

Power Plant: One unspecified axial-flow turbojet rated at 15,500 lb.s.t. and 22,050 lb.s.t. with afterburning.
Armament: Four Alkali beam-riding AAMs.
Performance: Max. speed (clean), 1,190 m.p.h. at 40,000 ft. (Mach 1.8), with four Alkali AAMs, 990 m.p.h. (Mach 1.5); initial climb rate, 27,000 ft./min.; time to 40,000 ft., 4.5 min.; service ceiling, 55,000 ft. Weights: Loaded (clean), 25,500 lb.; max., 29,000 lb. Dimensions: Span, 31 ft. 0 in.; length, 55 ft. 0 in.; height, 16 ft. 0 in.; wing area, 425 sq. ft.

SUKHOI FITTER

Intended primarily for close support and ground attack, the Fitter employs the same fuselage and tail surfaces as the initial production Fishpot interceptor, but the 57° swept delta wing is replaced by longer-span swept wings with 62° of leading-edge sweepback, accompanied by a new undercarriage and cannon

(FITTER)

Sukhoi Fitter close support and ground attack fighters with small underwing rocket pods.

armament. Like the Fishpot, the Fitter appeared over Tushino as a prototype in 1956, entering service with the V.-V.S. some three years later, and being used primarily by the Frontovaia Aviatsiya.

The lower powered turbojet installed in the initial production version of the Fishpot appears to have been retained, and built-in armament comprises a pair of 30-mm. cannon in the wing roots. There are four external stores pylons, two beneath the fuselage and two beneath the wings. The fuselage pylons normally carry two 132 Imp. gal. drop tanks or 1,100-lb. bombs side by side, although such installations are likely to result in considerable interference drag between the stores, and the underwing pylons are apparently restricted to fuel tanks or relatively light loads such as pods housing nineteen 55-mm. unguided rockets.

FITTER SPECIFICATION

Power Plant: One unspecified axial-flow turbojet rated at 14,500 lb.s.t. and 20,000 lb.s.t. with afterburning.
Armament: Two 30-mm. cannon and two 1,100-lb. bombs plus two pods each housing nineteen 55-mm. unguided rockets or two 550-lb. bombs.
Performance: Max. speed (clean), 1,056 m.p.h. at 36,000 ft., with two drop tanks and two rocket pods, 790 m.p.h. (Mach 1.2); initial climb rate (clean), 30,000 ft./min., (with external stores) 23,500 ft./min.
Weights: Loaded (clean), 27,000 lb.; max., 30,500 lb.
Dimensions: Span, 32 ft. 3 in.; length, 55 ft. 0 in.

TUPOLEV TU-16 BADGER

Broadly comparable in both rôle and performance with the B-47 Stratojet, the Tupolev Tu-16 medium bomber first entered service with the V.-V.S.'s Dalnaya Aviatsiya (Long-range Aviation) during 1954–55, design work having presumably been initiated in the late 'forties, with prototypes entering the test phase in 1952. Featuring moderately swept surfaces, the wing outer panels being swept 37° at the leading edge, increasing to 45° inboard, the Tu-16's most remarkable feature was the size and power of its turbojets which, in their initial AM-3 form as installed in early production bombers, possessed a rating of 18,080 lb.s.t.,

two power plants of this type being recessed into the fuselage sides. The main undercarriage members comprised four-wheel bogies housed in fairings extending aft of the wing trailing edges, seven crew members were carried, and the defensive armament system was apparently a rationalised development of that of the piston-engined Tu-4—the Russian copy of the Boeing B-29 Superfortress which the Tu-16 supplanted.

The Tu-16 was allocated the code-name "Badger" in the West, and several versions are currently in service.

An electronic reconnaissance version of the Tu-16 Badger-A with a scanner pod under the port wing, and various aerials.

TU-16 (BADGER-C)

BADGER-A: In production, the standard strategic bombing version of the Tu-16 was fitted with progressively more powerful engines, the principal of these being apparently the AM-3M of 19,180 lb.s.t. Defensive armament comprises a single 23-mm. cannon mounted in the starboard side of the fuselage nose and fixed to fire forward, twin 20-mm. or 23-mm. weapons in a tail turret, a similar armament in a semi-recessed dorsal barbette aimed from a position immediately aft of the flight deck, and a further pair of cannon in an aft ventral barbette aimed from blisters below the tailplane. A maximum bomb load of the order of 20,000 lb. can be housed internally and with which the maximum practical radius of action is

(Above) An electronic reconnaissance Badger-A featuring several radomes and numerous aerials, and (below, left) a reconnaissance version of the Badger-C with large search radar in modified nose.

TU-16 (BADGER-A)

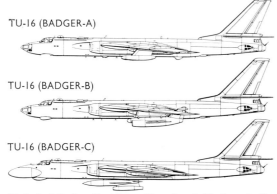

TU-16 (BADGER-B)

TU-16 (BADGER-C)

(Below) A Badger-B with two Kennel anti-shipping missiles.

approximately 1,250 miles. Some two dozen Tu-16s of this type have been supplied to the air arm of the United Arab Republic.

Several reconnaissance variants of the Badger-A exist, some having cameras in the weapons bay and others carrying two scanner pods on underwing pylons, these presumably shadowing naval forces by passive homing on their radar emissions and using the distance between the pods as a base for triangulation.

BADGER-B: The Badger-B is an adaptation of the -A to carry two Kennel anti-shipping missiles on pylons beneath the outboard wing panels. This missile is a relatively simple turbojet-driven weapon with a warhead of about 1,000 lb., a range of less than 100 mls., and radar-homing for the terminal attack phase. It is likely that some internally-housed free-falling weapons are combined with the two Kennel missiles on the Badger-B to provide maximum flexibility of attack, but radius of action is reduced to some 1,150 miles. The Badger-B is used in some numbers by the shore-based naval air arm, the A.V.-M.F., acting as a medium-range complement to the Tu-20 in the maritime strike and reconnaissance rôle, and a number of Kennel-armed Badger-Bs have been supplied to the Indonesian Republican Air Force, equipping Nos. 41 and 42 Squadrons.

BADGER-C: The third current service version of the Tu-16, the Badger-C, is employed in both long-range reconnaissance and missile-carrying rôles, the nose of this model being extensively modified to accommodate an extremely large search radar, increasing overall length by some 5 ft. to approximately 126 ft. The missile-carrying variant has the forward portion of the weapons bay eliminated as a result of extensive structural modifications dictated by the need to partly submerge the Kipper stand-off missile. An air-breathing weapon bearing a superficial resemblance to the AGM-28 Hound Dog carried by the B-52 Stratofortress, the Kipper is believed to have a range of some 200 mls., but with the improved range and definition of the launching aircraft's radar, the missile could theoretically be dropped right up to the radar horizon.

Between 1,500 and 2,000 Tu-16s are believed to have been produced, although a considerable proportion of these are now no doubt held at maintenance units as a strategic reserve.

TUPOLEV TU-16 (BADGER-A)
SPECIFICATION

Power Plants: *Two Mikulin AM-3M turbojets each rated at 19,180 lb.s.t.*

Armament: *(Defensive) One fixed forward-firing 23-mm. cannon and two 20-mm. or 23-mm. cannon in each of two remotely-controlled (forward dorsal and aft ventral) barbettes and tail turret. (Offensive) Maximum load of 20,000 lb. of free-falling bombs in internal weapons bay.*

Performance: *Max. speed, 620 m.p.h. at 10,000 ft. (Mach 0.85), 610 m.p.h. at 20,000 ft. (Mach 0.87); normal cruise, 495 m.p.h. at 38,000 ft. (Mach 0.75); max. unrefuelled range (with 7,000-lb. bomb load), 3,800 mls., (with 20,000-lb. bomb load), 2,500 mls.*

Weights: *Approx. max. loaded, 170,000 lb.*

Dimensions: *Span, 110 ft.; length, 121 ft.; height, 36 ft.; wing area, 1,815 sq. ft.*

(Above) A Badger-C with a Kipper stand-off missile.

TUPOLEV TU-20 (BEAR)

Unique in being the only turboprop-driven strategic bomber to have entered first line service with any air arm, and in combining airscrews with a swept wing—a combination widely held at one time to be pointless since airscrews were considered to be unusable at speeds above Mach 0.75 and wing sweepback is unnecessary below this speed—the Tu-20 has now been largely relegated to the rôles of missile carrier and electronic and photographic reconnaissance. However, before its designed task was assumed by the ICBM, it was undoubtedly the largest single factor justifying the North American continental defence system and, thus, an outstanding economic success from the Russian viewpoint as it necessitated a completely disproportionate counter effort on the part of the U.S.A.

Development of this turboprop-powered strategic bomber began during the early 'fifties under the Tupolev design bureau designation Tu-95, and the first prototype made its public début at Tushino in

1955. Five examples were demonstrated a year later, suggesting that development was proceeding to roughly the same time scale as the contemporary turbojet-driven Myasishchev Mya-4. Both the Tupolev and Myasishchev heavy bombers had been designed to meet specifications formulated by the Dalnaya

(Below and above right) The reconnaissance version of the Bear-B. Like the missile-carrying variant, this type has the large duck-billed nose radome housing high-definition search radar.

A Bear-B with Kangaroo stand-off missile.

Aviatsiya (Long-range Aviation) which provides Russia's strategic bombing arm, and both entered service during 1957–58, the Tupolev bomber receiving the official designation Tu-20. In the event, the Mya-4, dubbed Bison in the West, remained in first-line bomber service for a relatively brief period, allegedly due to the fact that its range failed to reach the critical figure, continuing in service in only small numbers for the tanker and photographic/electronic reconnaissance rôles, whereas, contrary to western forecasts, the Tu-20 continues to serve in substantial numbers.

The success of the Tu-20 was largely dependent on the development of an unprecedentedly powerful turbo-prop unit, and this task was allocated to the Junkers Collective at Kuibischev, which, headed by Dipl. Ing. Ferdinand Brandner, and staffed by some eight hundred German and Austrian engineers, was attached to the Kuznetsov engine design bureau. The turboprop, ultimately designated Kuznetsov NK-12, has been said to have offered 12,000 e.s.h.p., but in practice it was limited to 8,000–9,000 e.s.h.p., according to Andrei N. Tupolev, and it was this power plant that was installed in the prototype Tu-20 when it began flight trials in 1954. Late series Tu-20s undoubtedly switched to the improved NK-12M which is stated to be rated at 14,750 e.s.h.p. for take-off.

According to Dipl. Ing. Brandner, the Tu-20 was designed to attain 560 m.p.h. at 36,000 ft. (Mach 0.85) with the 16.4-ft. airscrews turning at 750 r.p.m., corresponding to a tip speed of Mach 1.08. However, it was not stated that the Tu-20 had, in fact, attained the design speed, and the "over the target" speed of 500 m.p.h. at 41,000 ft. (Mach 0.76) ascribed to the aircraft by U.S.A.F. intelligence sources would seem to be nearer to the bomber's true capability, this giving an airscrew tip speed of Mach 0.98. Of course, it should be borne in mind that, in April 1960, a Tu-114 transport—a derivative of the Tu-20 with an appreciably larger fuselage—completed a 3,130-mile closed-circuit with a 55,000-lb. load at an average speed of 545 m.p.h.

In the West, the Tu-20 has received the appellation of Bear, and two principal variants are currently in service.

BEAR-A: In its initial strategic bomber production form, the Tu-20 featured a glazed bomb-aiming nose, and defensive armament comprised one fixed forward-firing cannon of 20-mm. or 23-mm. calibre in the starboard side of the fuselage nose, and two weapons of similar calibre in each of a rear ventral barbette and

tail turret. An exceptionally large weapons bay reputedly accommodated a maximum of 25,000 lb. of free-falling conventional or nuclear weapons which load, according to U.S. Defence Secretary Robert S. McNamara, was accompanied by a 3,900-mile radius of action. However, assuming that additional fuel tanks are accommodated in the weapons bay for reconnaissance—now the Bear-A's principal task—tactical radius may be increased to some 4,500 miles.

In 1958 some publicity was given to a high-speed transport conversion of the Tu-20 bomber to which the designation Tu-114D was applied. Simply a Bear-A with a small pressurised cabin for passengers in the aft fuselage, the Tu-114D flew Moscow-Irkutsk-Moscow non-stop, a distance of 5,300 miles at an average speed of 503 m.p.h., giving an indication of the high-speed cruise performance of the early production Tu-20.

BEAR-B: During the early 'sixties, an attempt was made to extend the operational life of the Tu-20 by means of a major modification programme which resulted in the Bear-B, first seen publicly over Tushino in 1961. Two versions of the Bear-B are known to be in service, the first being a carrier for a stand-off weapon known as the Kangaroo, and the second being a specialised reconnaissance model. Both feature an extensively modified nose embodying a large duck-billed radome housing high-definition search radar, and a large in-flight refuelling probe. An additional gun barbette has been introduced in an aft dorsal position, and its single weapon could conceivably be used to fire tracer and "window" as a form of counter-measure, the intention being to confuse the missiles of opposing interceptors.

The largest of Russia's known stand-off weapons, the turbojet-driven Kangaroo has an overall length of some 46 ft., and guided by the Bear-B's radar is likely to cruise over a range of some 250 miles at a speed of the order of Mach 1.3. Presumably possessing a multi-megaton warhead, the Kangaroo may provide the Bear-B with a second-strike capability following the first-strike ICBM salvo. Refuelled once by a Bear-A tanker, the Bear-B could carry the Kangaroo more than 5,000 miles from Soviet territory.

Although the number of Tu-20s built is not known with certainty, it is believed that some 150 bombers of this type provided the Dalnaya Aviatsiya's principal striking force in the late 'fifties, and production probably totalled some 300 aircraft.

TUPOLEV TU-20 (BEAR-B) SPECIFICATION

Power Plants: *Four Kuznetsov NK-12M single-shaft turboprops each rated at 14,750 e.s.h.p. for take-off.* Armament: *(Defensive) Two 20-mm. or 23-mm. cannon in a rear turret and rear ventral barbette. (Offensive) One Kangaroo turbojet-driven supersonic stand-off missile.*
Performance: *Max. speed, 550 m.p.h. at 36,000 ft. (Mach 0.83); max. cruise, 500 m.p.h. at 40,000 ft. (Mach 0.76); range cruise, 440 m.p.h. at 36,000 ft. (Mach 0.67); unrefuelled range (recce. mission), 9,000 mls.; unrefuelled radius of action (with single Kangaroo stand-off weapon), 3,000 mls.; service ceiling, 44,000 ft.* Weights: *Normal loaded, 330,000–340,000 lb.; max., 370,000 lb.*
Dimensions: *Span, 163 ft.; length, 150 ft.; height, 40 ft.; wing area, 3,000 sq. ft.*

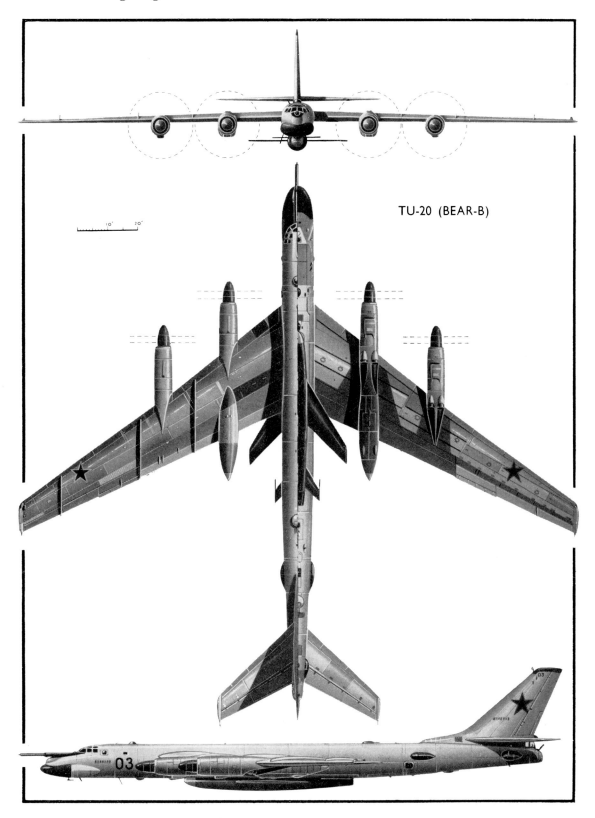

TU-20 (BEAR-B)

TUPOLEV BLINDER

Intended for bombing and reconnaissance missions of intermediate range and possessing supersonic dash capability, the Blinder is generally believed to be a

product of one of the design bureaux headed by Andrei N. Tupolev, and its configuration is unique in that its two turbojets are mounted side-by-side above the extreme rear fuselage. Displayed publicly at Tushino in June 1961, by which time it is believed to have attained pre-service status with the V.-V.S., the Blinder is likely to have flown in prototype form in 1957–58, and is in the same weight class as the R.A.F.'s V-bombers.

The Blinder appears to carry four crew members, and two versions were displayed at Tushino: the standard reconnaissance-bomber variant, nine examples of which were seen, and a modified variant having a drooped and broader nose radome, a prominent refuelling probe above the radar, and a large air-to-surface missile mounted semi-recessed in the lower fuselage. Only one example of the missile-carrying Blinder was seen at Tushino, and the operational status of this version is not known with certainty. The standard version has a short weapons bay positioned well aft, and has a single, remotely-controlled cannon in the tail which may be presumed to dispense a mixture of tracer and "chaff" to confuse the radar of intercepting fighters and the guidance systems of missiles.

The wing planform has a low overall taper ratio, and leading edge sweep varies from 70° at the root to 50° outboard, and the fairings housing the main undercarriage bogies project aft of the wings. Windows on either side of the bomb-aiming position indicate an emphasis on reconnaissance, and additional camera windows are situated further aft.

BLINDER SPECIFICATION

Power Plants: *Two unspecified turbojets rated at approx.* 19,200 *lb.s.t. and* 26,500 *lb.s.t. with afterburning.*
Armament: (*Standard version*) *Various combinations of free-falling weapons in internal bay.*
Performance: *Max. speed,* 925 *m.p.h. at* 40,000 *ft.* (*Mach* 1.4)*; cruising,* 630 *m.p.h. at* 40,000 *ft.* (*Mach* 0.95)*; tactical radius* (*unrefuelled*), 1,400 *mls.; service ceiling,* 60,000 *ft.*
Weights: *Approx. max. loaded,* 185,000 *lb.*
Estimated Dimensions: *Span,* 91 *ft.; length,* 133 *ft.; height,* 17 *ft.; wing area,* 2,030 *sq. ft.*

(Below and immediately above left) The missile-carrying version of the Blinder with broad-nose radome and refuelling probe, and (top and centre photographs above) the initial service version with smaller radome.

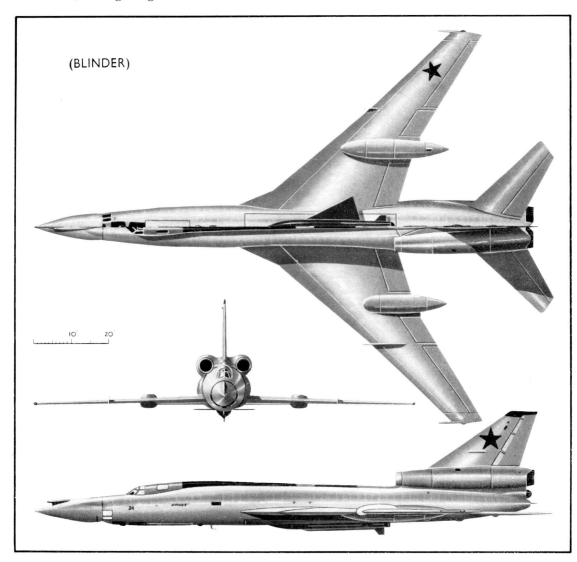

(BLINDER)

10′ 20′

Aerodynamically, the Blinder is one of the most sophisticated of current Russian warplanes, and it is roughly comparable with the B-58 Hustler although apparently possessing a substantially lower perfor-mance. However, little information is available concerning this aircraft other than can be gleaned from photographs, and the specification should be considered as highly provisional.

The standard reconnaissance-bomber version of the Blinder with short weapons bay and remotely-controlled tail cannon.

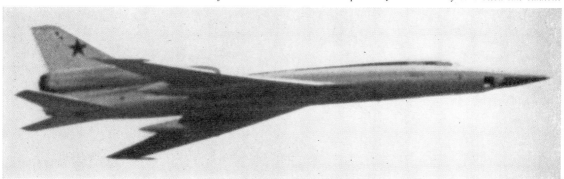

YAKOVLEV YAK-25 AND DERIVATIVES

Few post-war basic combat aircraft designs have given birth to more variants and derivatives than has the Yak-25, the I.A.-P.V.O.'s first twin-jet all-weather interceptor. The original Yak-25, which flew as a prototype in 1952–53, was uninspired in concept, and when it entered service in 1955 it was out-performed by western aircraft that pre-dated it. Yet, for more than a decade the Yak-25 has been constantly developed, and its "third generation" derivatives are among the latest combat aircraft to enter service with the V.-V.S.

Although both the R.A.F. and the U.S.A.F. introduced radar-equipped, two-seat all-weather interceptors during 1951–52, the V.-V.S. possessed no

A close-up view of the cockpits of the Yak-25 Flashlight-A all-weather and night fighter.

comparable combat aircraft until 1955 and the service début of the Yak-25. Aesthetically an unattractive aircraft of modest size, the Yak-25 had only a moderate performance considering that it was intended to intercept such targets as the Vickers Valiant and the B-47 Stratojet, and relied heavily on the relatively long search range radar which employed a large dish scanner. The Soviet Union was a late starter in the field of airborne fire control, and the Yak-25 had to use the stern chase, visual contact method of interception.

In its initial production form, the Yak-25 was powered by non-afterburning RD-5 turbojets of 4,800 lb.s.t., but at a relatively early stage in its service life it was re-engined with RD-9s of roughly 5,500 lb.s.t. The code-name "Flashlight" was allocated to the type, and later, in 1956, when further derivatives of the basic design appeared, the suffix letter "A" was added to distinguish the basic Yak-25 from its more advanced progeny.

FLASHLIGHT-A: The initial production model of the Yak-25, the Flashlight-A, employed a simple, 45° swept, untapered wing mounted in mid position, the two crew members were seated in tandem ejector seats, and the most unusual feature of the design was its novel undercarriage which was of zero-track tricycle layout—the aircraft being virtually balanced on the twin-wheel aft member with outrigger units on the wingtips. Built-in armament comprised two 37-mm. N-type cannon mounted semi-externally and

YAK-25 (FLASHLIGHT-A)

(Above and below, right) The initial production version of the Yak-25, the Flashlight-A two-seat night and all-weather interceptor, now being phased out of first line service with the V.-V.S.

forming a pack with snap-opening missile launcher housing 55-mm. unguided rockets. By detaching the gun barrels, the armament pack could be winched down for rearming.

FLASHLIGHT-B: Two "second generation" derivatives of the basic Yak-25 design made their appearance over Tushino in 1956, the first of these, the Flashlight-B, being a small tactical strike and reconnaissance aircraft in which the observer was moved into the front fuselage, ahead of the pilot, and a sharply-pointed, glazed nose was introduced, together with a small ventral radome. Afterburners were added to the RD-9 turbojets, the engine nacelles being lengthened accordingly, and a highly swept extension was added to the inboard wing leading edge, raising the critical Mach number slightly, and possibly improving stall behaviour.

At a later stage the wing fences were dropped and the wingtips extended to provide an overall span of approximately 38 ft. 6 in., but production of this aircraft was restricted to relatively small numbers, possibly as a result of the extremely limited radius of action offered by the Flashlight-B with its external load of bombs or rockets.

FLASHLIGHT-C: Demonstrated at the same time as the Flashlight-B, the -C also featured afterburners and similar wing modifications but was intended as an improved night and all-weather interceptor with tandem seating for the two crew members and a sharply-pointed nose radome to lessen drag and reduce rain erosion. Development of the Flashlight-C may be assumed to have been dropped owing to the marginal increase in performance over the -A, and to the fact that it possessed only a short time lead over later all-weather interceptors.

FLASHLIGHT-D: The only "second generation" Yak-25 development to attain really large-scale service status—if the Mandrake, representing a major re-design, is discounted—was the Flashlight-D tactical reconnaissance aircraft which first entered service with the V.-V.S.'s Frontovaia Aviatsiya in 1959 and currently serves in substantial numbers.

There is no direct western counterpart of the Flashlight-D, its rôle being performed by such types

as the Hunter F.R.Mk.10 and the RF-84F Thunder-flash, and this type embodies all the progressive aerodynamic improvements first tested on the Flashlight-B and -C. In addition, the outer wing panels feature drooped leading-edge extensions. The disposition of the two crew members and the glazed, pointed nose are similar to those of the Flashlight-B, cameras are installed in the extreme nose, and defensive armament comprises one 30-mm. cannon mounted semi-externally in the starboard side of the forward fuselage.

FLASHLIGHT-A SPECIFICATION

Power Plants: *Two Klimov RD-9 axial-flow turbojets each rated at approx. 5,500 lb.s.t.*

Armament: *Two 37-mm. Nudelmann N-37 cannon and 55-mm. unguided missiles in ventral pack, plus four Alkali beam-riding AAMs, or four pods each housing nineteen 55-mm. unguided rockets.*

Performance: *Max. speed, 630 m.p.h. at sea level (Mach 0.83), 594 m.p.h. at 36,000 ft. (Mach 0.9); range cruise, 495 m.p.h. at 40,000 ft. (Mach 0.75); initial climb rate, 10,000 ft./min.; low-level radius of action, 200 mls. at 570 m.p.h. (Mach 0.75); service ceiling, 50,000 ft.*

Weights: *Approx. normal loaded, 22,000 lb.*

Dimensions: *Span, 36 ft.; length, 51 ft.; height, 12 ft. 6 in.; wing area, 302 sq. ft.*

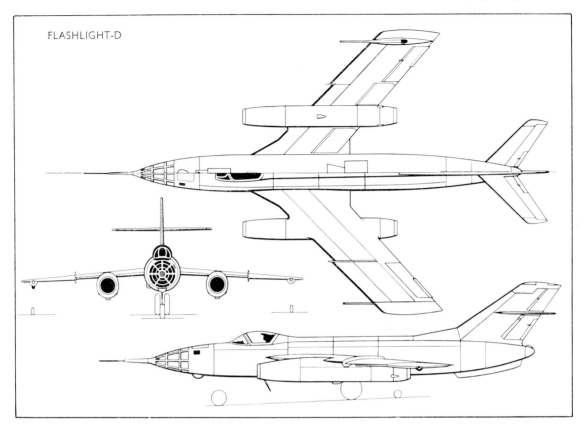

FLASHLIGHT-D

MAESTRO: The Maestro is a dual-control training variant of the Firebar for operational conversion, dual checks and instrument training.

MANDRAKE: A lighter, lower-powered equivalent of the Martin RB-57D, the Mandrake high-altitude

(Above) The Flashlight-D and (below) the Brewer.

FLASHLIGHT-D SPECIFICATION

Power Plants: *Two Klimov RD-9 axial-flow turbojets each rated at approx. 5,500 lb.s.t. and 7,200 lb.s.t. with afterburning.*
Armament: *One 30-mm. cannon in starboard side of forward fuselage.*
Performance: *Max. speed, 686 m.p.h. at sea level (Mach 0.9), 627 m.p.h. at 40,000 ft. (Mach 0.95); low-level cruise, 570 m.p.h. (Mach 0.75); initial climb, 16,000–18,000 ft./min.; tactical radius, 200 mls. at 1,000 ft., 500 mls. at 36,000 ft.; service ceiling, 50,000 ft.*
Weights: *Approx. normal loaded, 25,000 lb.*
Dimensions: *Span, 38 ft. 6 in.; length, 53 ft. 6 in.; height, 12 ft. 6 in.; wing area, 342 sq. ft.*

strategic reconnaissance aircraft is, in its standard form at least, a single-seater employing the standard Flashlight-A or -D rear fuselage, tail assembly and undercarriage, and the afterburning RD-9 turbojets of the latter. To these components have been married a new, non-swept, long-span wing measuring some 75 ft. from tip to tip. This new wing is mounted further aft on the fuselage to maintain the c.g., and has been raised to shoulder position.

The Mandrake is believed to have entered service with the V.-V.S.'s specialised strategic reconnaissance units in 1959, and has been seen in Europe and over India's northern territories, but few details of the capabilities of this aircraft are available, although it is believed to have been the Mandrake which, referred to as the "RV", established two payload-to-altitude records on July 29, 1959, by lifting 2,205 lb. to 67,113 ft., and 4,409 lb. to 66,188 ft. Assuming that every

The Brewer is currently in service in both reconnaissance and attack bomber versions, the latter having a small internal weapons bay, this space presumably being taken up by fuel in the reconnaissance model.

effort has been made to reduce weight, resulting in a take-off weight of the order of 22,000 lb. with 7,000 lb. of internal fuel, the Mandrake is likely to cruise at an altitude of about 56,000 ft., drifting up to 62,000 ft. as the fuel is burned off. A greater altitude would only be attained at a penalty in range, but it may be assumed that it will reach a maximum altitude of approximately 70,000 ft. Average cruise speed and normal radius of action are likely to be about 475 m.p.h. and 1,200 miles respectively.

BREWER: During the late 'fifties the Yakovlev design bureau was engaged in developing the well-proven Yak-25 airframe to permit operation at

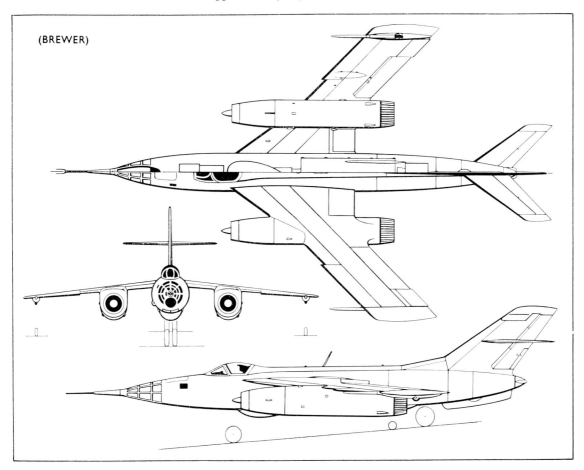

(BREWER)

appreciably higher weights and speeds by introducing further aerodynamic refinements, increasing the wing area and installing larger, more powerful turbojets. This new stage in the development of the basic 1950-design was to result in "third generation" versions for the reconnaissance, strike and all-weather intercept rôles, and the success that attended the Yakovlev bureau's efforts may be gauged from the fact that all three versions have attained service status with the V.-V.S.

At the Tushino display of 1961 all three variants made their public début and, initially, were dubbed in the West as Firebar-A, -B and -C. The Firebar-A was the tactical reconnaissance version, two examples of which appeared, differing one from the other only in that one featured a ventral radome; the Firebar-B was an all-weather interceptor variant, and externally very similar to the -A was the Firebar-C tactical strike model. The last-mentioned version was temporarily code-named "Brassard", but like the -A is now known as the Brewer. The Brewer differs from earlier Yak-25 derivatives in a number of major respects, and apart from an overall similarity of configuration is, to all intents and purposes, a new design. Nevertheless, there is some likelihood of observers confusing the Brewer with the Flashlight-D that it replaces. The later aircraft may be distinguished by its fatter engine nacelles with central intake cones, its modified wing planform, and the fact that the wing is mounted higher on the fuselage, simultaneously raising the jet pipes clear of the ground and providing more space for fuel or equipment.

The wing of the Brewer and other "third generation" Yak-25 derivatives has a straight inboard trailing edge and a further increase in leading-edge sweep inboard of the engine nacelles, increasing gross area by some 60 sq. ft. The vertical tail surfaces have been increased

in area, tailplane sweep has been increased, and the "zero-track tricycle" undercarriage of all earlier Yak-25 developments has given place to a widely spaced "bicycle" gear, the aircraft's weight being divided between the two twin-wheel fuselage-mounted units.

The tactical strike Brewer has an internal weapons bay which occupies the space in the fuselage presumably taken up by fuel in the reconnaissance version. This weapons bay, which is positioned well aft of the c.g., is presumably intended to accommodate quite modest loads, and has necessitated some flattening of the lower fuselage contours and the introduction of a pair of ventral strakes ahead of the rear undercarriage unit housing. The contents of the internal weapons bay may be supplemented by stores mounted on two underwing pylons, and gun armament remains the same as that of the reconnaissance version, consisting of a single 30-mm. weapon mounted in the starboard side of the fuselage. The radome aft of the forward wheel housing probably houses ground mapping and terrain avoidance radar. The Brewer apparently entered service with Frontovaya Aviatsiya units during 1961–62, and has progressively replaced the Ilyushin Il-28.

FIREBAR: Originally known as the Firebar-B, the two-seat night and all-weather interceptor member of the trio of "third generation" Yak-25 derivatives no longer has a suffix letter attached to its code name since the renaming of its fellows, and the differences between this and the Brewer are limited to the fuselage, the second crew member being in this case located behind the pilot à la Flashlight-A, the glazed nose being replaced by an A.I. radar.

Possessing a generally similar performance to that of the Brewer, and believed to have entered service with I.A.-P.V.O. units during 1962–63, the Firebar

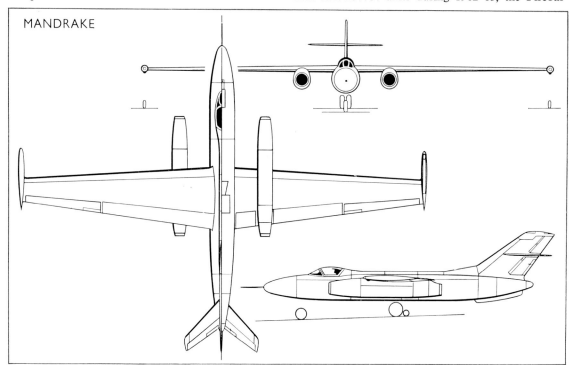

MANDRAKE

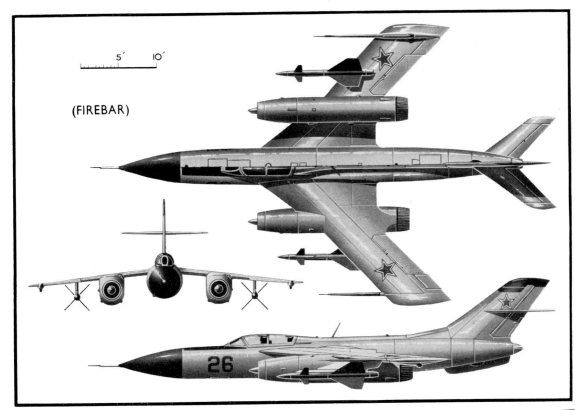

(FIREBAR)

carries two 13 ft. 6 in. missiles which are presumably semi-active radar homing weapons each weighing about 500 lb. and possessing a range of 6–7 miles, and the A.I. radar is believed to have a range of 35–40 miles.

MANGROVE: An operational training conversion of the Flashlight-D has been allocated the code-name Mangrove in the West. Several training versions of the Flashlight exist, including a pilot trainer with dual controls and the A.I. dish scanner removed from the nose, and a version for training navigators in the use of interception radar, but the Mangrove is apparently intended primarily for low-level attack and navigational training.

BREWER SPECIFICATION

Power Plants: *Two unspecified axial-flow turbojets each rated at 9,500 lb.s.t. and 12,500 lb. with after-burning.*
Armament: *One tactical nuclear store or alternative free-falling weapon in internal bay and conventional bombs or ASMs on two underwing pylons, plus one 30-mm. cannon in starboard side of forward fuselage.*
Performance: *Max. speed, 735 m.p.h. at 35,000 ft. (Mach 1.1), 725 m.p.h. at sea level (Mach 0.95); tactical radius, 230 mls. at 630 m.p.h. at sea level, 575 mls. at 570 m.p.h. at 35,000 ft., initial climb rate, 28,000 ft./min.; service ceiling, 55,000 ft.*
Weights: *Approx. loaded, 35,000 lb.*
Dimensions: *Span, 38 ft. 6 in.; length 59 ft. 0 in.; height, 13 ft. 0 in.; wing area, 400 sq. ft.*

YAKOVLEV FIDDLER

A multi-mission two-seat long-range all-weather fighter and reconnaissance-strike aircraft, the Fiddler was first reported in 1959 when it was assumed to be a variant of the so-called Backfin, a Yakovlev-designed light bomber with supersonic dash capability which failed to attain service status with the V.-V.S. Aerodynamically, the Fiddler does, in fact, bear a relationship to the abortive Backfin, apparently employing a basically similar wing, and similarly arranged power plants, but there the resemblance ends. The nearest comparable western aircraft appears to be the TSR-2 which is roughly in the same weight category, but whereas the Russian design emphasizes economical

high-altitude operation, the TSR-2's design is biased towards low-level flying.

Evolved during the mid 'fifties, the Fiddler is believed to have entered service during 1962–63, and has been seen with a large ventral radar bulge which may be presumed to house high definition ground mapping radar for reconnaissance missions, and two Ash AAMs which are believed to be infra-red homers. These missiles are mounted under the outboard wing panels and it may be assumed that various other types of missiles can be carried. For the strike mission, the ventral radar is likely to be replaced by an internal weapons bay. In the interceptor rôle the Fiddler can

75

Currently one of the most advanced of Russia's combat aircraft, the Fiddler multi-mission, two-seat, long-range, all-weather fighter and reconnaissance-strike aircraft is illustrated above with an Ash AAM under each wing. The large ventral bulge is assumed to house ground mapping radar.

apparently operate well beyond the range of ground-based radar control, and in addition to carrying its own early warning radar to detect low-flying intruders, it is believed to carry passive homing devices, frequency-switching A.I., and navigational aids of unusually long range.

FIDDLER SPECIFICATION

Power Plants: *Two unspecified turbojets of approx. 18,000 lb.s.t. and 22,000 lb.s.t. with afterburning.*
Armament: (*Intercept*) *Various AAMs mounted underwing, including the Ash infra-red homer.* (*Strike*) *Free-falling weapons in internal bay and ASMs underwing.*
Performance: *Max. speed, 1,056 m.p.h. at 40,000 ft. (Mach 1.6); cruising, 630 m.p.h. at 40,000 ft. (Mach 0.95); time to 40,000 ft., 5 min.; service ceiling, 60,000 ft.; range (internal fuel), 2,000 mls.*
Weights: *Estimated normal loaded, 80,000 lb.*
Dimensions: *Span, 56 ft.; length, 85 ft.; height, 20 ft.; wing area, 800 sq. ft.*

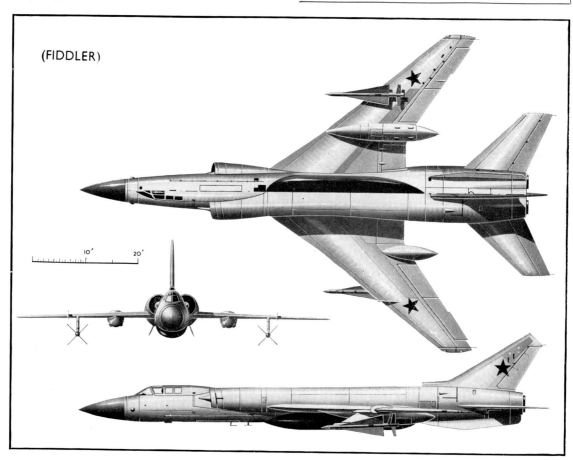

(FIDDLER)

HELOUAN HA-300

The HA-300 single-seat point defence interceptor, currently in the initial stages of production at Military Aircraft Factory No. 36 at Helouan, has a unique background in having been designed originally by a Germano-Spanish team led by Professor Willi Messerschmitt to meet a Spanish Air Force requirement, development being initiated by the Spanish Hispano-Aviación concern who built a full-scale glider model, the HA-23P, before, in 1960, the project was transferred lock, stock and barrel to Egypt, the United Arab Republic assuming the sponsorship of the fighter.

As originally conceived, the HA-300 was a tailless delta powered by a single Bristol Siddeley Orpheus B.Or.12 turbojet offering a dry thrust of 6,740 lb. and 8,170 lb. with afterburning, stipulated maximum speed being Mach 1.5. Prior to the transfer of the project from Spain to Egypt, a swept tailplane had been introduced at the base of the rear fuselage, and considerable development of the basic design was then undertaken by a team of German, Spanish and Egyptian engineers, who have adapted the design for the E-300 turbojet evolved in Egypt by Dipl. Ing. Ferdinand Brandner, and for speeds of the order of Mach 2.0.

The first prototype HA-300 flew for the first time on March 7, 1964 powered for initial trials by a 4,850 lb. s.t. Bristol Siddeley Orpheus turbojet. In its initial form, this aircraft is intended for relatively low-speed trials, having subsonic engine air intakes and a non-powered rudder, but the second prototype, which was scheduled to join the flight test programme during the spring of 1965, will have supersonic intakes and a rudder power control system, and, after initial flight trials of the E-300 turbojet in an HF-24 Marut test-bed, will be re-engined with the indigenous power plant.

An extremely small aircraft, roughly comparable in size and weight with the Fiat G.91 and the Northrop F-5A, the HA-300 has a mid-mounted delta wing with a thickness/chord ratio of about four per cent and a leading edge sweep of 57.5°. In view of the moderately large approach incidences associated with highly loaded deltas such as the HA-300, the pilot of this interceptor would appear to suffer an exceptionally poor view for landing, and it is therefore possible that the production version will employ some form of mechanical nose droop. Armament for the intercept rôle is likely to comprise a pair of infra-red homing AAMs, such as the Russian Atoll, and it is probable

---

HA-300 SPECIFICATION

Power Plant: *One Hezouan E-300 turbojet rated at approx. 7,500 lb.s.t. and 11,000 lb.s.t. with afterburning.*
Armament: *Probably two infra-red homing AAMs and two 20-mm. or 30-mm. cannon.*
Estimated Performance: *Max. speed, 1,320 m.p.h. at 40,000 ft. (Mach 2.0), (with two AAMs), 1,120 m.p.h. (Mach 1.7); initial climb, 40,000 ft./min.; combat radius (clean), 400 mls.*
Weights: *Estimated loaded (clean), 12,000 lb.*
Estimated Dimensions: *Span, 20 ft.; length, 38 ft.; height, 10 ft.; wing area, 185 sq. ft.*

The first Egyptian fighter of indigenous construction, the HA-300 has been developed by a team of German, Spanish and Egyptian engineers, and was first flown in 1964 with an Orpheus turbojet.

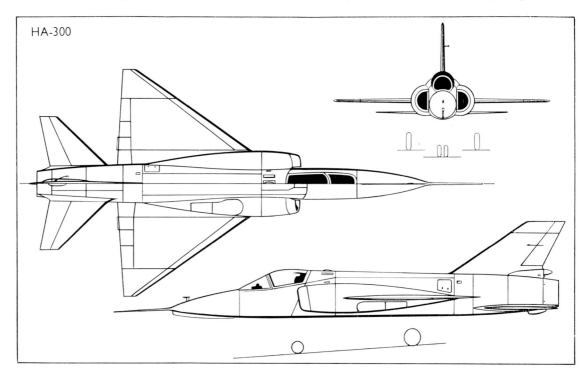

HA-300

that cannon armament will be included for the ground-attack task, although the highly loaded tailed delta configuration offers serious shortcomings in the latter rôle.

Additional prototypes or pre-production aircraft are expected to join the HA-300 test programme during the course of 1965, and production deliveries are likely to commence before the end of 1966.

A small point-defence interceptor with limited attack capability, the HA-300 is not likely to enter service before late 1966 or early 1967.

ARMSTRONG WHITWORTH SEA HAWK

Withdrawn from first line Royal Navy service in December 1960, and from the Royal Netherlands Navy in December 1964, the Sea Hawk shipboard single-seat ground-attack fighter today remains in service with the Indian and Federal German navies.

Although originally a Hawker design, the parent company manufactured only a small initial production batch, and all subsequent development and production became the responsibility of the former Sir W. G. Armstrong Whitworth Aircraft Limited, now a component of the Avro Whitworth Division of the Hawker Siddeley Group.

A carrier-borne interceptor derivative of the P.1040 experimental land-based fighter which was not ordered into production as it was not considered to offer a sufficient advance over the Meteor F.Mk.4, the Sea Hawk was first tendered to the Admiralty in January 1946. Specification N.7/46 was drawn up around this proposal, and three prototypes were ordered, the first of these (VP401) flying on September 2, 1947 with a 4,500 lb.s.t. Nene 1. This aircraft carried no naval equipment, but the second prototype (VP413), which flew a year later, on September 3, 1948, had arrester gear, upward-folding outer wing panels and an armament of four 20-mm. cannon with 200 r.p.g. The final prototype (VP422) flew on October 17, 1949, this featuring provision for R.A.T.O.G. and drop tanks, and faster undercarriage retraction.

In the meantime, a production contract had been placed for 151 aircraft, and the first Sea Hawk F.Mk.1 (WF143) with a 5,000 lb.s.t. Nene 101 engine flew on November 14, 1951. Hawker's other commitments

necessitated transfer of the Sea Hawk programme to Sir W. G. Armstrong Whitworth Aircraft after the completion of only thirty-five Sea Hawk F.Mk.1s, and a further sixty shipboard fighters of this type were produced before production switched to the F.Mk.2 in which power-boosted ailerons were introduced to improve roll rate. The first Sea Hawk F.Mk.2 (WF240) flew on February 24, 1954, forty machines being manufactured.

Whereas provision had been made in both the F.Mks.1 and 2 for two 90 Imp. gal. drop tanks, no other stores were carried externally, and with the development of a strengthened wing, permitting two 500-lb. bombs to be carried in place of the drop tanks, the rôle of fighter-bomber was added to the Sea Hawk's repertoire, and the designation was changed to F.B.Mk.3, the first aircraft of this type (WF280) flying on March 13, 1954. One hundred and sixteen Sea Hawks of this version were followed by ninety-seven F.G.A.Mk.4s with pick-up points for up to four 500-lb. bombs or two bombs and twenty 60-lb. rockets. The first Sea Hawk F.G.A.Mk.4 (WV792) flew on August 26, 1954, and many ground attack fighters of this type were later converted to the definitive F.G.A.Mk.6 standard.

The Sea Hawk F.B.Mk.5 was merely a conversion of the F.B.Mk.3 with the Nene 101 engine replaced by a Nene 103 rated at 5,400 lb.s.t., and the final production version for the Royal Navy was the F.G.A.Mk.6 which was similar to the F.G.A.Mk.4 apart from the more powerful Nene 103. Eighty-six Sea Hawk F.G.A.Mk.6s were manufactured for the Royal Navy,

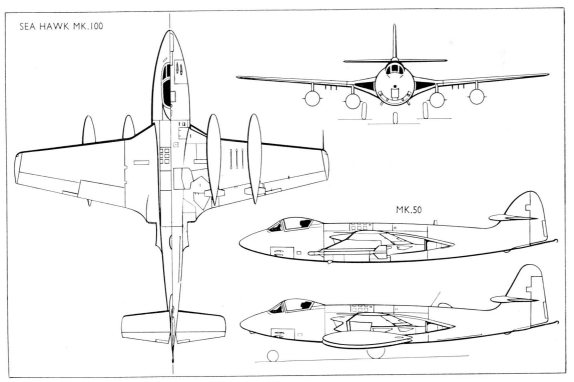

SEA HAWK MK.100

The Sidewinder-equipped Sea Hawk Mk.50 equipped No. 860 Squadron of the R.Neth.N.A.S. until December 1964. Twenty-two aircraft of this type were supplied to the Netherlands during 1956–7.

apart from conversions mentioned earlier, and although the production line had been dismantled in 1956, in the autumn of 1959 the Indian Navy placed orders for twenty-four shipboard ground-attack fighters of this type, including new aircraft and some refurbished ex-Royal Navy aircraft, for service aboard the I.N.S. *Vikrant*. The first Indian Sea Hawk F.G.A.Mk.6 was delivered on January 22, 1960, and the type entered service with the Indian Navy's No. 300 Squadron with which it still serves.

SEA HAWK MK.50: Twenty-two examples of the Sea Hawk F.G.A.Mk.6 were supplied to the R.Neth. N.A.S. during 1956–57 for service aboard the *Karel Doorman*. One R.Neth.N.A.S. squadron, No. 860, operated the Sea Hawk Mk.50 until December 1964,

(Above) A Sea Hawk F.G.A.Mk.6 of the Indian Navy and (below) a Sea Hawk Mk.100 fighter-bomber of Federal Germany's Marineflieger der Bundeswehr.

the cannon armament of which was supplemented for the intercept rôle by a pair of Sidewinder infra-red homing missiles.

SEA HAWK MK.100: Simultaneous with the placing of the Netherlands contract, the Federal German government placed an order for sixty-eight Sea Hawks of which thirty-four were fighter-bombers essentially similar to the F.G.A.Mk.6 but featuring a revised cockpit layout, U.S. radio equipment and other internal changes. Externally, the Sea Hawk Mk.100, as the fighter-bomber version was designated, differed from the F.G.A.Mk.6 in having a taller fin and rudder which increased overall height by 13.5 inches. The remaining thirty-four aircraft on the German order were equipped with Ekco Type 34 search radar mounted in a pod beneath the starboard wing to suit them for use in the all-weather rôle. The all-weather version was designated Mk.101, and delivery to the Kriegsmarine was completed during 1960. Although shore-based, the Sea Hawk Mks.100 and 101 are equipped with full arrester gear to permit their use from NATO carriers. They are scheduled to be withdrawn from first-line service during 1965 when they will be replaced by the F-104G Starfighter.

SEA HAWK F.G.A.MK.6 SPECIFICATION

Power Plant: *One Rolls-Royce Nene 103 turbojet rated at 5,400 lb.s.t.*
Armament: *Four 20-mm. Hispano cannon with 200 r.p.g. and four 500-lb. bombs, or two 500-lb. bombs and twenty 3-in. or sixteen 5-in. rockets.*
Performance: *Max. speed, 590 m.p.h. at sea level (Mach 0.79), 587 m.p.h. at 20,000 ft. (Mach 0.83); initial climb rate, 5,700 ft./min.; time to 35,000 ft., 11 min. 50 sec.; service ceiling, 44,500 ft.; combat radius (clean), 230 mls., (with two 90 Imp. gal. drop tanks and two 500-lb. bombs), 288 mls., (with four 90 Imp. gal. drop tanks), 386 mls.*
Weights: *Empty, 9,720 lb.; loaded (clean), 13,200 lb., (with two 90 Imp gal. drop tanks), 15,198 lb.; max., 16,200 lb.*
Dimensions: *Span, 39 ft. 0 in.; length, 39 ft. 8 in.; height, 8 ft 8 in.; wing area, 278 sq. ft.*

AVRO SHACKLETON

Despite the fact that it traces its ancestry back to the wartime Lancaster bomber and entered operational service in 1951, the Shackleton remains R.A.F. Coastal Command's sole maritime reconnaissance aircraft, equipping the eight M.R. squadrons of Nos. 18 and 19 Groups comprising that force, and destined apparently to soldier on into the late 'sixties. Although progressively up-dated during its long career, and to be subjected in its M.R.Mk.3 form to a further modification programme in which 2,500 lb.s.t. Viper turbojets are to be added to each outboard engine nacelle to avoid over-boosting the ageing Griffon piston engines during maximum weight take-offs, doubts were being expressed during 1964 that the Shackleton could continue to maintain the R.A.F.'s full maritime reconnaissance commitment after 1966, and consideration was being given to the Breguet Atlantic as a possible interim replacement aircraft for the M.R.Mk.2 version.

The Shackleton was evolved to meet the requirements of specification R.5/46, and utilized the basic wing structure of the Lincoln heavy bomber which, together with the main undercarriage units, was married to an entirely new fuselage and Griffon 57 engines driving six-blade contra-rotating airscrews. The first of three prototypes (VW126) was flown for the first time on March 9, 1949, this event having been preceded by some three years by the placing of the first production order. Designated Shackleton M.R.Mk.1, the first production aircraft (VP254) flew on October 24, 1950, and deliveries to R.A.F. Coastal Command began during the following year, the first aircraft going to No. 120 Squadron.

The Shackleton M.R.Mk.1 carried the primary search radar in a chin housing under the fuselage nose, and defensive armament comprised two 20-mm. Hispano cannon in the fuselage nose, two similar weapons in a dorsal turret, and two 0.5-in. guns in a tail turret. The power plants of initial production aircraft were not interchangeable between inner and outer nacelles, but later production aircraft possessed this interchangeability and were known as M.R.Mk. 1As, and a total of seventy-seven M.R.Mks.1 and 1A Shackletons was built before the introduction of the much-improved M.R.Mk.2.

SHACKLETON M.R.MK.2: During the production of the Shackleton M.R.Mk.1, various modifications had been tested on the original prototype, these including the re-positioning of the primary radar from the nose to the aft fuselage, the redesign of the nose, and the deletion of the tail turret and its replacement by a tapered, transparent cone for observation purposes. The new retractable ventral radome permitted an uninterrupted 360° scan. These features were also applied to a production M.R.Mk.1A (WB833) which served as a prototype for the M.R. Mk.2, flying in its new guise for the first time on June 17, 1952.

Powered by 2,450 h.p. Griffon 57A engines, the Shackleton M.R.Mk.2 attained a maximum speed in fully loaded condition of 272 m.p.h. at 10,000 ft. Maximum and economical cruising speeds were 255 m.p.h. and 200 m.p.h. respectively, initial climb rate was 920 ft./min., and endurance was 7.5 hours. Possessing a maximum loaded weight of 98,000 lb., it

A Shackleton M.R.Mk.3 of No. 120 Squadron R.A.F. Coastal Command.

carried ten crew members and defensive armament comprised twin 20-mm. Hispano cannon and, initially, two 0.5-in. guns in a dorsal turret. This turret was removed, however, from all service aircraft in 1955. Production deliveries of the Shackleton M.R.Mk.2 (commencing WG530) to R.A.F. Coastal Command began late in 1952, sixty-nine aircraft of this version being manufactured. The third production aircraft (WG532) was experimentally fitted with an airborne lifeboat, and the thirty-eighth (WL789) was used for a trial installation of MAD (Magnetic Anomaly Detection) equipment in a tail "stinger".

From 1961, all remaining M.R.Mk.2s were progressively modernised as M.R.Mk.2Cs, their internal electrics, ECM and ASW equipment being brought up to the standard of that of the later M.R.Mk.3 which it currently operates alongside in R.A.F. Coastal Command, serving with Nos. 37, 38, 42, 205 and 224 Squadrons.

SHACKLETON M.R.MK.3: The final production model of the Shackleton, the M.R.Mk.3, introduced a nosewheel undercarriage, a rearranged flight deck, revised outboard wing panels, and a modified fuel system of increased capacity (4,248 Imp. gal.) and incorporating fixed wingtip tanks. Other modifications included a frameless flight deck canopy and the provision of a sound-proofed wardroom. The nosewheel undercarriage was incorporated at some minor expense of weapons-bay capacity. For instance, a typical offensive load for tactical operations consists of twelve 1,000-lb. bombs as compared with fifteen carried by the M.R.Mk.2C. A typical ASW stores load is three Mk.30 acoustic homing torpedoes, nine Mk.11 depth charges, twelve Mk.2 marine markers, and twelve sonobuoys. For the emergency transport rôle, the M.R.Mk.3 can carry twenty-nine troops with their equipment stowed in special weapons-bay panniers.

The first Shackleton M.R.Mk.3 (WR970) flew on September 2, 1955, and deliveries began eighteen months later, in 1957, forty-two being produced of which eight were supplied to the South African Air Force and currently equip No. 35 Squadron of that service's Maritime Command, R.A.F. M.R.Mk.3 squadrons including Nos. 120, 201, and 206.

R.A.F. Coastal Command Shackleton M.R.Mk.3s are now being progressively modified to take a single 2,500 lb.s.t. Bristol Siddeley Viper turbojet in each outboard engine nacelle to provide supplementary take-off power. Simultaneously, provision is being made for the emergency jettisoning of all fuel.

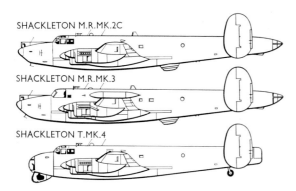

SHACKLETON M.R.MK.2C

SHACKLETON M.R.MK.3

SHACKLETON T.MK.4

Shackletons modified in this fashion are scheduled to enter service in 1965, with the first fully-modified aircraft commencing its test programme early in the year. The ASW systems of the aircraft have been constantly up-dated during its service career, such items as the Autolycus ionization-detecting system for tracking the exhaust of snorkeling submarines being added.

SHACKLETON T.MK.4: During 1956–57, a small number of Shackleton M.R.Mk.1s were converted for use as crew trainers at the Maritime Operational Training Unit under the designation T.Mk.4. Additional radar positions were installed for instructors and students, and all armament was removed.

SHACKLETON M.R.MK.3 SPECIFICATION

Power Plants: *Four Rolls-Royce Griffon 57A liquid-cooled piston engines each rated at 2,450 h.p. (to be augmented by two 2,500 lb.s.t. Bristol Siddeley Viper turbojets).*
Armament: *Two 20-mm. Hispano cannon in nose and (typical ASW) nine Mk.II depth charges and three Mk. 30 homing torpedoes, or (tactical operations) twelve 1,000-lb. general-purpose bombs in internal weapons bay.*
Performance: *Max. speed (at 85,000 lb.), 302 m.p.h. at 12,000 ft.; max. cruising, 253 m.p.h. at 10,000 ft.; econ. cruising, 200 m.p.h.; initial climb (at 100,000 lb.), 850 ft./min.; service ceiling, 19,200 ft.; max. range, 4,215 mls. at 200 m.p.h. at 1,500 ft.*
Weights: *Empty, 57,800 lb.; max. loaded, 100,000 lb.*
Dimensions: *Span, 119 ft. 10 in.; length, 92 ft. 6 in.; height, 23 ft. 4 in.; wing area, 1,458 sq. ft.*

(Above left and below) A Shackleton M.R.Mk.3 (XF707)—the twenty-ninth example of this mark built—of No. 201 Squadron, R.A.F. Coastal Command. Phase 3 modifications will include the introduction of auxiliary turbojets in outboard nacelles.

A Shackleton M.R.Mk.3 of No. 35 Squadron of the South African Maritime Command which received eight aircraft of this type.

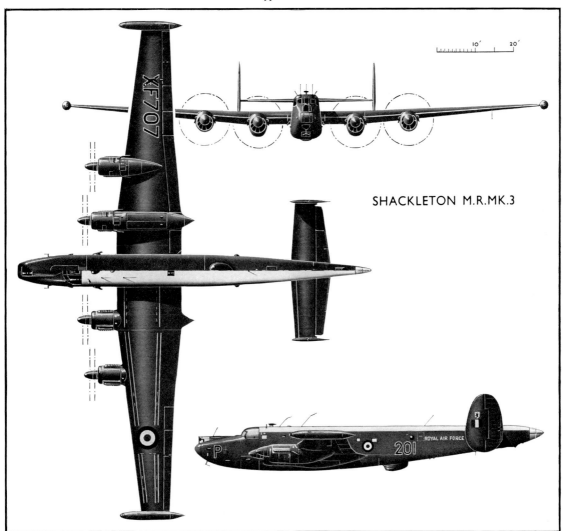

SHACKLETON M.R.MK.3

BAC TSR-2

Currently one of the most advanced combat aircraft in production, the TSR-2 tactical strike and reconnaissance aircraft, the first of twenty pre-production and development examples of which (XR219) flew for the first time on September 27, 1964, has been evolved from an operational requirement (GOR.339) formulated in 1958, and intended to provide a versatile, supersonic replacement for the Canberra with short field capability.

In its present form, the TSR-2 is claimed to be suitable for all types of attack missions, from strikes against armoured forces using such weapons as the Nord AS.30 ASM, to semi-strategic sorties with a thermonuclear stand-off weapon currently under development in the United Kingdom. The TSR-2 will also carry the Anglo-French television-guided tactical ASM being evolved by Hawker Siddeley and MATRA. Equipment has been stated to include high-definition

SLAR (Side-Looking Aircraft Radar) and cameras, and a self-contained radar-reconnaissance pack may be mounted amidships for specific reconnaissance sorties.

The two crew members are seated in tandem ground-level ejector seats, and the navigation-attack system utilises a Doppler/inertial mix for dead reckoning, corrected by fixes from the SLAR equipment. Forward-looking terrain avoidance radar housed in the nose maintains the aircraft at a pre-set altitude above local ground level under manual or automatic control in all weathers. Short field performance results from a combination of blown flaps and a high thrust-to-weight ratio. Flap blowing extends over the entire wing span, apart from the anhedral wingtips, and take-off performance is further enhanced by an extendable nose landing gear leg which increases the incidence of the aircraft on the ground. The 60° swept delta wing has no ailerons, the all-moving tailplane commanding both pitch and roll control, acting in the conventional manner to achieve the former and differentially for the latter. This so-called "taileron" system is also employed by the North American A-5 Vigilante.

Power is provided by two Bristol Siddeley Olympus Mk.320 engines each possessing a potential after-burning thrust of 33,000 lb., and mounted side-by-side in the rear fuselage, these are fed by lateral variable-area type intakes with movable half-cone shock bodies. The thin, 60° delta wing planform provides the optimum compromise of small area and low gust response demanded by low-level supersonic flight, and assuming a mean thickness/chord ratio of approximately four per cent, the TSR-2 should be capable of speeds of the order of Mach 2.0 at altitude and about Mach 1.15–1.2 at sea level. On a Hi-Lo-Hi strike-reconnaissance mission it should be capable of achieving a radius substantially in excess of 1,000

(Above left and below) The first of twenty pre-production and development TSR-2 tactical strike and reconnaissance aircraft (XR219) at the Aeroplane and Armament Experimental Establishment at Boscombe Down during initial trials.

The TSR-2 is currently one of the most advanced combat aircraft in production, and should enter service in 1967-68.

miles, and unrefuelled ferry range is likely to be of the order of 4,000 miles. No details of the TSR-2's weights had been officially revealed at the time of closing for press, but it may be assumed that gross weight exceeds 90,000 lb., and overall span and length are 37 ft. and 89 ft. respectively.

Several pre-production TSR-2s are expected to join the test programme during the course of 1965, and it has been revealed that the initial production order will call for thirty aircraft which are likely to enter R.A.F. service during 1967–68, but the total R.A.F requirement is understood to be for 100–130 aircraft.

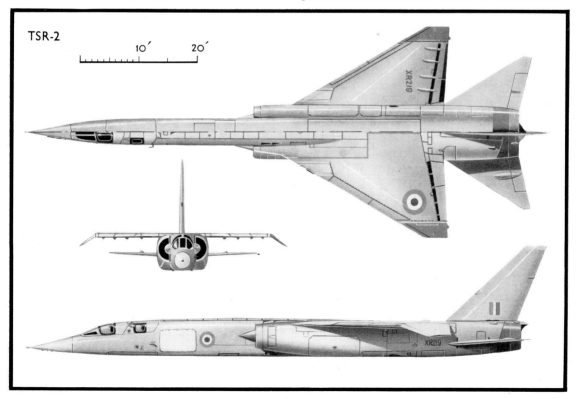

TSR-2

ENGLISH ELECTRIC LIGHTNING

Currently the fastest climbing service interceptor, the Lightning will equip seven R.A.F. Fighter Command squadrons by the end of 1965, and is expected to remain in service until the early 'seventies. Unique in the disposition of its twin turbojets, these being superimposed one above the other in the centre fuselage, the Lightning is also unusual in employing a wing planform in which the ailerons are mounted across the tips of the wings which are swept 60° on the leading edges, joining the extremities of the leading and trailing edges to form what has been referred to as a "notched delta", although, aerodynamically, it has little in common with a true delta wing.

Stemming from the P.1A research aircraft which attained Mach 1.53 during the course of its test programme, and originally known as the P.1B, the Lightning was developed under the direction of F. W.

Page and, in its initial form, was envisaged as a pursuit-type weapons system, using classic stern-chase tactics to position itself for an attack with cannon, unguided rockets or AAMs. The limited-thrust Sapphire engines of the P.1A were supplanted by Avon 200 series engines of R.A.24R rating which offered 11,250 lb.s.t. dry and 14,430 lb.s.t. with afterburning, these power plants being fed by means of a circular pitot-type two-shock intake with a fixed conical centre-body. The fuselage was almost entirely redesigned, and changes included the raising of the pilot's cockpit to improve view for combat, and fairing the new canopy into a dorsal spine.

The original contract under which the P.1A had been developed had also called for the construction of three operational prototypes, and the first of these (XA847) was flown on April 4, 1957, being followed by the second and third prototypes (XA853 and 856) for engine, weapon and structural testing. On November 25, 1958, the first of these prototypes gained the distinction of becoming the first British aircraft to attain Mach 2.0 in level flight, maintaining that speed at the minimum afterburning setting while carrying a ventral tank, missile pylons and heavy instrumentation. The aircraft also displayed outstanding low-speed characteristics, being flown down to something of the order of 115 m.p.h., and thus demonstrating the remarkable speed range of 13 : 1. Long before the first aerodynamic prototype had flown an order had been placed for twenty pre-production aircraft for development purposes (XG307–313 and XG325–337), and the first of these flew on April 3, 1958. The first three pre-production aircraft differed in no major way from the prototypes, but the fourth (XG310) introduced a taller fin and rudder assembly, the thirty per cent increase in area being intended to compensate for the de-stabilising effect of the externally-mounted Firestreak AAMs. The pre-production aircraft were not intended for

(Above left and below) Lightning F.Mk.1As of No. 111 Squadron which was scheduled to commence re-equipment with the F.Mk.3 late in 1964. The refuelling probe under the starboard wing is detachable.

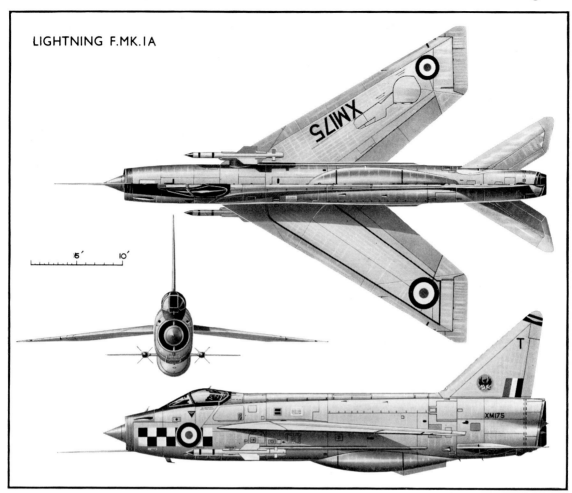

LIGHTNING F.MK.1A

squadron service and were assigned to various development programmes encompassing power plants, weapons, autopilot and associated instrument flying, etc., and although the last three machines of this batch were not entirely to full production standards, they were accepted by the Central Fighter Establishment for handling trials.

LIGHTNING F.MKS.1 AND 1A: An initial production contract for the Lightning had been placed in November 1956, and the first production Lightning F.Mk.1 (XM134) was rolled out and flown at Samlesbury on October 29, 1959, the first C.A. release of an operational aircraft to the Central Fighter Establishment following in December 1959, and the first delivery of a fully-equipped production aircraft to an operational squadron (No. 74) taking place on July 30, 1960.

The Mk.1, powered by the Avon 201 of R.A.24R rating but lacking fully modulated afterburning, being instead provided with four afterburner nozzle settings for fixed-thrust outputs, could take-off, cruise and land on either of its engines, and was undoubtedly the first fighter in the world to fly supersonically at *half* power. The main and leading-edge integral wing tanks were supplemented by tanks occupying a substantial part of

the flap volume, and a 250 Imp. gal. ventral tank was normally carried. The fixed intake cone housed the quickly-removable pressurized capsule for the Ferranti Airpass (Airborne Interception Radar and Pilot's Attack Sight System), and built-in armament comprised a pair of 30-mm. Aden Mk.4 cannon flanking the cockpit. In addition, an interchangeable weapons pack could be fitted, this housing the equipment

Lightning F.Mk.1As of No. 56 Squadron R.A.F. Fighter Command.

(Above) The twelfth production Lightning F.Mk.2 (XN734), one of several examples of this interim version employed for F.Mk.3 development, seen here with overwing ferry tanks which are to be employed by the later model.

(Above) The fifth production F.Mk.3 which has served as a testbed for the new ventral tank and modified wing.

associated with two Firestreak infra-red homing AAMs, two retractable boxes containing a total of forty-eight 2-in. rockets, or two additional Aden cannon and their ammunition. These weapons packs could be interchanged within an hour.

Possessing an initial climb rate in excess of 50,000 ft./min., the Lightning F.Mk.1 could reach its operational ceiling in about two minutes from take-off. It could accelerate from Mach 0.9 to Mach 2.0 in little more than three minutes, and could normally take-off and land within 1,000 yards.

The Mk.1 was only issued to one squadron, No. 74 at Coltishall (which re-equipped with the F.Mk.3 during 1964), for after delivery of some twenty aircraft, the addition of UHF and provision for a flight refuelling probe beneath the port wing resulted in the Lightning F.Mk.1A, distinguished from its predecessor externally by a cable duct on each side of the fuselage. The F.Mk.1A, the first of which was XM169, had been delivered to Nos. 56 and 111 Squadrons by mid-1961, and currently remains in service with the former unit, the latter having been in process of converting to the F.Mk.3 late in 1964.

LIGHTNING F.MK.2: The initial production order for the Lightning F.Mk.1 placed in November 1956 had been supplemented by a further order on April 28, 1958, but only some sixty F.Mk.1s and 1As were produced before the improved F.Mk.2 began to come off the line (commencing with XN723). The first F.Mk.2 flew on July 11, 1961, and this variant of the Lightning was considered as an interim version pending the introduction of the definitive F.Mk.3, between forty and fifty interceptors of this type being produced and entering service with Nos. 19 and 92 Squadrons.

The F.Mk.2 carries the same armament as the F.Mk.1, and overall dimensions and fuel capacity remain the same. Some changes were introduced in the electrical systems, liquid replaced gaseous oxygen, an integrated instrument panel was provided for the first time, and fully variable afterburning was fitted to the Avon 210 engines. Loaded weight was increased and overall performance was generally similar to that of the earlier mark.

LIGHTNING F.MK.3: The current production model of the single-seat interceptor version of the Lightning, the F.Mk.3 represents a major advance over earlier variants, and is considered to be the definitive production type which will equip the bulk of R.A.F.

LIGHTNING F.MK.2 SPECIFICATION

Power Plants : *Two Rolls Royce Avon Mk.210 turbojets each rated at 11,250 lb.s.t. dry and 14,430 lb.s.t. with afterburning.*

Armament : *Two 30-mm. Aden Mk.4 cannon and interchangeable weapons pack with two Firestreak infra-red homing AAMs, two 30-mm. Aden cannon, or forty-eight 2-in. unguided rockets.*

Performance : *Max. speed, 1,320–1,450 m.p.h. (Mach 2.0–2.2) at 40,000 ft.; normal cruise, 530–595 m.p.h. (Mach 0.8–0.9) at 36,000 ft.; initial climb, 50,000 (plus) ft./min.; time to operational altitude at Mach 0.9, 2.5 min.; acceleration from Mach 0.9 to Mach 2.0, 3–3.5 min.; service ceiling, 60,000 (plus) ft.*

Weights : *Loaded, 37,000–38,000 lb.*

Dimensions : *Span, 34 ft. 10 in.; length (including probe), 55 ft. 3 in.; height, 19 ft. 7 in.; wing area, 458.5 sq. ft.*

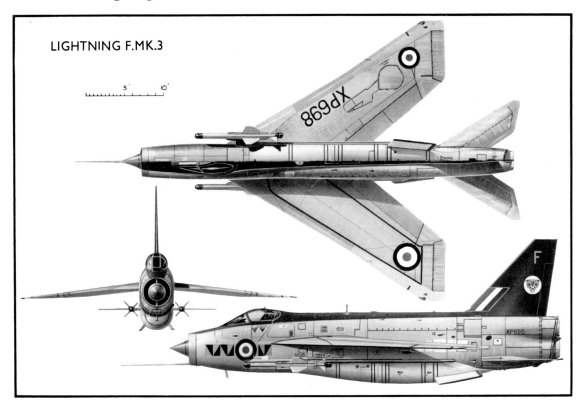

LIGHTNING F.MK.3

Fighter Command squadrons. Capable of employing far more sophisticated interception techniques and carrying a later Airpass A.I. system enabling either Red Top or Firestreak infra-red homing AAMs to be carried as required, the F.Mk.3 has no built-in cannon armament, and its Avon 301 turbojets each provide 13,220 lb.s.t. dry and 16,600 lb.s.t. with afterburning.

Initially, the only external change was the new and angular vertical tail surfaces of fifteen per cent greater area to offset the effect of the larger Red Top missiles, this being first tested in flight on June 16, 1962, on one of the pre-production aircraft (XG310), and the first production F.Mk.3 (XP693) flew in 1963, being used,

together with the second aircraft (XP694), for development trials. On January 1, 1964, the Central Fighter Establishment took delivery of its first Lightning F.Mk.3 (XP695), and a few months later, No. 74 Squadron began to convert from its early F.Mk.1s to the new variant, Nos. 23 and 111 Squadrons also commencing conversion before the end of 1964, with No. 64 Squadron being scheduled to convert during 1965.

Further changes have been introduced on the F.Mk.3 since the delivery of the initial aircraft to the R.A.F., these including a modified wing configuration incorporating camber and a leading-edge extension at

Lightning F.Mk.3s of No. 74 Squadron, the first unit to re-equip with this variant of the fighter. The modified wing configuration and new ventral tank are to be applied retrospectively.

approximately one-third span, and a substantially larger ventral fuel pack, these changes increasing range by some twenty per cent but incurring virtually no performance penalty. The wing and fuel pack modifications are being made retrospectively to all early production F.Mk.3s. Overall dimensions remain

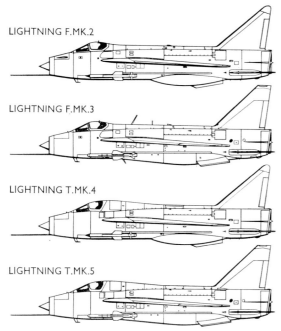

LIGHTNING F.MK.2

LIGHTNING F.MK.3

LIGHTNING T.MK.4

LIGHTNING T.MK.5

similar to those of earlier versions apart from a marginal increase in gross wing area.

The new ventral tank, which, together with the modified wing, was first fitted to the fifth pro-

duction F.Mk.3 (XP697), is retained during combat manoeuvres, and may be supplemented for ferry purposes by a pair of overwing tanks which were first tested on the third production Lightning F.Mk.2 (XN725) which has served as a systems test aircraft for the F.Mk.3. These overwing tanks were originally developed for the combat rôle but would have had to be jettisoned.

LIGHTNING T.MK.4: Work on a two-seat dual-control operational weapons system trainer variant of the basic Lightning design began in 1957, the forward fuselage being widened by almost one foot to accommodate side-by-side Martin-Baker Mk.4BST ejector seats, plus duplicated pilot attack sights and radar scopes. The cabin profile was derived from Hunter T.Mk.7 front fuselage loftings, and this had only a marginal effect on performance, enabling the two-seater to undertake fully operational two-man sorties, the only change in armament from that of the early single-seat marks being the deletion of the 30-mm. Aden cannon.

Designated T.Mk.4, the first two-seat Lightning (XL628) flew on May 6, 1959, this being followed by a small production batch of machines for Lightning operational conversion units plus one or two for each Fighter Command squadron.

LIGHTNING T.MK.5: The dual-control two-seat Lightning T.Mk.5 is fulfilling the same functions with Fighter Command squadrons equipped with the F.Mk.3 as does the earlier T.Mk.4 with units operating the F.Mks.1A and 2, and the aerodynamic prototype of the T.Mk.5 (XM967), differing from its predecessor solely in having similar vertical tail surfaces to those of the F.Mk.3 and provision for carrying Red Top missiles, flew for the first time on March 29, 1962. Presumably, the Lightning T.Mk.5 will be adapted to incorporate the cambered and extended wing and enlarged ventral fuel pack of the single-seat F.Mk.3.

ENGLISH ELECTRIC CANBERRA

Britain's first essay in the jet bomber field, the Canberra was manufactured continuously for twelve years—a record in jet combat aircraft production longevity—and every variant other than prototype or experimental version remains in service today, sixteen years after the prototype's maiden flight. One or another model of the Canberra currently serves with eleven air arms, and this remarkable warplane is likely to remain on the first line operational strength of a number of these, including the R.A.F., well into the 'seventies.

Development of the light tactical jet bomber that was to crystallize as the Canberra began in 1944, an official specification, B.3/45, calling for a high-speed high-altitude bomber utilizing a radar bomb-sight and relying on the highest possible performance for defence, being issued in the following year. The question of wing sweepback was studied from the outset, but the final analysis indicated that the Mach numbers attainable on the power likely to be available within the development life of the aircraft rendered this feature unnecessary. The "state of the art" knowledge available at that time led to a twin-engined two-seater with a comparatively lightly loaded, low aspect ratio wing with a modest thickness/chord ratio

—ranging from twelve per cent at the root to nine per cent at the tip.

Four prototypes were ordered on January 7, 1946, but before the first of these (VN799) flew on May 13, 1949, it had become obvious that the essential radar bomb-sight would not be available for installation, necessitating the provision of a visual bomb-aiming position and a third crew member to act as bomb-aimer. At this stage, however, prototype construction was too far advanced to make radical changes, and therefore all four prototypes were completed as two-seaters and were dubbed Canberra Mk.1s. Whereas the first prototype was powered by 6,000 lb.s.t. Avon RA.2 turbojets, the second (VN813), which flew on November 9, 1949, was powered by centrifugal-type Nenes as a safeguard against development of the new axial-flow Avon falling seriously behind schedule. In the event, Avon development continued to schedule, and both the third and fourth prototypes (VN828 and VN850) were Avon-powered, flying on November 22 and December 20, 1949 respectively.

CANBERRA B.MK.2: The initial production model, the B.Mk.2 to specification B.5/47, differed from the prototypes in that the original radar nose was elimin-

A Canberra B.Mk.2 of the Royal Rhodesian Air Force. One Rhodesian squadron, No. 5, currently operates this type.

ated, the fuselage framing was extended forward, and a transparent nose was substituted, incorporating an optically flat panel which was offset to enable the bomb-aimer to crawl around the pilot's feet. Whereas the B.Mk.1 had featured side-by-side seating for pilot and navigator, the B.Mk.2 had the pilot on the port side of the cockpit with the navigator and bomb-aimer side-by-side aft.

The first of two prototypes of the B.Mk.2 (VX165) flew on April 23, 1950, the first production aircraft (WD929) following on October 8, 1950, No. 101 Squadron converting to the type in May 1951. Production was stepped up rapidly, the impetus being provided by the Korean War, and A. V. Roe, Handley Page and Short Brothers all established production lines, the first two mentioned companies building seventy-five and sixty-five Canberra B.Mk.2s respectively, and Short Brothers going on to build later variants of the aircraft after completing seventy-six B.Mk.2s.

Before the design was fully "productionized", it was ordered by the R.A.A.F., five B.Mk.2s being delivered to Australia to act as pattern aircraft for licence manufacture by the Government Aircraft Factory. Australian production comprised forty-nine aircraft which, essentially similar to the B.Mk.2, were designated as B.Mk.20s, the first flying on May 29, 1953, and the bulk being powered by the Australian-built Avon 109 engine. The Canberra B.Mk.20 currently equips Nos. 1, 2 and 6 Squadrons of the R.A.A.F., and is scheduled to be replaced by the General Dynamics F-111A from 1968 onwards. Two of the original British-built B.Mk.2s and five B.Mk.20s have been converted as T.Mk.21 dual-control trainers, and serve with the R.A.A.F.'s No. 1 (Bomber) Operational Conversion Unit. A manufacturing licence was also obtained by the American Glenn L. Martin Company following a U.S.A.F. decision to acquire the Canberra in quantity (see page 182), one B.Mk.2 being supplied to the United States as a pattern aircraft.

English Electric manufactured a total of 203 Canberra B.Mk.2s—bringing total production in the United Kingdom to 424 machines—of which six were sold to Venezuela early in 1953 and currently remain in service alongside Canberra B.(I).Mk.8s in one of the two bomber squadrons of the Fuerzas Aéreas Venezolanas. Fifteen ex-R.A.F. B.Mk.2s were later (in 1959) supplied to the Royal Rhodesian Air Force and operated by Nos. 5 and 6 Squadrons of that service until the dissolution of the Federation of

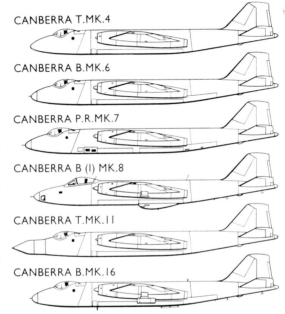

CANBERRA T.MK.4

CANBERRA B.MK.6

CANBERRA P.R.MK.7

CANBERRA B (I) MK.8

CANBERRA T.MK.11

CANBERRA B.MK.16

Rhodesia and Nyasaland when the last-mentioned squadron was disbanded.

Powered by 6,500 lb.s.t. Avon 101s, the Canberra B.Mk.2 attained maximum speeds of 518 m.p.h. at sea level (Mach 0.68) and 570 m.p.h. at altitude (Mach 0.82). Initial climb rate was 3,800 ft./min., and maximum operational altitude was limited by aircrew breathing equipment to 48,000 ft. The maximum internal bomb load totalled 6,000 lb., with which the B.Mk.2 had a range of 2,660 miles and a maximum take-off weight of 46,000 lb.

CANBERRA P.R.MK.3: At an early stage in Canberra development a requirement was formulated for a photographic reconnaissance version, and to specification PR.31/46, a prototype photographic version (VX181) was built and flew on March 19, 1950. Similarly powered to the B.Mk.2, the photographic version featured a 14-in. additional section in the forward fuselage for a camera bay, the size of the bomb-bay was reduced to the minimum needed to carry photo-flash bombs, and fuel capacity was increased from 1,377 Imp. gal. to 1,917 Imp. gal. which could be supplemented, as could that of the B. Mk.2, by wingtip tanks each housing 244 Imp. gal.

A Canberra B.Mk.15 (WH967) equipped with Nord AS.30 ASMs, installation trials for which have been undertaken by Boulton Paul Aircraft.

Carrying seven cameras, the photo-reconnaissance Canberra entered production as the P.R.Mk.3, the first example (WE135) flying on July 31, 1952, and a total of thirty-six being built by the parent company, the first unit to re-equip with this type being No. 541 Squadron. The performance of the P.R.Mk.3 was generally similar to that of the B.Mk.2 apart from the range, which was increased to 3,585 miles on internal fuel and 3,660 miles with wingtip tanks.

CANBERRA T.MK.4: Evolved from the B.Mk.2 to meet the requirements of specification T.2/49, the Canberra T.Mk.4 operational trainer embodied a new cockpit with side-by-side seats and dual controls for the pupil and instructor, the navigator's position being retained on the port side, aft of the pupil. The prototype (WN467) flew on June 6, 1952, and seventy-five were manufactured while others were converted from B.Mk.2s. Two were supplied to Venezuela, seven to India, and three ex-R.A.F. T.Mk.4s were delivered to Rhodesia, while two aircraft modified by Boulton Paul for use by the R.N.Z.A.F. received the designation T.Mk.13.

Apart from the Australian T.Mk.21 mentioned earlier, there was one other trainer variant of the Canberra, the T.Mk.11, six of which were converted from B.Mk.2s by Boulton Paul for the training of pilots and navigators in the use of airborne intercept radar. With A.I. radar in an extended nose, the T.Mk.11 flew for the first time on March 29, 1958, and six conversions were produced for the R.A.F. Two Mk.2s were converted to similar standards for the Royal Swedish Air Force in 1960, these serving under the designation Tp 52.

CANBERRA B.MK.6: Specification B.22/48 called for a target marking version of the Canberra with a special nose radar installation, and one prototype (VX185) was produced to meet this requirement as the Canberra B.Mk.5. This aircraft was the first to feature integral wing tanks and 7,500 lb.s.t. Avon 109 turbojets, but in the event the requirement was cancelled and no production of the B.Mk.5 was undertaken. However, the more powerful Avon 109s and the integral wing tanks distinguished the next bomber variant to attain production, the B.Mk.6, which was

otherwise similar to the B.Mk.2. There was no prototype of the B.Mk.6, the first aircraft (WJ754) being the first production example which flew on January 26, 1954, eighty-eight being built by the parent company and a further thirty by Short Brothers.

The B.Mk.6 supplanted the B.Mk.2 in service with No. 101 Squadron during 1954, and six examples were supplied to Ecuador for service with the Fuerza Aérea Ecuatoriana, while a further six were delivered to the Centre d'Essais en Vol at Bretigny for use in connection with France's missile development programme.

For service with the 2nd Tactical Air Force in Germany, a number of Canberra B.Mk.6s were converted to carry a ventral pack containing four 20-mm. cannon which was mounted in the rear half of the bomb-bay, and fitted with underwing pylons for two 1,000-lb. bombs or two packs of thirty-seven 2-in. rockets. With the gun pack installed, the forward portion of the bomb-bay could still house three 1,000-lb. bombs. This conversion was designated B.(I).Mk.6, the first example (WT307) flying on March 31, 1955, and entering service with No. 213 Squadron in Germany in the intruder rôle from 1956, this unit remaining the sole B.(I).Mk.6 squadron in R.A.F. service. The performance of the B.(I).Mk.6 is similar to that of the B.(I).Mk.8 (which see specification), and maximum loaded weight is similar at 56,250 lb., but normal loaded weights with and without wingtip tanks are slightly higher at 51,448 lb. and 55,590 lb.

Most B.Mk.6s in R.A.F. service have now been modified as follows:

Canberra B.Mk.15: Currently serving with Nos. 32, 73 and 249 Squadrons in the Near East Air Force and No. 45 Squadron in the Far East Air Force, the B.Mk.15 is a conversion of the B.Mk.6 to take new equipment, including UHF and HF communications radio, a forward-facing F.95 camera in the nose and a G.45 camera in the starboard wing leading edge, Decca roller-map with feed-in from the Doppler navigation system, and underwing attachments for two 1,000-lb. bombs or two Microcell pods each containing thirty-seven 2-in. rockets. The existing F.24 camera is retained in the rear fuselage, and the internal bomb load remains unchanged at 6,000 lb.

Canberra B.Mk.16: Generally similar to the B.Mk.

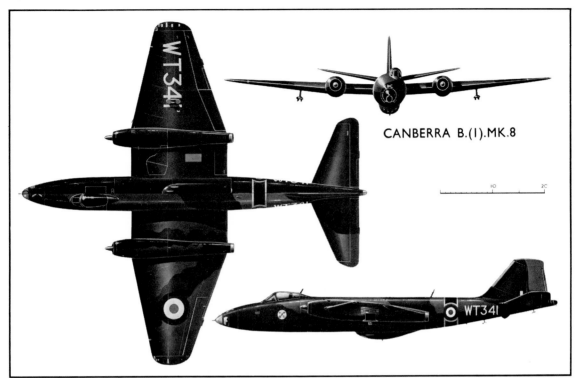

CANBERRA B.(I).MK.8

15, the B.Mk.16 retains some of the original radar aids of the B.Mk.6 and was developed specifically for use by squadrons of the 2nd. T.A.F. in Germany, although it also serves with No. 6 Squadron based at Akrotiri, Cyprus. A variant to similar standards for Nos. 97 and 98 Squadrons, R.A.F. Signals Command, with additional radar and other equipment for guided weapon calibration is designated P.R.Mk.16.

CANBERRA P.R.MK.7: A photo-reconnaissance version of the B.Mk.6 with Avon 109 engines and similar integral tanks, the Canberra P.R.Mk.7 has a similar camera installation to that of the P.R. Mk.3

comprising seven cameras. The first production P.R.Mk.7 (WH774) flew for the first time on October 28, 1953, and seventy-four aircraft of this type were built by the parent company, eight of which were modified for use by the Indian Air Force under the designation Canberra P.R.Mk.57. Possessing a maximum speed of 580 m.p.h. (Mach 0.83), the Canberra P.R.Mk.7 carries 2,817 Imp. gal. of fuel internally to provide a range of 4,340 miles, 244 Imp. gal. wingtip tanks increasing this to 4,400 miles.

CANBERRA B.(I).MK.8: Whereas all production bomber versions prior to the B.(I).Mk.8 were three-

Canberra B.Mk.16s of No. 6 Squadron based at Akrotiri, Cyprus, and equipped with Microcell rocket pods underwing.

(Above and below left) An extensively modified version of the basic Canberra, the P.R.Mk.9 was manufactured by Short Brothers and Harland, forty-five being produced for R.A.F. Bomber Command. It is seen here in service with No. 58 Squadron.

seaters, this new mark introduced a major redesign in the form of a new two-seat forward fuselage in which the pilot was seated to port beneath a fighter-type canopy with the second crew member in the nose. A detachable pack containing four 20-mm. cannon was fitted in the rear portion of the bomb-bay for the night interdictor rôle, and provision was made for underwing loads of up to 2,000 lb. The prototype, originally the sole B.Mk.5 (VX185), flew initially on July 23, 1954, the first of seventy-four production Canberra B.(I).Mk.8s (WT326) followed on June 8, 1955, and this model serves with Nos. 3, 14, 16 and 213

CANBERRA P.R.MK.9

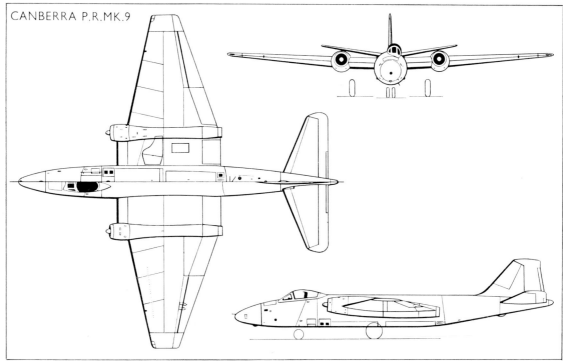

Squadrons with the 2nd. T.A.F. Peru and Venezuela each received eight B.(I).Mk.8 aircraft, and sixty-six supplied to the Indian Air Force received the designation Canberra B.(I).Mk.58.

CANBERRA P.R.MK.9: Intended for strategic reconnaissance at altitudes in excess of 60,000 ft., the Canberra P.R.Mk.9 was manufactured solely by Short Brothers and Harland who produced forty-five aircraft of this type. The prototype, a conversion of a P.R.Mk.7 (WH793), flew on July 8, 1955, this having 10,050 lb.s.t. Avon 206 turbojets and a wing of increased span (67 ft. 10 in.) and greater chord on the sections inboard of the engines. The production version, the first example of which (XH129) flew on July 27, 1958, also embodied a B.(I).Mk.8-type cockpit canopy, the navigator being seated in the nose with an ejector seat beneath a frangible hatch, the nose being hinged to facilitate entry and exit. The first unit to receive the Canberra P.R.Mk.9 was No. 58 Squadron with R.A.F. Bomber Command, followed by No. 39 Squadron, and production was completed in 1961.

CANBERRA U.MK.10: An unmanned target conversion of the B.Mk.2 developed by Short Brothers and Harland, the Canberra U.Mk.10 was evolved for advanced guided missile trials, and the first flight by auto-control was effected on June 11, 1957.

CANBERRA B.(I).MK.12: Basically similar to the B.(I).Mk.8, the B.(I).Mk.12 has been supplied to the R.N.Z.A.F., this service receiving twelve aircraft of this type which currently equip No. 14 Squadron at Ohakea, and to the S.A.A.F., six being supplied for use by No. 12 Squadron to provide strike-reconnaissance training prior to the delivery of the Buccaneer S.Mk.50.

(Above) A Canberra P.R.Mk.16 (WH961) of R.A.F. Signals Command. Like the B.Mk.16, this is a conversion of the B.Mk.6.

(Above) A Canberra U.Mk.10 (WJ987) conversion of B.Mk.2, and (below) a Canberra T.Mk.11 (WJ610).

CANBERRA B.(I).MK.8 SPECIFICATION

Power Plants: *Two Rolls-Royce Avon 109 turbojets each rated at 7,500 lb.s.t.*
Armament: *(Interdictor) Four 20-mm. Hispano cannon and sixteen 4.5-in. flares or three 1,000-lb. bombs internally, plus two 1,000-lb. bombs, two packs of thirty-seven 2-in. rockets or two Nord AS.30 ASMs on underwing pylons. (Bomber) Six 1,000-lb., one 4,000-lb. and two 1,000-lb. or eight 500-lb. bombs internally, plus two 1,000-lb. bombs externally.*
Performance: *Max. speed, 580 m.p.h. at 30,000 ft.*

(Mach 0.83), 518 m.p.h. at sea level (Mach 0.68); initial climb rate (at 55,134 lb.), 3,400 ft./min.; max. operational altitude, 48,000 ft.; range (interdictor rôle with combat allowances), 800 mls. at 403 m.p.h. at 2,000 ft.; max. ferry range (with two 244 Imp. gal. wingtip tanks), 3,630 mls.
Weights: *Empty, 23,173 lb.; normal loaded, 50,992 lb.; max. 56,250 lb.*
Dimensions: *Span, 63 ft. 11½ in.; length, 65 ft. 6 in.; height, 15 ft. 7 in.; wing area, 960 sq. ft.*

The Canberra B.(I).Mk.8 serves with four R.A.F. Squadrons in the 2nd T.A.F., and is illustrated in the markings of No. 16 Squadron.

FAIREY GANNET

The first aircraft in the world to fly solely on the power of a coupled turboprop and the only aircraft with such a power plant to attain quantity production, the Gannet was originally designed for the ASW rôle in which it has now been supplanted in Royal Navy service by the helicopter, but it still performs this function with the Royal Australian Navy and the naval air arms of Federal Germany and Indonesia, and serves operationally with the Royal Navy in its airborne early warning form.

The Gannet stemmed from specification G.R.17/45 formulated towards the end of 1945 and calling for a shipboard ASW aircraft, and a prototype contract was placed on August 12, 1946. The first of two prototypes (VR546) flew on September 19, 1949 with a 2,950 e.s.h.p. Double Mamba A.S.M.D.1 coupled turboprop, and was joined by the second prototype (VR557) on July 6, 1950. Both prototypes were two-seaters, but in June 1949 a contract had been placed for a third aircraft (WE488) which, flown on May 10, 1951, was a three-seater. Apart from the third cockpit, weapon development had dictated the lengthening of the weapons bay and the relocation of the retractable search radar further aft, and in this form the aircraft entered production as the Gannet A.S.Mk.1. The first production aircraft (WN339) flew on June 9, 1953, one hundred and sixty-nine examples of the initial model being built, and the type entering service with No. 826 Squadron on January 17, 1955.

Development of a dual-control training variant of the Gannet had been initiated in parallel with the ASW version, and the first T.Mk.2 trainer (WN365) flew on August 16, 1954, thirty-six aircraft of this type subsequently being produced at regular intervals along the A.S.Mk.1 production line. The Gannet T.Mk.2 featured a second set of flight controls in the forward observer's cockpit and a periscope for the instructor occupying this cockpit on training flights. Both the A.S.Mk.1 and T.Mk.2 were powered by the 2,950 e.s.h.p. Double Mamba 100, but with the availability of the Double Mamba 101 of 3,035 e.h.p., the new

engine was introduced on the production line with the 170th ASW Gannet (XA412) which, flown on April 13, 1956, became the first Gannet A.S.Mk.4, the similarly-powered training variant being the T.Mk.5.

Twenty Gannet A.S.Mk.4s were supplied to the Royal Australian Navy, ten of these being currently operated from H.M.A.S. *Melbourne* by No. 816 Squadron. Fifteen Gannet A.S.Mk.4s and one T.Mk.5 were supplied to the Federal German Kriegsmarine, these being operated from shore bases as are also the sixteen A.S.Mk.4s and two T.Mk.5s operated by the Indonesian Naval Air Arm. Some eighty Gannet A.S.Mk.4s were built, and a small number of these were fitted with modified electronic equipment as A.S.Mks.6 and 7.

GANNET A.E.W.MK.3: At a relatively early stage in the Gannet's life the possibility of developing the basic airframe to serve as a shipboard early warning aircraft had been considered, and an aerodynamic prototype of this version, the Gannet A.E.W.Mk.3 (XJ440), flew on August 20, 1958. Retaining hardly more than the wing of the earlier aircraft, the A.E.W.Mk.3 featured an entirely redesigned fuselage accommodating two radar observers. The vertical tail surfaces were redesigned and enlarged, a large radome was mounted ventrally, and a Double Mamba 102 was installed, this power plant being rated at 3,875 e.h.p. for take-off.

The first production Gannet A.E.W.Mk.3 (XL449) was flown on December 2, 1958, and the thirty-eighth and last aircraft of this type was completed in 1961, by which time it had entered service with No. 849 Squadron which provides airborne early warning flights for the Royal Navy's carriers, "A" and "B" Flights being based aboard H.M.S. *Victorious* and H.M.S. *Centaur* respectively in 1954, "C" and "D" Flights being deployed aboard H.M.S. *Ark Royal* and H.M.S. *Eagle*. The Gannet A.E.W.Mk.3 normally cruises on only one of the two components of its Double Mamba turboprop, each of these components being entirely independent, power being changed to the alternate component every hour.

A Gannet A.E.W.Mk.3 of No. 849 Squadron of the Royal Navy landing aboard H.M.S. Victorious.

Gannet A.S. Mk. 4s of 1 Marinefliegergeschwader of Federal Germany's Marineflieger der Bundeswehr. Fifteen Gannet A. S. Mk. 4s were supplied to the German Navy, and these are operated from shore bases.

GANNET A.S.MK.4 SPECIFICATION

Power Plant: *One Bristol Siddeley Double Mamba 101 coupled turboprop rated at 3,035 e.h.p.*
Armament: *(Internal) Two 1,000-lb. bombs and three depth charges, four 500-lb. bombs, two torpedoes or two mines and (external) twenty-four 3-in. HVARs or sixteen 5-in. HVARs.*
Performance: *Max. speed, 299 m.p.h. at sea level; range* *(radome retracted), 513 mls. at 242 m.p.h., 662 mls. at 194 m.p.h. at sea level; endurance (radome extended), 4.9 hr. at 150 m.p.h. at sea level; initial climb rate, 2,200 ft./min.*
Weights: *Empty, 14,069 lb.; loaded, 22,506 lb.*
Dimensions: *Span, 54 ft. 4 in.; length, 43 ft. 0 in.; height, 13 ft. 8½ in.; wing area, 490 sq. ft.*

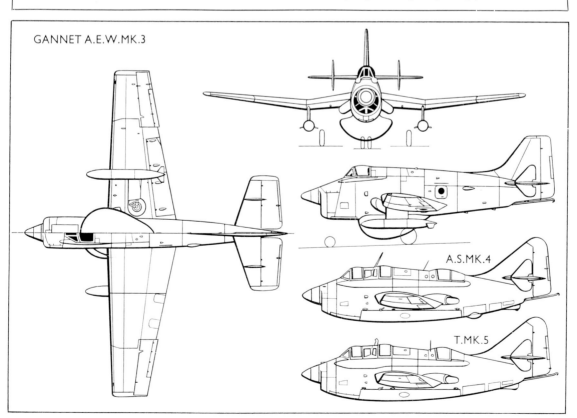

GANNET A.E.W.MK.3

A.S.MK.4

T.MK.5

GLOSTER JAVELIN

For some eight years the Javelin provided the backbone of Britain's night and all-weather fighter defence, but during 1965 this large and heavy interceptor, which was both the first twin-engined delta-wing aircraft to fly and the first British fighter developed specifically for all-weather operation, will disappear from R.A.F. Fighter Command with the re-equipment of No. 64 Squadron, the last Javelin-equipped unit

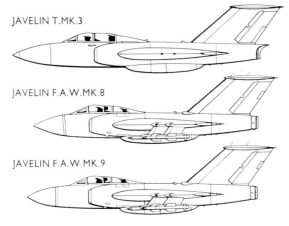

JAVELIN T.MK.3

JAVELIN F.A.W.MK.8

JAVELIN F.A.W.MK.9

attached to that Command. Three other Javelin squadrons are currently operational with the R.A.F., No. 60 with the Far East Air Force, and Nos. 5 and 11 with the 2nd T.A.F. in Germany.

The Javelin stemmed from project studies prepared to meet specifications F.43/46 and F.44/46 which demanded a day interceptor and a day and night interceptor respectively with alternative armaments of a 4.5-in. recoilless gun and four 30-mm. cannon. In February 1948, R.A.F. night fighter requirements crystallized in the form of specification F.4/48, to meet the requirements of which Gloster proposed the G.A.5, instructions to proceed with prototype construction being given on April 13, 1949, similar instructions being given to de Havilland whose D.H. 110 was then in direct competition with the Gloster fighter.

The original order called for four prototypes but this was later cut back to two prototypes, and it was not until eight months before the first prototype's initial flight that three additional interceptor prototypes plus a prototype of a training variant were ordered. Powered by two Sapphire A.S.Sa.3 turbojets each offering 7,000 lb.s.t., the first prototype (WD404) flew for the first time on November 26, 1951, some serious buffeting of the rudder being experienced, but after modifications to the rear fuselage fairing and the

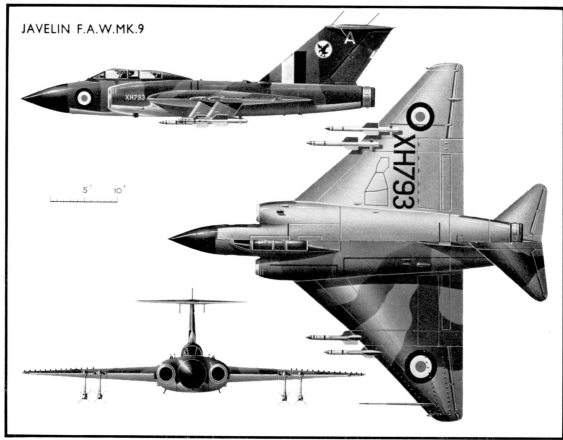

JAVELIN F.A.W.MK.9

5'   10'

A Javelin F.A.W.Mk. 8 (XH984)—the nineteenth production machine—which was operated by No. 41 Squadron from Wattisham until the unit was disbanded in December 1963.

extension of the jet pipe fairings this fault was cured and flight testing progressed relatively smoothly until the ninety-ninth flight, on June 29, 1952, when both elevators were lost and the aircraft written off. The second prototype (WD808) flew on August 20, 1952, followed by the third (WT827) on March 7, 1953.

In the meantime, a modified wing had been developed for the Javelin, an extension being added on each outer wing half so that the thickness/chord ratio diminished towards the tip, increasing lift before the onset of buffeting at high Mach numbers. The wing was first tested on the second prototype which was lost on June 11, 1953, but reappeared on the fourth prototype (WT830), which flew on January 14, 1954, and was subsequently standardized. The fifth (WT836) and sixth (XD158) prototypes flew on July 20, 1954 and October 31, 1955 respectively, the latter having U.S. radar and thus served as a prototype for the F.A.W.Mk.2.

Similar to the fifth prototype, the initial production version was designated Javelin F.A.W.Mk.1, and powered by 8,300 lb.s.t. Sapphire 102/103 turbojets, the first aircraft (XA544) flew on July 22, 1954. Forty were built, of which eleven were retained for flight test and development purposes, and No. 46 Squadron became the first Javelin unit in February 1956. The Javelin F.A.W.Mk.1 carried an armament of four 30-mm. Aden cannon, as did also the F.A.W.Mk.2 which, differing only in having U.S. in place of British A.I. radar, was also built in small numbers, the first of thirty (XA773) flying on April 25, 1956.

The dual-control training variant of the Javelin, the T.Mk.3, was developed by Air Service Training Limited and featured an extended front fuselage, a redesigned cockpit canopy, and a small radar ranging unit in the extreme nose, the large A.I. scanner of the interceptor models being removed. The prototype (WT841) flew on August 20, 1956, and the first production Javelin T.Mk.3 (XH390) was flown on January 6, 1958, the second featuring an all-flying tail similar to that evolved in the meantime for the F.A.W.Mk.4. A total of twenty-one T.Mk.3s was built, these going to No. 228 Operational Conversion Unit and to operational Javelin squadrons for dual checks and instrument training.

One of the shortcomings evinced by the initial production versions of the Javelin was the excessive stick force at high indicated speeds. To overcome this an all-moving tailplane with elevators acting as anti-balance tabs was developed and, introduced on the production line, resulted in the Javelin F.A.W.Mk.4, fifty examples of which were manufactured, this variant entering service with No. 141 Squadron early in 1957. Revision of the wing structure permitting a 250 Imp. gal. increase in fuel capacity produced the F.A.W.Mk.5 which was otherwise similar to the F.A.W.Mk.4 and of which sixty-four examples were produced. Deliveries to No. 151 Squadron began during 1957, the first example (XA641) having flown on July 26, 1956. The Javelin F.A.W.Mk.6 differed from the F.A.W.Mk.5 solely in having U.S. radar, and the first of thirty-three production interceptors of this mark (XA815) flew on December 14, 1956. This was the last of the "first generation" Javelins, as a major redesign of the interceptor had been undertaken to permit the installation of the more powerful Sapphire 200 series engines, the first of the "second generation" variants being the F.A.W.Mk.7.

JAVELIN F.A.W.MK.7: The availability of the appreciably more powerful 200 series Sapphire resulted in extensive structural re-engineering of the basic Javelin design. Wing fuel tankage was again increased, two of the 30-mm. Aden cannon were removed, later A.I. equipment was installed, provision was made for a primary armament of four Firestreak infra-red homing AAMs with their associated electronic equipment, two rows of vortex generators were added to the wings, the aileron trailing edges were thickened, and the rear fuselage was lengthened. Embodying all these changes, the first Javelin F.A.W. Mk.7 (XH704) flew on November 9, 1956, and more examples of this version of the Javelin were to be built than any other, ninety-six being delivered, of which thirteen were retained for development and trials purposes. The Javelin F.A.W.Mk.7 was first issued to No. 33 Squadron in August 1958.

JAVELIN F.A.W.MK.8: Differing from the F.A.W. Mk.7 only in having U.S. radar, drooped wing leading edges, a Sperry autopilot, and a simplified system of afterburning for its Sapphire turbojets, the F.A.W. Mk.8 was destined to be the final production version of the Javelin. The first example of this variant (XH966) flew on May 9, 1958, entering service with No. 41 Squadron early in 1960, and forty-seven were built to bring total Javelin production to 381 aircraft excluding

A Javelin F.A.W.Mk.9 (XH881)—originally the thirty-ninth production F.A.W.Mk.7. The Javelin is scheduled to be phased out of R.A.F. Fighter Command service early in 1965.

prototypes. Together with the F.A.W.Mk.9, the Javelin F.A.W.Mk.8 is currently operational with the R.A.F. The last production aircraft flew on August 16, 1960.

JAVELIN F.A.W.MK.9: Forty-six Javelin F.A.W.Mk. 7s were brought up to F.A.W.Mk.8 standards by the installation of U.S. radar, the addition of short after-burners, the drooping of the wing leading edges, and the provision of dampers on both yaw and pitch axes, as F.A.W.Mk.9s. Bag-type integral wing tanks have a total capacity of 915 Imp.gal., two 250 Imp.gal. ventral drop tanks may be carried, and provision is made for in-flight refuelling. The first F.A.W.Mk.9 conversion flew on May 6, 1959, and the first examples of this version of the Javelin were issued to No. 25 Squadron.

JAVELIN F.A.W.MK.8 SPECIFICATION

Power Plants: *Two Bristol Siddeley Sapphire 203/204 turbojets each rated at 10,630 lb.s.t. and 12,230 lb.s.t. with afterburning.*
Armament: *Two 30-mm. Aden cannon and four Firestreak infra-red homing AAMs.*
Performance: *Max. speed (at 35,180 lb.), 684 m.p.h. at sea level (Mach 0.9), 628 m.p.h. at 30,000 ft. (Mach 0.93), 620 m.p.h. at 40,000 ft. (Mach 0.94); optimum cruise, 353 m.p.h. at 10,000 ft. (Mach 0.48), 454 m.p.h. at 30,000 ft. (Mach 0.67), 508 m.p.h. at 45,000 ft.;*
initial climb (at 38,400 lb.), 12,250 ft./min.; time to 40,000 ft., 5.6 min., to 50,000 ft., 9.4 min.; service ceiling, 49,500 ft. (at 35,180 lb.), 51,330 ft.; range (with two 250 Imp. gal. drop tanks), 618 mls. at 20,000 ft., 783 mls. at 30,000 ft., 907 mls. at 40,000 ft., 930 mls. at 45,000 ft.
Weights: *Loaded (clean), 38,400 lb., (with two 250 Imp. gal. drop tanks), 42,930 lb.*
Dimensions: *Span, 52 ft. 0 in.; length, 56 ft. 3½ in.; height, 16 ft. 0 in.; wing area, 927 sq. ft.*

HANDLEY PAGE VICTOR

Sharing the task of spearheading Britain's deterrent force with the Vulcan B.Mk.2, the Victor B.Mk.2 forms a part of the equipment of No. 3 Group R.A.F. Bomber Command, but, ordered in smaller numbers

Victor B.Mk.1As of No. 10 Squadron at Cottesmore in the low-level camouflage finish introduced during 1964.

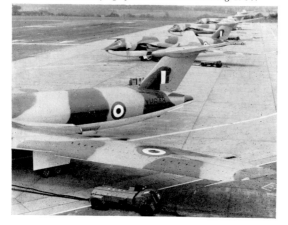

than the contemporary Hawker Siddeley bomber, equips proportionately fewer squadrons, these including Nos. 57, 100 and 139 Squadrons which, during 1964, completed conversion to the Blue Steel stand-off missile from free-falling weapons.

Possessing a unique crescent wing planform in which a constant critical Mach number is maintained from root to tip by means of graded sweepback, the Victor was designed to fulfil the same B.35/46 specification for which the Vulcan was projected, and, as the H.P.80, design work was initiated in 1947, a development contract being placed late that year, followed in 1949 by an order for two prototypes. The first prototype (WB771) flew for the first time on December 24, 1952, but nineteen months later, on July 14, 1954, the aircraft was lost as a result of a fatigue failure and the loss of the tailplane during a low-level run. The second prototype (WB775) flew on September 11, 1954, and the first production Victor B.Mk.1 (XA917) made its initial flight on February 1, 1956.

VICTOR B.MKS. 1 AND 1A: The production Victor B.Mk.1, the contract for which had been placed late in 1952, differed from the prototypes in several respects, the most noteworthy of which was the installation of 11,000 lb.s.t. Sapphire 202 engines in place of the 8,000 lb.s.t. 100 series engines; the lengthening of the forward fuselage by 40 inches to improve the c.g. range, and a 15-in. reduction in the height of the vertical tail surfaces. On June 1, 1957, the first production Victor exceeded Mach 1.0 inadvertently in a shallow dive at 40,000 ft. during a delivery flight to No. 232 Operational Conversion Unit, becoming the largest aircraft in the world known to have exceeded Mach unity at that time.

In April 1958, the Victor B.Mk.1 entered service with No. 10 Squadron, No. 15 Squadron also re-equipping with the bomber before the end of that year, and the planned total of four Victor B.Mk.1 squadrons (the others being Nos. 55 and 57) was completed early in 1960. No. 543 Squadron also received a number of examples of a reconnaissance conversion, the Victor B.(P.R.)Mk.1, and between sixty and seventy examples of the initial production model were built before the more advanced Victor B.Mk.2 was introduced on the line. Many B.Mk.1s were later brought up to B.Mk.1A standards by up-dating internal equipment and providing electronic countermeasures equipment in the extreme rear fuselage.

Unlike the aircrew of other V-bombers, the Victor's crew of five were seated together in one compartment, and the internal weapons bay could accommodate appreciably greater offensive loads than that of the contemporary Vulcan, the maximum conventional load being thirty-five 1,000-lb. bombs. Powered by four 11,000 lb.s.t. Bristol Siddeley Sapphire 202 turbojets, the Victor B.Mk.1 could fly at speeds only marginally lower than Mach 1.0 at altitudes between 40,000 and 50,000 ft., maximum cruise performance including a speed of 607 m.p.h. at 46,000 ft., and unrefuelled flight range at altitude being some 4,000 miles. Largely supplanted by the Victor B.Mk.2 in the strategic bombing rôle, the B.Mk.1 is being relegated to the photo-reconnaissance and tanker rôles in which it succeeds the Valiant. For flight refuelling, the Victor B.Mks.1 and 1A are being converted to "three-point" tankers, with a Mk.20B refuelling pod beneath each wing and a Mk.17 hose drum unit faired into the rear of the weapons bay. Structural alterations include the installation of two fuel tanks in the weapons bay which is faired over, the doors being dispensed with. A prototype conversion (XA918), the second production B.Mk.1, was made during the summer of 1964.

VICTOR B.MK.2: The second and final stage in the development of the basic Victor bomber is represented by the B.Mk.2 which, externally similar in appearance

A Victor B.Mk.1A (XH648)—the 46th production Victor—dropping its load of thirty-five 1,000-lb. bombs.

to its predecessor, has appreciably more powerful turbojets than the B.Mk.1 and some increase in wing span and gross area, these being raised from 110 ft. and 2,406 sq. ft. to 120 ft. and 2,597 sq. ft. respectively. The increases in span and area result from the insertion of stub-wing extensions inboard of the engines and slight extension of the wingtips. Two retractable air intakes on top of the rear fuselage can be extended at altitude to supply two ram-air turbo-alternators for emergency power supplies, a Bristol Siddeley-Turboméca Artouste turbine is installed in the starboard wing root to supply compressed air for engine starting and power for airframe systems, and the air intakes are enlarged to feed the Conway turbojets.

The first Victor B.Mk.2 (XH668) flew on February 20, 1959, but there were some delays in deliveries to R.A.F. Bomber Command, these not commencing until 1961, and the first Squadron to be equipped with this type, No. 139, did not begin conversion until February 1962. Initial production Victor B.Mk.2

(Below and above right) The prototype Victor B.K.Mk.1 tanker conversion (XA918)—originally the second production B.Mk.1—with a 150 Imp. gal. fuel reservoir, hose drum and drogue beneath each wing, and retractable fuselage hose drum unit.

A Victor B.Mk.2 of No. 139 Squadron with semi-externally mounted Blue Steel stand-off weapon.

bombers were powered by the 17,250 lb.s.t. Conway R.Co.11 but later aircraft received the 20,000 lb.s.t. Conway R.Co.17, these providing almost twice the thrust available to the Victor B.Mk.1. The greatly increased power is devoted mainly to increasing operating altitude and extending the cruising speed further toward the buffet boundary. A photo-reconnaissance version of the basic aircraft is designated B.(P.R.) Mk.2, and production of the Victor was virtually complete by the end of 1964.

The principal weapon of the Victor B.Mk.2 is now the Blue Steel which is mounted semi-externally,

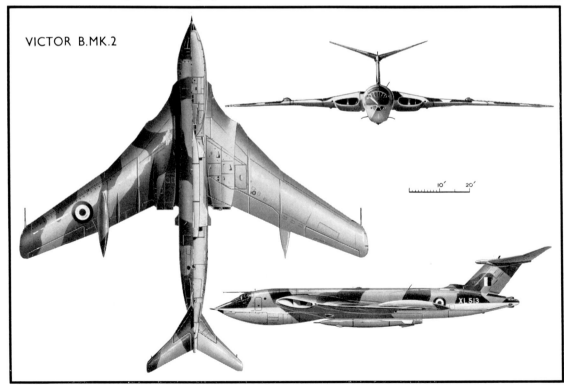

VICTOR B.MK.2

VICTOR B.MK.2 SPECIFICATION

Power Plants: *Four Rolls-Royce Conway R.Co.17 turbojets each rated at 20,000 lb.s.t.*

Armament: *One Avro Blue Steel Mk.1 rocket-driven supersonic stand-off missile or various loads of nuclear or conventional free-falling weapons, such as thirty-five 1,000-lb. general-purpose bombs.*

Performance: *Approx. max. speed, 640–645 m.p.h. at 40,000 ft. (Mach 0.97–0.98); max. cruise, 620 m.p.h. at 55,000 ft. (Mach 0.94), 570 m.p.h. at sea level (Mach 0.79); tactical radius (with Blue Steel), 1,730 mls. at low altitude, 2,300 mls. at high altitude. Service ceiling, 60,000 (plus) ft.*

Weights: *Approx. loaded, 200,000 lb.*

Dimensions: *Span, 120 ft. 0 in.; length, 114 ft. 11 in.; height, 30 ft. 1½ in.; wing area, 2,597 sq. ft.*

attached to a beam in the weapons bay and necessitating special cut-down weapons-bay doors, but the aircraft can be modified to carry free-falling nuclear or high-explosive weapons within 24–30 hours. The Blue Steel may be launched in a high- or low-level approach and only reduces performance by some two

(Right and below) Victor B.Mk.2s of No. 139 Squadron.

per cent. From late 1963, Victor B.Mk.2s were retrospectively modified by the fitting of fairings above the trailing edges of the wings, just outboard of the break in sweep angle. These resulted from a request to provide space for the stowage of radar "chaff" dispensers, and the discovery that these could be stowed in such fairings with beneficial effect on drag reduction at near-sonic speeds.

HAWKER HUNTER

Aesthetically perhaps the most attractive of jet fighters and undoubtedly the most successful of Britain's post-war combat aircraft, the Hunter serves in a variety of rôles with a number of the world's air forces, and has enjoyed an exceptionally long operational career in R.A.F. service, a career bidding fair to continue until at least the end of the 'sixties as this versatile aircraft's intended successor, the P.1154, is not expected to enter service until 1968–69. Although Hunter production was completed in the late 'fifties, at the end of 1964 the parent company was continuing the overhaul and conversion of F.Mks.4 and 6 interceptors for other tasks against foreign orders.

As the P.1067, the Hunter design originated in the Hawker project office in 1947, and, submitted to the Air Ministry in January 1948, influenced the writing of

specification F.3/48 for a single-seat transonic day interceptor. A contract for three prototypes was awarded in June 1948, and before the first of these (WB188) had flown, production orders had been placed (in October 1950) for 200 aircraft powered by the Rolls-Royce Avon and a similar quantity powered by the Armstrong Siddeley Sapphire. The first Avon-powered prototype flew on June 20, 1951, followed by the similarly-powered second prototype (WB195) on May 5, 1952. The third prototype (WB202), powered by the Sapphire, and flown on November 30, 1952, was considered as the prototype F.Mk.2.

The first production Avon-powered Hunter F.Mk.1 (WT555) flew on May 16, 1953, five months ahead of the first Sapphire-powered F.Mk.2 (WN888) which made its first flight on October 14th. The Hunter

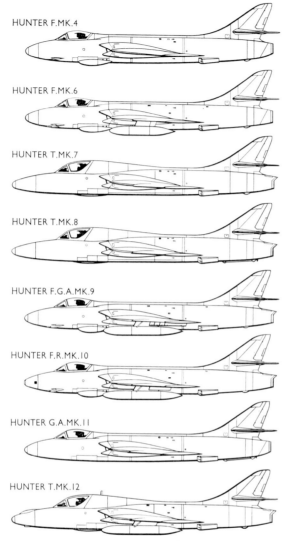

HUNTER F.MK.4

HUNTER F.MK.6

HUNTER T.MK.7

HUNTER T.MK.8

HUNTER F.G.A.MK.9

HUNTER F.R.MK.10

HUNTER G.A.MK.11

HUNTER T.MK.12

F.Mks.1 and 2 were essentially short-range day interceptors carrying four 30-mm. Aden cannon with 150 r.p.g., and lacking any provision for external stores. Powered by the 7,550 lb.s.t. Avon 113, the F.Mk.1 attained 617 m.p.h. at 36,000 ft. (Mach 0.935) and 693 m.p.h. at sea level (Mach 0.9), while the fractionally more powerful F.Mk.2, the Sapphire 101 turbojet of which was rated at 8,000 lb.s.t., attained 620 m.p.h. at 36,000 ft. (Mach 0.94) and 698 m.p.h. at sea level (Mach 0.905). Twenty of the 139 F.Mk.1s produced were retained for pre-production testing, and the interceptor entered service from mid-1954 with Nos. 43, 54, and 222 Squadrons of R.A.F. Fighter Command. Simultaneously, forty-five F.Mk.2s were built, these being issued to Nos. 257 and 263 Squadrons.

One of the principal shortcomings of the Hunter was its extremely limited operational radius and, in consequence, internal fuel capacity was increased from 334 to 414 Imp. gal., and two underwing pylons were provided, these each carrying a 100 Imp.gal. drop tank. The 140th Avon-powered production aircraft (WT701) embodying these changes, and flown on October 20, 1954, received the designation Hunter F.Mk.4, while the forty-sixth Sapphire-engined aircraft (WN954), which incorporated similar changes and actually flew on the previous day, October 19th, became the F.Mk.5. Only 105 examples of the last-mentioned version were built, these being issued to Nos. 1, 34, 41, 56, and 263 Squadrons, but 365 Hunter F.Mk.4s were built by the parent company, while, in addition, licence manufacture was undertaken in the Netherlands by Fokker and Aviolanda, and in Belgium by Avions Fairey and SABCA, the four companies between them manufacturing a total of 460 F.Mk.4s and the later F.Mk.6s, 268 being supplied to the R.Neth.A.F., and 192 to the R.Bel.A.F.

The first 159 British-built Hunter F.Mk.4s retained the Avon 113 of the F.Mk.1, but the 160th and subsequent machines received the Avon 115 embodying modifications intended to overcome surging experienced when the Aden cannon were fired. Initial deliveries of the F.Mk.4 were made to Nos. 54 and 111 Squadrons in the United Kingdom, and then to R.A.F.

(Below) One of twelve Hunter F.Mk.6 fighters which currently equip one squadron of Jordan's Royal Arab Air Force.

Hunter F.Mk.6s of No. 325 Squadron, R.Neth.A.F. No. 325 is the last Dutch Hunter squadron and will retain its present equipment for the low-level intercept rôle until 1966. Based at Soesterberg, No. 325 also operates a target towing flight.

HUNTER F.MK.6

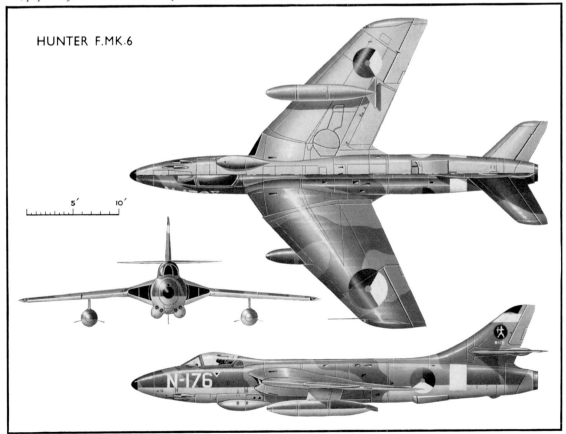

Hunter F.Mk.6s of the R.Neth.A.F.'s No. 325 Squadron are equipped with the Sidewinder AAM as illustrated here.

squadrons in Germany, subsequently serving with Nos. 3, 4, 14, 20, 26, 43, 66, 67, 71, 74, 92, 93, 98, 112, 118, 130, 222, 234 and 247 Squadrons. No Hunter F.Mk.4s remain in operational service with the R.A.F., the R.Neth.A.F. or the R.Bel.A.F., but there were three export versions as follows:

Hunter F.Mk.50: This designation was applied to 120 F.Mk.4s supplied to the R.Swed.A.F. (Flygvapnet) in 1955–56, subsequently serving as the J 34 with the Flottiljer 8, 9, 10 and 18. The F.Mk.50 was later adapted to carry two Rb 324 (Sidewinder) AAMs, and the last units to operate the type were F 9 at Save and F 10 at Angelholm which were in process of re-equipping with the J 35 Draken during 1964.

Hunter F.Mk.51: This designation was applied to thirty aircraft supplied to the R.Dan.A.F. in 1956 and subsequently operated by No. 724 Squadron until 1963.

Hunter F.Mk.52: Sixteen ex-R.A.F. Hunter F.Mk.4s were supplied to the Peruvian Air Force in 1956 as F.Mk.52s, these currently serving with one squadron of that air arm's Gruppo 12.

HUNTER F.MK.6: The final basic single-seat production version of the Hunter was the F.Mk.6, the prototype of which, as the P.1099 (XF833), flew for the first time on January 22, 1954. The production Hunter F.Mk.6, the first example of which (WW592) flew on March 25, 1955, received the 10,050 lb.s.t. Avon 203 turbojet, the installation of which resulted in much improved load-carrying capability. Initial aircraft were manufactured with straight wing leading edges, but high altitude handling trials prompted the addition of leading-edge extensions to counter possible pitch-up, a modification applied retrospectively to almost all F.Mk.6s and a number of F.Mk.4s, and for the intercept rôle gun blast deflectors were fitted to counter a tendency to pitch down during high altitude gun firing. On later F.Mk.6s a "flying tail" was introduced, with the power-operated elevator interconnected to change tailplane incidence.

The Hunter F.Mk.6 progressively supplanted the F.Mk.4 in R.A.F. service, equipping Nos. 4, 14, 19, 20, 43, 54, 63, 65, 66, 74, 92, 93, 111, 247 and 263 Squadrons, and in addition to those previously mentioned as being manufactured under licence in the Netherlands and Belgium, 415 were built as F.Mk.6s in the United Kingdom, fifteen of these being delivered to Iraq, twelve being supplied to Jordan, and six being delivered to the Lebanon, the last-mentioned country later taking delivery of a further six aircraft. In Belgium, the Hunter F.Mk.6 equipped the 7ème, 8ème, 22ème and 26ème Escadrilles, being finally withdrawn from service in 1963. In the Netherlands, Nos. 322, 323, 324 and 325 Squadrons have flown the Hunter F.Mk.6, and Nos. 322 and 323 have re-equipped with the F-104G, but No. 325 is scheduled to retain its Hunters until 1966, these serving in the low-level intercept rôle until 1966, No. 324 now being a SAM unit. A number of short-hour Hunter F.Mk.6s were delivered from Belgium and the Netherlands to the Hawker Blackburn Division of the Hawker Siddeley Group during 1963–64 for conversion, primarily to F.G.A.Mk.9 standards, and resale, and a number of F.Mk.6s remain in operational R.A.F. service in some seven mixed squadrons (see opposite page) which comprise primarily F.G.A.Mk.9s and a few F.R.Mk.10 versions on their strength. A substantial number of Hunters essentially similar to the F.Mk.6 were exported as follows:

Hunter F.Mk.56: One hundred and sixty aircraft powered by the Avon 203 were supplied to the Indian Air Force between October 1957 and February 1961, and currently remain in operational service with that air arm. The forty-ninth and subsequent aircraft were equipped with a 10 ft. 6in. diameter ring-slot landing parachute in the tail.

Hunter F.Mk.57: Four single-seat ground-attack fighter conversions of F.Mk.6s to F.G.A.Mk.9 standards supplied to Kuwait in 1964, the first aircraft of this type flying on November 27, 1963.

Hunter F.Mk.58: One hundred ground-attack fighter versions of the F.Mk.6 supplied to the Swiss Air Force during 1958–60. The last eighty-eight were completed to F.G.A.Mk.9 standards with gun blast deflectors and tail parachutes, and this type currently equips five staffeln, these being scheduled to remain in first-line service into the 'seventies.

Hunter F.Mk.59: Eighteen ex-Belgian F.Mk.6s converted to F.G.A.Mk.9 standards and delivered to Iraq in 1964 to supplement fifteen F.Mk.6s supplied earlier.

One of twenty Hunter T.Mk.7 side-by-side two-seat operational trainers delivered to the R.Neth.A.F.

HUNTER F.G.A.MK.9: The principal current operational version of the Hunter in R.A.F. service, equipping, together with F.Mk.6s and F.R.Mk.10s, several units, including Nos. 1, 8, 20, 28, 43, 54, and 208 Squadrons, the F.G.A.Mk.9 is a ground-attack fighter conversion of the F.Mk.6 with an Avon 207 in place of the Avon 203, a 10 ft. 6 in. diameter ring-slot landing parachute in the tail, increased oxygen reserves for the pilot, and cutaway landing flaps to permit the attachment of 230 Imp. gal. drop tanks. A stop-gap version introduced prior to the delivery of the definitive F.G.A.Mk.9 which simply included the modifications associated with the 230 Imp gal. drop tanks and was converted by R.A.F. Maintenance Units was known as the "Mk.6/Interim Mk.9". Twelve Hunter F.G.A.Mk.9s were supplied to Rhodesia in 1962–63, and currently equip No. 1 Squadron of the Royal Rhodesian Air Force.

HUNTER F.R.MK.10: The F.R.Mk.10 reconnaissance fighter, which currently serves with Nos. 2 and 4 Squadrons of the R.A.F., has all the features of the F.G.A.Mk.9, including the Avon 207 and tail parachute, and is a further conversion of the F.Mk.6. The first Hunter F.R.Mk.10 (XF429) flew on November 7, 1958, and while retaining normal cannon armament, this variant has one forward-facing and two oblique cameras in the nose.

HUNTER G.A.MK.11: A single-seat advanced ground-attack trainer serving with the Royal Navy's Nos.

HUNTER F.G.A.MK.9 SPECIFICATION

Power Plant: *One Rolls-Royce Avon 207 turbojet rated at 10,050 lb.s.t.*
Armament: *Four 30-mm. Aden cannon with 150 r.p.g. plus two 500-lb. or 1,000-lb. bombs, four 100 Imp. gal. napalm tanks, twenty-four 3-in. rockets or four 2-in. rocket pods.*
Performance: *Max. speed, 715 m.p.h. at sea level (Mach 0.938), 627 m.p.h. at 36,000 ft. (Mach 0.95); initial climb rate (clean), 17,200 ft./min.; time to 10,000 ft., 2.25 min., to 20,000 ft., 3 min., to 40,000 ft., 5.25 min.; absolute ceiling, 53,400 ft.; range (clean), 489 mls. at 30,000 ft., (with two 230 and two 100 Imp. gal. drop tanks), 1,854 mls. at 515 m.p.h.; radius of action (with two 1,000-lb. bombs and two 100 Imp. gal. drop tanks), 219 mls. at 1,000 ft., 350 mls. at 39,000 ft. Weights: Empty, 14,400 lb.; loaded (clean), 17,750 lb.; max. overload, 24,600 lb.*
Dimensions: *Span, 33 ft. 8 in.; length, 45 ft. 10½ in.; height, 13 ft. 1¾ in.; wing area, 349 sq. ft.*

(Above, right) An R.A.F. Hunter T.Mk.7 (WV383) in camouflage finish, and (below) a Hunter F.G.A.Mk.9 (XK151).

(Above) A high gloss blue and white Hunter T.Mk.8 (XL580) used by Admiral Gick at R.N.A.S. Yeovilton.

(Above) A Hunter G.A.Mk.11 advanced ground-attack trainer of the type serving with the Royal Navy.

738 and 764 Squadrons, the Hunter G.A.Mk.11 is a conversion of the F.Mk.4 with a 7,575 lb.s.t. Avon 122 engine, guns and gunsight removed, comprehensive wing store wiring for a variety of weapons loads ranging from 1,000-lb. bombs to AGM-12B Bullpup-A ASMs, an airfield emergency arrester hook, and TACAN equipment. During conversion all G.A.Mk. 11s received wing leading edge extensions, and a three-camera nose is interchangeable with the "plain" nose fitted as standard. Between forty and fifty F.Mk.4s were converted to G.A.Mk.11 standards, and the first Hunter G.A.Mk.11 flew on January 24, 1962.

HUNTER TWO-SEATERS: A two-seat side-by-side operational training version of the Hunter was called for by specification T.157D issued in 1954. The first prototype, the P.1101 (XJ615), was basically an F.Mk.4 with an Avon 113 engine and a new front fuselage, fully duplicated flying controls and gunsights being provided for instructor and pupil. The new two-seat nose, which was the subject of considerable development, increased overall length to 48 ft. 10½ in., and, in the first prototype, armament comprised a pair of semi-externally mounted Aden cannon. This first aircraft flew on July 8, 1955, and was followed by a second prototype (XJ627) on November 17, 1956, this being based on an F.Mk.6 airframe.

Production orders were placed for sixty-five examples of the lower-powered training version as the Hunter T.Mk.7, ten of these being diverted to the Fleet Air Arm as the T.Mk.8, and ten to the R.Neth. A.F. which service later increased its order by a further ten machines. The T.Mk.7 powered by the 7,575 lb.s.t. Avon 122 retained only the starboard-mounted 30-mm. cannon, and with a clean A.U.W. of 17,200 lb. attained maximum speeds of 660 m.p.h. at 20,000 ft. (Mach 0.935) and 615 m.p.h. at 40,000 ft. (Mach 0.93). Initial climb rate was 10,500 ft./min., and an altitude of 40,000 ft. was attained in 9.5 min.

The first production Hunter T.Mk.7 (XL563) flew on October 11, 1957, and the type entered service with No. 229 Operational Conversion Unit in mid-1958, some aircraft going to the Central Fighter Establishment and operational squadrons as instrument flying check-out aircraft.

The Hunter T.Mk.8 for the Royal Navy, the first example of which (WW664) flew on March 3, 1958, differed from the R.A.F.'s T.Mk.7 in having naval radio equipment and an airfield arrester hook. The ten new aircraft already referred to were joined by eighteen additional aircraft converted from F.Mk.4 airframes, and the T.Mk.8s currently equip Nos. 738 and 759 Squadrons. Further single-seaters were converted as two-seat T.Mks.8B and 8C during 1963–64, these differing from the standard T.Mk.8 only in equipment fitted, gunsight, gun and nose radar being deleted, and OR.946 instrument display and, in some aircraft, TACAN equipment being introduced. One non-training two-seater, the Hunter Mk.12 (XE531) powered by the Avon 207, is used at the Royal Aircraft Establishment to test certain equipment associated with the TSR-2, including a head-up display, and export versions of the two-seater are as follows:

Hunter T.Mk.53: Essentially similar to the T.Mk.7, the T.Mk.53 was a version for the R.Dan.A.F., two examples of which were supplied without the wing leading edge extensions.

Hunter T.Mk.62: One aircraft essentially similar to the T.Mk.7 supplied to the Peruvian Air Force.

Hunter T.Mk.66: Powered by the 10,050 lb.s.t. Avon 203 turbojet and equipped with two 30-mm. Aden cannon and tail parachute, the T.Mk.66 was developed for the Indian Air Force, the delivery of twenty-two commencing in 1959.

Hunter T.Mk.66A: Hawker Siddeley's demonstration aircraft basically similar to the T.Mk.66. During 1964 this aircraft was engaged on a training commitment in Iraq.

Hunter T.Mk.66B: Powered by the Avon 207 and carrying an armament of two 30-mm. Aden cannon, the T.Mk.66B was a version for Jordan, two examples being supplied in 1960–61.

Hunter T.Mk.67: Two Avon 207-powered aircraft essentially similar to the T.Mk.66 supplied in 1963–64 to Kuwait.

Hunter T.Mk.69: Two Avon 207-powered aircraft similar to the T.Mk.66 delivered in 1964 to Iraq.

HAWKER SIDDELEY KESTREL

Under development since 1957, when design work was initiated as a private venture, the P.1127, subsequently named Kestrel, was the world's first V/STOL strike and reconnaissance fighter, and during 1964 a tripartite evaluation squadron comprising personnel from the R.A.F., the Federal German Luftwaffe, the U.S.A.F. and the U.S. Navy was in process of being formed and equipped with this revolutionary warplane.

The Kestrel was designed around the unique Pegasus turbofan engine which, basically an Orpheus driving a two-stage ducted fan, discharges air through two pairs of nozzles mechanically connected together and capable of rotation, thus permitting all the installed thrust to be vectored to match the demands of vertical or short take-off and landing at one end of the scale and climb acceleration and level speed at the other. The design of the Kestrel crystallized by 1958 as a relatively simple, single-seat tactical strike and re-connaissance fighter halfway in size between the Gnat and the Hunter. At this time, the Kestrel was envisaged as a potential replacement for the R.A.F.'s Hunter in the ground attack rôle but, more specifically, as a "third generation" NATO lightweight strike and reconnaissance aircraft.

In June 1958 the first tangible support for the project was provided by the decision to support financially the development of the Pegasus vectored-thrust engine from the Mutual Weapons Development Programme, and actual construction of the Kestrel

commenced as a private venture in May 1959, but it was not until June 1960 that a Ministry of Aviation contract was placed for two prototypes, a contract for an additional four prototypes later being negotiated.

The first Kestrel (XP831) with an early Pegasus engine developing 11,300 lb.s.t. rose vertically off a grid for the first time on October 21, 1960, and on March 13, 1961 effected its first horizontal take-off and conventional flight. On July 7, 1961, the second prototype (XP836) made a conventional first flight, and eventually, on September 12th, complete take-off and landing transitions were carried out. Unfortunately, the second prototype was lost three months later, on December 14th, when one of the fibreglass nozzles became detached in flight, but the third prototype (XP972) joined the test programme on April 5, 1962, this, like the fourth aircraft (XP976), initially being powered by the 12,500 lb.s.t. Pegasus 2, the first prototype having been re-engined in the meantime with a Pegasus 3 rated at 13,500 lb.s.t. The fourth Kestrel had flown on July 12, 1962, by which time a service test batch of nine aircraft had been ordered for a multilateral evaluation squadron.

Minor changes had been introduced on the third and fourth aircraft, the third having modified stabilizing wheels and a reduction in sweep angle on the extreme outboard sections of the wing leading edges, and the fourth, which reverted to the original outrigger fairings, had modified intakes and tip-nozzle

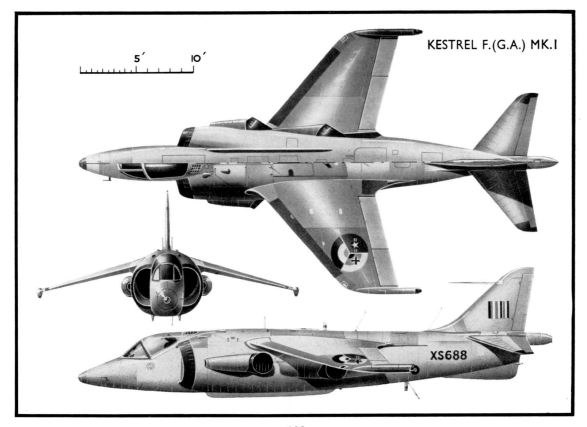

KESTREL F.(G.A.) MK.I

5′　　10′

XS688

fairings, and a kinked wing leading edge intended to combine the pitch-up characteristics of the "dog

(Above) The first Kestrel prototype (XP831) and (below) the third (XP972) with the original non-swept wings.

(Below) The second Kestrel prototype (XP836) which was lost when an exhaust nozzle became detached in flight.

tooth" with smoothing the streamwise distribution. Tests were made with simulated 250-lb. bombs under the wings to check control inertia in hovering, and the first prototype underwent deck trials aboard H.M.S. *Ark Royal*. The fifth prototype (XP980), which joined the test programme on February 24, 1963, had streamwise wingtips, and its anhedral tailplane and ventral strakes were fitted retrospectively to the earlier prototypes.

Although the first five prototypes differed in detail, they all had unswept wing trailing edges and an overall wing span of 24 ft. 4 in., and with the Pegasus 3 engine attained level flight speeds only marginally below Mach unity, speeds in excess of Mach 1.0 being reached at dive angles of a few degrees. The sixth prototype (XP984), which flew on February 13, 1964, differed from its predecessors in a number of respects and was, in fact, representative of the definitive model for the tripartite evaluation squadron excepting for operational equipment. Powered by the Pegasus 5 engine of 15,200 lb.s.t., the sixth aircraft embodied a slight increase in overall length (from 41 ft. 2 in. to 42 ft. 0 in.), some 10° of sweepback on the wing trailing edges, full ventral strakes, rectangular air brake/mainwheel doors, and some modifications to the undercarriage and rear nozzle fairings. Only three weeks later, on March 7th, the first of the tripartite Kestrel F.(G.A.)Mk.1s (XS688) was flown for the first time.

KESTREL F.(G.A.)Mk.1: The Kestrel F.(G.A.)Mk.1 for the tripartite evaluation squadron at West Raynham has provision for full operational equipment, and all nine aircraft of this type were scheduled to be completed by the end of 1964. The most marked external difference from the sixth prototype is the provision of a camera nose, and strong points are provided beneath the wings for four stores pylons, external ordnance loads being similar to those of the Hunter F.G.A.Mk.9. Dominant features include the large cheek engine air intakes and the zero-track tricycle undercarriage with low-pressure tyres to permit operation from unprepared surfaces. The Kestrel has been designed fatigue-wise to cope with the exacting requirements of

(Below) Two prototypes of the Kestrel, the first (XP831) in the foreground, and the third (XP972) in the background.

(Above and below right) The first tripartite Kestrel (XS688) which, together with its eight fellows, will be evaluated by a special three-nation squadron in 1965. They will be joined by the surviving four prototypes, the first of which, XP831, has been rebuilt to tripartite standards. The evaluation programme will not now include any weapons trials.

the high subsonic speed low-level rôle, and generous internal and external fuel capacity permits a ferry range well in excess of that of the Hunter. With the 15,200 lb.s.t. Pegasus 5 and flying at Mach 0.8 with maximum internal fuel with ten per cent reserves over a maximum 2,420-mile range for a low-level sortie at 500 ft., the Kestrel has a 45-mile radius of action in the target area. The effective radius of action varies considerably from the VTO low-level strike at the one extreme to the STO "top hat" profile at the other, and although intended primarily for the strike-reconnaissance task, the Kestrel's very high thrust-to-weight ratio endows it with a high climb rate and a comparatively high ceiling, providing a useful secondary intercept capability.

P.1154: The Kestrel is the forerunner of the heavier and very much more powerful P.1154 which is now being developed for the R.A.F. as a successor to the Hunter. Evolved from experience gained with the Kestrel, the P.1154 will be powered by the Bristol Siddeley BS.100 and the detailed design submission to specification ASR.356 was made in August 1954, and at the time of closing for press the placing of a development order—probably for eight aircraft, the first to fly two years later—was awaited. Service deliveries are likely to begin in 1968–69. The technical winner of the abortive NATO BMR.3 contest for a V/STOL reconnaissance-strike fighter, the P.1154 will possess dual intercept-ground attack capability, although emphasis is being placed on the latter.

No details of the P.1154 have been revealed, but by comparison with the Kestrel it is logical to suppose that, in view of the electronic equipment, various types of armament and quantities of fuel that will have to be carried, the fineness ratio of the fuselage will be increased by substantial lengthening, as the larger engine, which must be installed on the c.g., will not permit any reduction of the cross section. The BS.100 vectorable turbofan will deliver approximately 9,500 lb. thrust from the forward nozzles and about 18,000 lb. thrust from the rear nozzles, maximum dry thrust being of the order of 27,500 lb., and plenum chamber burning upstream of the forward pair of nozzles will boost this by some thirty per cent to about 36,000 lb. Much of the fuel is likely to be carried around the engine, and it may be assumed that the swivelling nozzles will be arranged so that they lie in the lee of the air intakes.

KESTREL F.(G.A.)MK.1 SPECIFICATION

Power Plant: *One Bristol Siddeley Pegasus 5 rated at 15,200 lb.s.t.*

Armament: *Possible external loads include two 1,000-lb. or 500-lb. bombs, four 100 Imp. gal. napalm tanks, twenty-four 3-in. rockets or four 2-in. rocket pods.*

Estimated Performance: *Max. speed, 690 m.p.h. at sea level, 670 m.p.h. at 36,000 ft. (Mach 1.02); radius of action (STOL), 220 mls. at 1,000 ft., 350 mls. at 40,000 ft.; max. range, 2,500 mls.; initial climb, 35,000 (plus) ft./min.; time to 50,000 ft., 4 min.; service ceiling, 50,000 ft.; absolute ceiling, 55,000 ft.*

Estimated Weights: *Loaded (VTOL), 13,000 lb., (STOL), 18,000 lb.; max. overload, 21,000 lb.*

Dimensions: *Span, 22 ft. 10 in.; length, 42 ft. 0 in.; height, 10 ft. 9 in.; wing area, 186 sq. ft.*

HAWKER SIDDELEY (BLACKBURN) BUCCANEER

Developed by the Hawker Blackburn Division of the Hawker Siddeley Group as a two-seat shipboard low-level strike aircraft, the Buccaneer is currently serving in its initial S.Mk.1 production version with Nos. 800, 801 and 809 Squadrons of the Fleet Air Arm, and will be supplemented in service in 1965 and eventually supplanted by the more powerful Buccaneer S.Mk.2, the present production model.

Designed to meet the requirements of specification NA.39 which, formulated in the early 'fifties, called for a two-seat strike aircraft capable of sustained flight at extremely high subsonic speeds at sea level, the Buccaneer began life as the B.103. NA.39 imposed limitations on gross weight and overall size, and in order to meet the range requirement, the total installed engine thrust had to be held to the minimum necessary for flight at just below Mach unity. To achieve maximum lift, the B.103 adopted boundary layer control over the wings, flaps, ailerons and tailplane, this being obtained by bleeding compressed air from the engines; the fuselage was area-ruled to delay the drag rise towards Mach unity, provide better control response and afford a smoother ride during high-speed low-level flight, and in order to provide an airframe life comparable with that of a high-flying aircraft, a detailed study was made of fatigue induced by low-level turbulence.

In 1955, the B.103 design was selected to fulfil the NA.39 specification, and in July of that year an order was placed for twenty pre-production machines, the first of which (XK486) flew for the first time on April 30, 1958 with two 7,000 lb.s.t. Gyron Junior DGJ.1 turbojets, and was essentially an empty shell for aerodynamic tests. This and the next eight pre-production aircraft were intended primarily for manufacturer's trials. The second aircraft (XK487) featured thicker wing skins and was used for aerodynamic and flutter tests, and the third (XK488) was similar but allocated for engine development. The fourth machine (XK489) was the first fully navalised aircraft, with folding wings and nose, arrester hook etc., this being employed on preliminary carrier trials; the fifth (XK490) was fitted with the hydraulically-

actuated rotating bomb door, wing strong points, etc., for armament trials, and the sixth (XK491) had the full electrical system.

The seventh, eighth and ninth pre-production machines (XK523–525) had the full electronics and navigation systems, incorporated the final detail design, and had the complete weapon/electronics systems respectively, and the tenth to the fourteenth aircraft (XK526–530) were all completed to the same standards as the ninth aircraft, and were allocated to the Ministry of Aviation for further development. By this time, the B.103 had been officially designated Buccaneer S.Mk.1, and an initial production order had been announced (in October 1959). The last five pre-production aircraft (XK531–535) were issued to an Intensive Flying Trials Unit, No. 700Z Flight, which was formed at R.N.A.S. Lossiemouth with the responsibility of proving the Buccaneer for Naval service.

BUCCANEER S.MK.1: The first production Buccaneer S.Mk.1 (XN924) was flown on January 23, 1962, and the first squadron to receive this type, No. 801, was commissioned on July 17, 1962, embarking aboard H.M.S. *Ark Royal* in February 1963. Two further Buccaneer S.Mk.1 squadrons were subsequently formed, Nos. 800 and 809, and these have progressively supplanted the Fleet Air Arm's Scimitar squadrons for the strike rôle.

Powered by two 7,100 lb.s.t. Gyron Junior 101 turbojets, the Buccaneer S.Mk.1 has, according to American sources, an estimated fatigue life of 1,000 hours at low altitude or 1,000 deck landings, and can carry a wide variety of conventional or nuclear stores on the rotating bomb door, or a camera pack for reconnaissance. Four underwing pylons, each with a capacity of 1,000 lb., may carry a Martin AGM-12B Bullpup-A ASM, a 2-in. or 3-in. rocket pack, or a range of bombs from 1,000 lb. down to 25 lb.

Tactically, the Buccaneer is intended to operate below the detection limits of radar, approaching its target at high subsonic speed and delivering its internally-housed store by toss-bombing. It possesses full all-weather capability, and a typical mission would call for cruise from carrier to within 300 miles of the target at 20,000 ft., a descent to sea level maintaining a cruising speed of some 460 m.p.h. to within 100 miles of the target, and then acceleration to 600–650 m.p.h.

BUCCANEER S.MK.2: During the development of the Buccaneer modern turbofan engines such as the Rolls-Royce Spey became available, offering appreciably lower fuel consumption and substantially increased power. Thus, at an early stage it was decided that the bulk of the Royal Navy's Buccaneers would have these highly efficient power plants which afford a higher all-round performance and a major increase in range.

Two of the pre-production Buccaneers were re-engined with 11,200 lb.s.t. RB.168-1 Spey turbofans as prototypes for the S.Mk.2, as the Spey-engined production version of the Buccaneer was designated, the first of these (XK526) flying on May 17, 1963, and the second (XK527) flying on August 19, 1963. The first production Buccaneer S.Mk.2 (XN974) flew on June 5, 1964, following the last of the fifty production examples

(*Above and below*) *The Buccaneer S.Mk.1 which equips Nos. 800, 801 and 809 Squadrons of the Fleet Air Arm.*

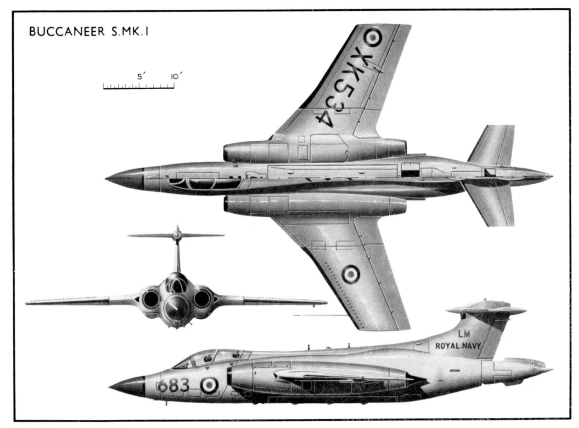

BUCCANEER S.MK.1

of the S.Mk.1. The production order for the S.Mk.2 was announced in January 1962, and it is anticipated that this more advanced version of the strike aircraft will enter service with Fleet Air Arm squadrons during 1965.

BUCCANEER S.MK.50: A version of the Buccaneer basically similar to the S.Mk.2 has been ordered by the South African Air Force as its standard Maritime Command strike and reconnaissance aircraft. Designated Buccaneer S.Mk.50 and scheduled to enter

The thirtieth production Buccaneer S.Mk.1 (XN953) flying with the first Buccaneer S.Mk.2 prototype (XK526).

The first production Buccaneer S.Mk.2 (XN974). This version of the Buccaneer is expected to enter service during 1965.

service with the S.A.A.F. during 1965, the South African version will carry two 250 Imp. gal. underwing tanks for long-range shore-based operations, and the twenty aircraft of this type ordered will be fully navalised to enable them to cross-operate with Fleet Air Arm units, although no South African aircraft carriers are envisaged. The Buccaneer S.Mk.50 will equip two S.A.A.F. squadrons, and it is likely that the crews will be trained to operate from Royal Navy carriers under the Simonstown Agreement. In addition to twenty complete aircraft, the equivalent of four aircraft is being supplied in the form of components, and late in 1964 negotiations for a further sixteen aircraft were taking place.

BUCCANEER S.MK.1 SPECIFICATION

Power Plants: *Two Bristol Siddeley Gyron Junior 101 turbojets each rated at 7,100 lb.s.t.*
Armament: *Various conventional or nuclear stores mounted on rotary door of internal weapons bay, and underwing pylons for four 1,000-lb., 750-lb., or 500-lb. general-purpose bombs, four Martin AGM-12B Bullpup ASMs, or four 2-in. or 3-in. rocket pods.*
Performance: (*Note: The following figures are quoted from "Aviation Week" and have not been officially corroborated) Max. speed, 720 m.p.h. at sea level (Mach 0.95); low-level cruise, 645 m.p.h. (Mach 0.85); range cruise, 460 m.p.h.; initial climb rate (at 27,000 lb.), 14,000 ft./min., (at 45,000 lb.), 7,700 ft./min.; ferry range, 3,850 mls.*
Weights: *Normal loaded, 38,500 lb.; max. loaded, 46,000 lb.*
Dimensions: *Span, 42 ft. 4 in.; length, 63 ft. 5 in.; height, 16 ft. 6 in.; wing area, 500 sq. ft.*

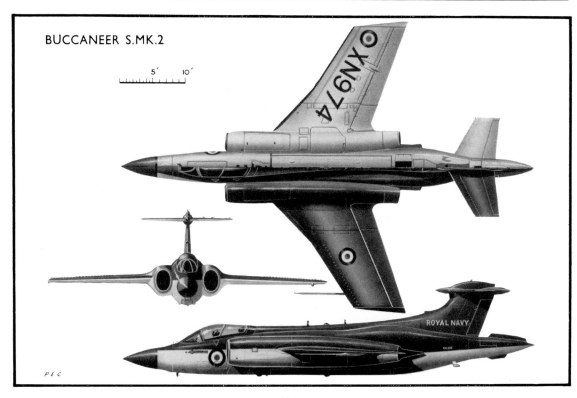

BUCCANEER S.MK.2

HAWKER SIDDELEY (FOLLAND) GNAT

Currently being manufactured under licence in India and serving with the Indian Air Force and Finnish Air Force, the Gnat single-seat lightweight fighter was designed by the former Folland Aircraft concern and, as the Fo.141, was evolved from experience gained with the Fo.139 Midge powered by a 1640 lbs.t.,. Viper 101 turbojet.

The prototype Gnat, powered by a 3,285 lb.s.t. Orpheus B.Or.1, flew for the first time on July 18, 1955, prior to which, in March 1955, the British Ministry of Supply had announced its intention to acquire six aircraft for trials purposes. This contract was placed in August 1955, and the first of the six aircraft (XK724) flew on May 26, 1956, this being employed for gun-firing trials with two 30-mm. Aden cannon. The second and third aircraft (XK739 and XK740) were used for performance and engine development purposes, the latter having a 4,520 lb.s.t. Orpheus B.Or.2, the fourth (XK741) was test flown with the full range of underwing stores, and the fifth (XK767) was used primarily to develop a "flying" tail.

In the meantime, the Indian government had begun to evince interest in the Gnat and, on September 15, 1956, concluded an agreement for the licence manufacture of the fighter in India by Hindustan Aircraft Limited. The agreement included the supply of twenty-five complete aircraft and fifteen sets of components for assembly in India, and the sixth Gnat on the M.o.S. contract was diverted to the Indian contract. The Gnat was cleared by the Indian Air Force for squadron service in mid-1959, the first fighters of this type to be manufactured completely by Hindustan Aircraft (now Hindustan Aeronautics) being delivered in 1962, and some sixty of the order for approximately 100 machines having reportedly been delivered by the end of 1964 when four I.A.F. squadrons were operating this type.

The second foreign customer for the Gnat was the Finnish Air Force which placed an order for twelve aircraft in November 1956, two of these being reconnaissance-fighters each having three 70-mm. Vinten cameras in a modified nose. The first two Gnats were delivered to Finland on July 30, 1958, and the type currently equips HLeLv 21 at Jyväskylä. Two other single-seat Gnats were acquired for evaluation purposes by the Yugoslav Air Force.

GNAT T.MK.1: The tandem two-seat advanced training Fo.144 evolved from the Gnat lightweight fighter aroused interest on the part of the R.A.F. in 1957, and this crystallized in 1958 with a pre-production order for fourteen machines, the first of which flew on August 31, 1959. Successive production orders called for a further ninety-one machines, and the pre-production aircraft entered R.A.F. service in February 1962 as the Gnat T.Mk.1.

Apart from having tandem seats with full dual control the Gnat T.Mk.1 differs from the single-seat model in having a 40 per cent increase in wing area, outboard ailerons, conventional flaps, larger vertical tail surfaces, and a 4,230 lb.s.t. Orpheus 101 turbojet. The Gnat T.Mk.1 carries no built-in armament, and although intended primarily for the advanced training rôle, can carry external stores to enable it to fulfil operational tasks. With a normal loaded weight of 8,039 lb., the Gnat T.Mk.1 attains a maximum speed of 636 m.p.h. at 31,000 ft. (Mach 0.95), has an initial climb rate of 7,620 ft./min., and, with two 59 Imp. gal. slipper tanks, has a maximum range of 1,151 mls.

(Below) A Gnat fighter of the Finnish Air Force's 21st Squadron at Jyväskylä, and (above right) one of the two reconnaissance Gnats with three 70-mm. Vinten cameras in a modified nose.

A Gnat T.Mk.1 tandem two-seat trainer (XM706) from the Central Flying School, Little Rissington. Production of the Gnat trainer was being phased out late in 1964.

GNAT SPECIFICATION

Power Plant: *One Bristol Siddeley Orpheus 701 turbojet rated at 4,700 lb.s.t.*

Armament: *Two 30-mm. Aden cannon with 115 r.p.g. plus two 500-lb. bombs or twelve 3-in. rockets.*

Performance: *Max. speed, 695 m.p.h. at 20,000 ft., 647 m.p.h. at 36,000 ft. (Mach 0.98); max. climb rate,*

20,000 *ft./min.; time to 45,000 ft., 5.25 min.; service ceiling, 50,000 ft.; tactical radius (with two 66 Imp. gal. drop tanks), 500 mls. at 400 m.p.h.; endurance (clean), 1.25 hr., max., 2.5 hr.*
Weights: *Loaded (clean), 6,650 lb.; max., 8,885 lb.*
Dimensions: *Span, 22 ft. 2 in.; length, 29 ft. 9 in.; height, 8 ft. 10 in.; wing area, 136.6 sq. ft.*

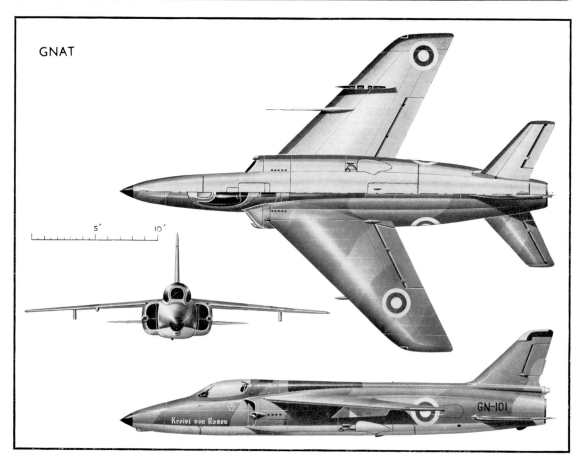

GNAT

HAWKER SIDDELEY (D.H.) SEA VIXEN

The Royal Navy's standard shipboard two-seat all-weather fighter, the Sea Vixen was the first British aircraft to be designed as an integrated weapon system, the first to attain operational status with guided missiles, and the first to have all gun armament deleted. In its initial production F.A.W.Mk.1 version it is currently serving with three Fleet Air Arm squadrons afloat, Nos. 890, 892, and 893, and with No. 766B Squadron for all-weather training.

Design of the Sea Vixen was initiated in 1946 to meet the requirements of specification N.40/46 which called for an advanced carrier-borne all-weather fighter and, in "de-navalised" form, the contemporary specification F.44/46 for a generally similar land-based aircraft. A succession of specification changes followed, the naval requirement eventually being re-issued as N.14/49 and the R.A.F. specification as F.4/48, and in 1949 two prototypes of the land-based version were ordered to meet the requirements of the latter. At this time, the fighter was designated D.H.110, and the first prototype (WG236), powered by two 7,300 lb.s.t. Rolls-Royce Avon engines, flew for the first time on September 26, 1951. The second prototype (WG240) flew on July 25, 1952, but a few weeks later, the first prototype was lost as a result of an unpredicted combination of roll rate and high acceleration at low altitude, and the second did not resume the flight test programme until June 1953, by which time the R.A.F. had selected the competitive Javelin for the all-weather intercept rôle.

In June 1954, by which time Naval interest in the design had been reinstated, the surviving prototype embarked upon a new series of trials with a slab-type tail, and work was progressing on a further prototype (XF828) which was "semi-navalised" in that it was fitted with catapult and arrester hooks but lacked wing folding or military equipment. Having more powerful "second generation" Avon engines, this aircraft flew for the first time on June 20, 1955, six months after an initial production order had been placed. The first production aircraft and, incidentally, the first fully-navalised machine (XJ474), flew on March 20, 1957, featuring upward-folding outer wing panels and a hinged nose radome, and receiving the designation Sea Vixen F.A.W.Mk.1. The first ten production aircraft (XJ474–483) were allocated to development flying, service introduction began in November 1958 with the formation of an Intensive Flying Trials Unit,

No. 700Y Flight, and the first Sea Vixen squadron, No. 892, was commissioned on July 2, 1959.

The Sea Vixen F.A.W.Mk.1's only built-in armament comprises two retractable fuselage packs each housing fourteen 2-in. unguided rockets, but four of the six underwing pylons (the outboard pylons normally carrying two 150 Imp. gal. fuel tanks) can carry a wide variety of weapons ranging from Fire-

(Above) The 81st production Sea Vixen F.A.W.Mk.1 (XN649), and (below) the Microcell rocket batteries extended.

(Below) The first Sea Vixen F.A.W.Mk.2 (XN684), the ninety-second production aircraft, has served as a trials machine.

(Above and foot of opposite page) The Sea Vixen F.A.W.Mk.2 entered service in 1963 with No. 899 Squadron and carries a quartette of Red Top AAMs as alternatives to the Firestreak carried by the F.A.W.Mk.1.

streak infra-red homing AAMs or Bullpup-A ASMs to 500-lb. bombs or rocket packs. Considerable internal fuel tankage is provided within the wings and between the intake ducts, and provision for flight refuelling is standard, a probe being mounted in the port wing. The two crew members are seated side-by-side in Martin-Baker 4DS ejector seats, that of the navigator being situated on a lower level than that of the pilot, whose canopy is therefore offset to port.

Production of the F.A.W.Mk.1 version of the Sea Vixen, which was completed in 1963, totalled some one hundred machines, and it is to be expected that these will be progressively replaced in first-line squadrons by the later F.A.W.Mk.2 version.

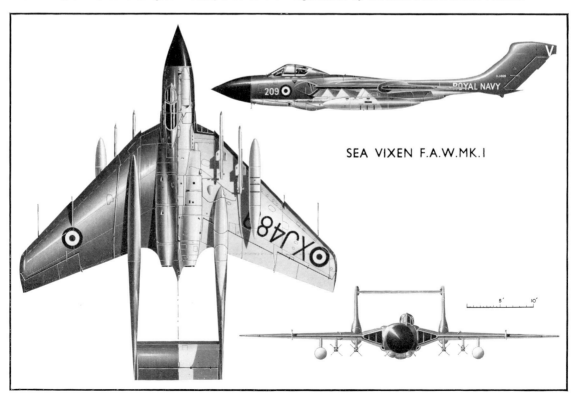

SEA VIXEN F.A.W.MK.1

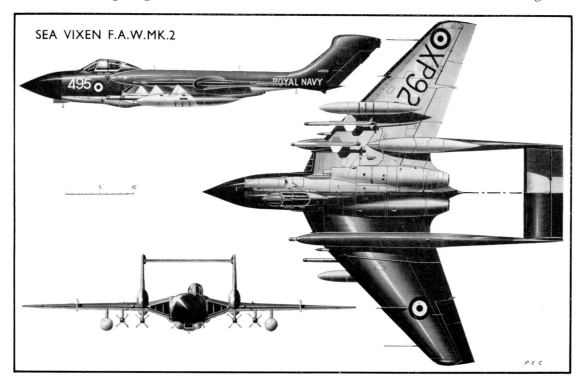

SEA VIXEN F.A.W.MK.2

SEA VIXEN F.A.W.MK.2: Although the F.A.W.Mk.2 version of the Sea Vixen currently entering Fleet Air Arm service is basically similar to the F.A.W.Mk.1, and possesses a similar overall performance, its equipment provides it with a far more sophisticated interception potential, particularly in respect of collision-course tactics, through the installation of Red Top missiles as alternatives to the original Firestreaks.

The ninety-second Sea Vixen F.A.W.Mk.1 (XN684) was modified on the production line late in 1962 to serve as a prototype for the F.A.W.Mk.2, this differing from its predecessors chiefly in having tail booms of deeper section which were carried over and projected well forward of the wing. It may be presumed that the enlarged and extended booms house additional fuel tankage. The first production Sea Vixen F.A.W.Mk.2 (XP919) was delivered in 1963, and the type entered service with No. 899 Squadron at Yeovilton early in 1964. The F.A.W.Mk.2 has the same internally-mounted rocket packs as the F.A.W.Mk.1 and can carry the same variety of external stores as alternatives to the quartette of Red Top AAMs.

SEA VIXEN F.A.W.MK.1 SPECIFICATION

Power Plants: *Two Rolls-Royce Avon 208 turbojets each rated at 10,000 lb.s.t.*
Armament: *Two retractable rocket packs each housing fourteen unguided 2-in. rockets and four Firestreak infra-red homing AAMs, two Firestreaks and two packs of twenty-four 2-in. rockets, four 500-lb. bombs and two clusters of six 3-in. HVARs, four clusters of six 3-in. HVARs, four packs of twenty-four 2-in. rockets. Two Martin AGM-12B Bullpup-A ASMs or two 1,000-lb. bombs may be mounted on the outboard pylons in place of the 150 Imp. gal. fuel tanks.*
Performance: *Approx. max. speed, 645 m.p.h. at 10,000 ft. (Mach 0.92), 610 m.p.h. at 40,000 ft.; time to 40,000 ft., 6–7 min.; service ceiling, 48,000 ft.*
Weights: *Approx. loaded, 35,000 lb.*
Dimensions: *Span, 50 ft. 0 in.; length, 55 ft. 7 in.; height, 10 ft. 9 in.; wing area, 648 sq. ft.*

HAWKER SIDDELEY (AVRO) VULCAN

Representing, together with the Victor B.Mk.2, the ultimate in transonic medium bomber design, the Vulcan B.Mk.2 currently equips No. 1 Group of R.A.F. Bomber Command, including Nos. 9, 12, 27, 35, 50, 83 and 617 Squadrons, and shares with its Handley Page contemporary the task of providing Britain's nuclear deterrent.

Development of the Vulcan was initiated in 1947 with the issue of specification B.35/46 which called for a strategic bomber offering twice the speed and ceiling of the then current piston-engined Lincoln, combined with greater range and weapon-carrying capacity. A series of design studies were undertaken by A. V. Roe and Company, later to become the Avro Whitworth Division of the Hawker Siddeley Group, under the generic designation Type 698, and in January 1948 a contract was awarded for two prototypes, the first of which (VX770) flew on August 30, 1952 with four 6,500 lb.s.t. Rolls-Royce Avon R.A.3 turbojets, the more powerful Bristol B.E.10 (which was later to be named Olympus) not then being available for installation. A year later, the Avons were replaced by 7,500 lb.s.t. Sapphire A.S.Sa.6 engines which were, in turn, destined to be supplanted by 9,500 lb.s.t. Olympus 100 series engines with which the second prototype (VX777) flew for the first time on September 3, 1953.

VULCAN B.MK.1A: A production contract for the Type 698 was awarded in June 1952, and as the Vulcan B.Mk.1, the first production aircraft (XA889) flew on February 4, 1955. This aircraft had a similar

wing to that of the prototypes, featuring an unbroken sweep angle of 52° on the leading edge, but in the meantime it had been discovered that application of *g* at high altitudes could generate minor buffeting which posed a fatigue problem in the outer wings. As this buffet regime was uncomfortably near the performance boundary anticipated for later production Vulcan B.Mk.1s, it was found necessary to effect some wing redesign. Thus, on October 5, 1955, the second prototype flew with a modified wing on which the leading edge sweep angle was reduced by 10° at half-span and increased further outboard. This increased the incidence of the buffet threshold by some twenty per cent. Associated with the extension in chord was a distinct droop on the leading edge and a series of vortex generators to re-energize the boundary layer. Relatively few Vulcan B.Mk.1s had been completed with the original wing, and these were modified retrospectively.

The first production Vulcan B.Mk.1 completed preliminary acceptance trials in the spring of 1956, and deliveries to No. 230 Operational Conversion Unit began in the following August, the first squadron to be formed on the type being No. 83 which began conversion in May 1957. Other units to receive the B.Mk.1 were Nos. 50 and 617 Squadrons, both of which subsequently re-equipped with the more advanced B.Mk.2 version of the Vulcan, and Nos. 44 and 101 Squadrons, and planned re-equipment of No. 1 Group units with this type was completed by the beginning of 1960.

The B.Mk.1 was successively fitted with 11,000 lb.s.t. Olympus 101, 12,000 lb.s.t. Olympus 102 and 13,000 lb.s.t. Olympus 104 engines, and carried the standard V-bomber crew complement of five members. The internal weapons bay could accommodate free-falling nuclear weapons or, for "limited war" purposes, a maximum of twenty-one 1,000-lb. general-purpose bombs. Cruise performance included a speed of 607 m.p.h. at 50,000 ft. (Mach 0.92), maximum speed being of the order of 625 m.p.h. (Mach 0.95) at the same altitude, service ceiling exceeding 55,000 ft., and high-altitude tactical radius being about 1,700 miles. The Vulcan B.Mk.1s were progressively brought up to

Vulcan B. Mk. 2s XM649 (above, left) and XM645 (below) in the new high-gloss, low-level camouflage scheme of grey and green upper surfaces with anti-radiation white underneath, signifying the under-the-radar concept.

(*Above*) *A Vulcan B.Mk.2 (XM572) with the Blue Steel stand-off weapon. Units include Nos. 9, 12, 35, 50, 83 and 617 Sqdns.*

B.Mk.1A standards by the up-dating of internal equipment and the provision of electronic counter-measures equipment in the extreme rear fuselage, but apart from aircraft employed for special purposes, this first production version of the Vulcan had been largely phased out of first line operational service in favour of the B.Mk.2 variant by the end of 1964.

VULCAN B.MK.2: Before the service introduction of the Vulcan B.Mk.1 substantial increases in power were being offered by new versions of the Olympus engine, and to take advantage of the more powerful turbojets it was decided to reduce substantially the thickness/chord ratio over the outer portions of the Vulcan's wing and simultaneously increase both span and area. The new wing was fitted to the second prototype Vulcan (VX777) which flew in its new form on August 31, 1957. It was immediately obvious that the new wing offered a substantial improvement in operational altitude when combined with the more powerful Olympus turbojets, and permitted the pulling of appreciably higher *g*. The decision was therefore taken to introduce this innovation at an early stage on the Vulcan production line, the B.Mk.1 thus becoming an interim model pending the introduction of the B.Mk.2 with the new wing and more powerful engines, these changes being made on the forty-sixth and subsequent aircraft.

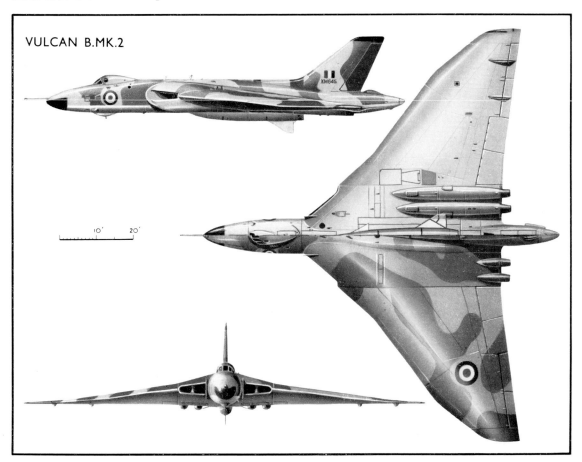

VULCAN B.MK.2

The first Vulcan B.Mk.2 (XH533) flew on August 19, 1958 with 17,000 lb.s.t. Olympus 201 engines, the new wing increasing span and gross area from 99 ft. 0 in. and 3,554 sq. ft. to 111 ft. 0 in. and 3,964 sq. ft. respectively, increasing operational altitude by some 5,000 ft. over that of the initial production model. Deliveries of the B.Mk.2 to R.A.F. Bomber Command began on July 1, 1960, the first unit to re-equip being No. 83 Squadron followed by No. 617 Squadron, the latter being the first unit to receive the Avro Blue Steel Mk.1 stand-off missile which, with a range of about 200 mls. and a speed of the order of Mach 1.6, can be launched at both high and low level, and is now a standard weapon for V-bomber squadrons. Mounted semi-externally, the Blue Steel reduces the performance of the Vulcan B.Mk.2 by only two per cent.

One Vulcan B.Mk.2 (XH557) employed in the engine development rôle was flown on May 19, 1961 with 20,000 lb.s.t. Olympus 301 turbojets in the outboard engine bays, and this more powerful engine has since been adopted as standard, all B.Mk.2s being pro-gressively re-engined. During 1964 the mission capability of the Vulcan B.Mk.2, like that of the Victor B.Mk.2, was being extended to include low-level penetration.

VULCAN B.MK.2 SPECIFICATION

Power Plants: *Four Bristol Siddeley Olympus* 301 *turbojets each rated at 20,000 lb.s.t.*
Armament: *One Avro Blue Steel Mk.1 rocket-driven supersonic stand-off missile or twenty-one 1,000-lb. general-purpose bombs.*
Performance: *Approx. max. speed, 640–645 m.p.h. at 40,000 ft. (Mach 0.97–0.98); maximum cruise, 627 m.p.h. at 55,000 ft. (Mach 0.95), 530 m.p.h. at sea level (Mach 0.75); low-altitude tactical radius (unrefuelled), 1,700 mls.; high-altitude tactical radius (unrefuelled), 2,300 mls.; approx. unrefuelled range, 4,750 mls.; service ceiling, 65,000 (plus) ft.*
Weights: *Loaded, 180,000–200,000 lb.*
Dimensions: *Span, 111 ft. 0 in.; length, 99 ft. 11 in.; height, 27 ft. 2 in.; wing area, 3,964 sq. ft.*

VICKERS SUPERMARINE SCIMITAR

Now largely supplanted in the strike rôle by the Buccaneer S.Mk.1, the Scimitar F.Mk.1 currently equips only one operational Fleet Air Arm squadron, No. 803, which embarked aboard H.M.S. *Ark Royal* during 1964. The Scimitar single-seat day fighter and strike aircraft has been in service with the Royal Navy since June 1958 when No. 803 Squadron was commissioned, other units subsequently operating this type including Nos. 800, 804 and 807 Squadrons.

The Scimitar was the end-product of a complex evolutionary process, and its forebears can be traced back to 1945 when the Admiralty began to evince interest in an undercarriageless shipboard fighter to be catapulted from a carrier and landed on a flexible flight deck. From the design proposals submitted to meet this requirement, a series of developments finally culminated in the Type 544, as the Scimitar was originally known. Prototypes to specification N.113D were ordered early in 1951 with a production contract to N.113P following in December 1952.

The first Type 544 prototype (WT854) was flown on January 20, 1956, the second (WT859), which had provision for flap blowing although the Avon 200 series engines did not at that time have the appropriate

The Scimitar F.Mk.1 strike fighter is now nearing the end of its operational career, and is expected to be phased out of first line service during the course of 1965.

SCIMITAR F.MK.1 SPECIFICATION

Power Plants: *Two Rolls-Royce Avon 202 turbojets each rated at 11,250 lb.s.t.*
Armament: *Four 30-mm. Aden cannon and various external loads on four underwing pylons with a maximum load of 2,000 lb. per pylon. Typical external loads include four 1,000-lb. bombs, twenty-four 3-in. HVARs, forty-eight 2-in. rockets in four pods, or four Martin AGM-12B Bullpup-A ASMs.*
Performance: *Approx. max. speed, 635 m.p.h. at 36,000 ft. (Mach 0.95), 648 m.p.h. at sea level (Mach 0.9); unrefuelled tactical radius (clean), 250–300 mls.; ferry range, 1,300–1,500 mls.; service ceiling, 50,000 ft.*
Weights: *Normal loaded, 33,000–35,000 lb.; max., 40,000 lb.*
Dimensions: *Span, 37 ft. 2 in.; length, 55 ft. 4 in.; height, 15 ft. 3 in.*

that intercept effectiveness would be improved by removing the Aden cannon and replacing them with Sidewinder infra-red AAMs. The decision to make this modification was taken in principle following assessment of practice interceptions which revealed that in war conditions the cannon armament would have proved relatively ineffective. In the event, the relatively short remaining operational life of the Scimitar motivated against this change, and the cannon armament has been retained. To supplement the nine internal fuel cells the underwing pylons may carry four 150 or 200 Imp. gal. drop tanks, or two 150 and two 250 Imp. gal. tanks, endowing the Scimitar with an excellent ferry range, and an interchangeable camera nose is available.

(Below) A Scimitar F.Mk.1 of No. 803 Squadron, the last operational unit equipped with this strike fighter.

bleed system, and third (WW134) with a fully operational blown flap system following before the end of the year. The first production Scimitar F.Mk.1 flew on January 11, 1957, and the type began to supplant the Sea Hawk in Royal Navy service during the following year. The original production contracts called for one hundred aircraft, but these were eventually cut back to seventy-six machines, the last of which was delivered in September 1960, by which time four squadrons had been formed on the Scimitar.

Basically the Scimitar is a strike aircraft rather than a high-level interceptor, and in 1960 it was proposed

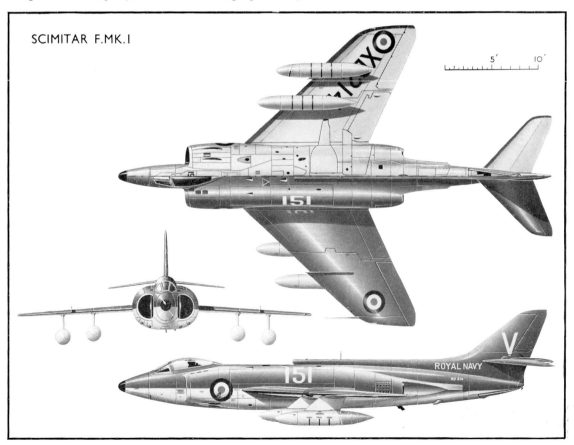

SCIMITAR F.MK.I

VICKERS VALIANT

The first of R.A.F. Bomber Command's V-bombers, the Valiant has now been entirely phased out of Britain's deterrent force but still equips a small tactical force assigned to NATO, a strategic photographic reconnaissance force, and a tanker force which is available to both Bomber and Fighter Commands. Others are currently held in storage.

Less radical than the Victor and Vulcan, the Valiant was also originally tendered to meet the requirements of specification B.35/46 as the Type 660. The Vickers proposal did not fulfil the specification in all respects, but it evinced considerable promise and appeared simpler and quicker to produce than the more advanced designs which were to result in the Victor and Vulcan and, in 1948, a less stringent specification, B.9/48, was drawn up around the Type 660 which, by this time, was considered as an interim strategic bomber. Two prototypes were ordered, the first of which (WB210) flew on May 18, 1951 with four 6,500 lb.s.t. Avon RA.3 turbojets. The second prototype (WB215) followed on April 11, 1952, differing from the first aircraft primarily in having 7,500 lb.s.t. Avon RA.7s fed via enlarged, redesigned intakes. An initial production order had been placed in April 1951 calling for five pre-production and twenty production aircraft, and the first of the five pre-production Valiant B.Mk.1s (WP199–203) flew on December 21, 1953 with Avon 200 series engines.

Deliveries to R.A.F. Bomber Command began in

1954, the first production aircraft being issued to No. 230 Operational Conversion Unit, and the first operational unit, No. 138 Squadron, began to re-equip early in 1955. Valiants were also issued to Nos. 7, 49, 90, 148, 207, 214 and 543 Squadrons, and to No. 199 Squadron for special duties. Apart from the initial production B.Mk.1, three versions of the Valiant were produced, the first of these being the B.(P.R.) Mk.1 equipped for the dual reconnaissance bombing rôle, eleven of these being built at intervals along the B.Mk.1 production line. The B.(P.R.) K.Mk.1 was another multi-rôle version which added the flight-refuelling tanker rôle to its capabilities, a hose-reel pack being inserted in the bomb-bay. Fourteen of these were interspersed on the B.Mk.1 production line before the final variant, the B.K.Mk.1, reached the line. The Valiant B.K.Mk.1 was essentially similar to the basic B.Mk.1 but featured a refuelling probe in the nose and had provision for a hose-reel pack in the bomb-bay. Forty-eight Valiants of this type were produced, the last flying on August 27, 1957, bringing total pro-

VALIANT B.MK.1 SPECIFICATION

Power Plants: *Four Rolls-Royce Avon 204 or 205 turbojets each rated at 10,050 lb.s.t.*
Armament: *Max. internal load comprises twenty-one 1,000-lb. general-purpose bombs, or various combinations of nuclear or high-explosive free-falling weapons.*
Performance: *Max. speed, 554 m.p.h. at 36,000 ft. (Mach 0.84), 414 m.p.h. at sea level; max. cruise, 540 m.p.h. at 40,000 ft. (Mach 0.82); econ. cruise, 495 m.p.h. at 46,000 ft. (Mach 0.75); initial climb (at 140,000 lb.), 4,000 ft./min.; service ceiling, 54,000 ft.; range (clean with 10,000-lb. bomb load half way), 3,450 mls., (with two 1,645 Imp. gal. underwing tanks), 4,500 mls.*
Weights: *Empty, 75,880 lb.; loaded (10,000-lb. bomb load), 138,000 lb.; max. overload, 175,000 lb.*
Dimensions: *Span, 114 ft. 4 in.; length, 108 ft. 3 in.; height, 32 ft. 2 in.; wing area, 2,362 sq. ft.*

(Above) The 23rd production Valiant, a B.(P.R.)K.Mk.1 (WP221), and (below) B.K.Mk.1 (XD870) with the Mk.16 hose drum refuelling unit in action. R.A.F. Bomber Command has two Valiant tanker units, Nos. 90 and 214 Squadrons.

The 84th production Valiant, a B.K.Mk.1 (XD829), sporting the new low-level camouflage. A small force of Valiants is assigned to the Supreme Allied Commander Europe (SACEUR) for tactical operations in the defence of the Continent.

duction to 104 machines plus three prototypes, the third prototype being the sole B.Mk.2 designed for high-speed low-level operations.

Late in 1964 some six squadrons of Valiants remained in R.A.F. service, including Nos. 49, 148, 207 and 214 Squadrons forming a tactical wing which, based at Marham, is assigned to SACEUR (Supreme Allied Commander Europe) for the defence of the Continent, No. 543 Squadron employed in the photo-reconnaissance rôle, and No. 90 serving as a tanker unit. The Valiant tankers frequently support fighter squadrons in overseas deployments, in addition to providing service for the V-force bombers.

The Valiant B.Mk.2 (WJ954), which flew for the first time on September 4, 1953, featured a lengthened fuselage, a reinforced wing, and trailing-edge nacelles to accommodate four-wheel bogie-type main undercarriage members. During its trials, the Valiant B.Mk.2 attained 552 m.p.h. at sea level compared with 414 m.p.h. for the standard B.Mk.1.

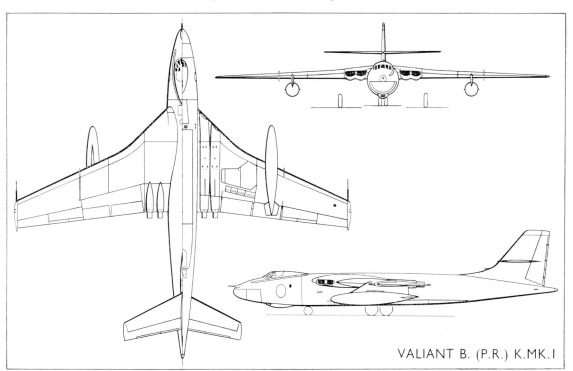

VALIANT B. (P.R.) K.MK.I

BOEING B-47 STRATOJET

Possessing the distinction of having been the first swept-wing jet bomber to attain quantity production, and built in larger numbers than any post-war western strategic aircraft, the B-47 Stratojet is in process of being phased out of the active U.S.A.F. inventory, and is scheduled to have disappeared from the operational strength of the Strategic Air Command by 1966, although in September 1964 more than five hundred Stratojets of all types remained in U.S.A.F. service, and equipped nine S.A.C. wings.

The Stratojet, which provided the backbone of the Strategic Air Command throughout the 'fifties, was exceptionally bold in concept and, like the contemporary F-86 Sabre interceptor, owed much to German wartime research into wing sweepback. Boeing initiated design work on a medium jet bomber in the autumn of 1943, and various design studies were prepared before, with the availability of German research data two years later, the project took final form as the Model 450 on which a thin, flexible wing of high aspect ratio, swept at an angle of 35°, carried six turbojets in underwing pods. To aid the flexible wing with relieving moments, the pods were distributed along the wing span—four paired in two nacelles at approximately one-third span and two in individual nacelles near to the tips. As neither wing nor engine pods offered stowage space for the main undercarriage members, a tandem type landing gear was adopted, the two twin-wheel units retracting fore and aft of the weapons bay into the large, oval-section fuselage. This undercarriage arrangement was to offer the disadvantage that landing speed had to be calculated on the bomber's all-up weight to within 2 m.p.h., the pilot ensuring that both pairs of wheels touched the runway simultaneously. Small outrigger wheels retracted into the inboard jet pods to provide lateral stability although, under normal circumstances, these were not intended to come into contact with the ground.

Two prototypes of the bomber were ordered by the U.S.A.F. in May 1946, the designation XB-47 being applied, and the first of these (46-065) was flown on December 17, 1947 with six 3,750 lb.s.t. Allison J35-A-2 turbojets. A little more than a year later, on February 8, 1949, this aircraft was to make a trans-continental flight covering a distance of 2,289 mls. in 3 hr. 46 min.—an average speed of 607.8 m.p.h. Similarly powered, the second XB-47 (46-066) flew in July 1948, and was later re-engined with 5,000 lb.s.t. J47-GE-3 engines, flying for the first time with the new turbojets on October 7, 1949. By that time an initial contract had been awarded for ten production aircraft with 5,200 lb.s.t. J47-GE-11 engines, K-24 (later K-4A) navigational and bombing radar, and an A-2 armament system comprising twin 0.5-in. guns in a radar-directed tail barbette. Designated B-47A, the first of these (49-1900) flew on March 1, 1950, but the cautious attitude of the U.S.A.F., which had been engendered understandably enough by the radical nature of the Stratojet's design, had given place under the stimulus of technical development and international events to undisguised enthusiasm for the bomber's performance potential, and substantial production contracts had been awarded an improved version, the B-47B, the first of these—for eighty-seven aircraft—having been placed in November 1948.

The B-47A Stratojets were employed for engine and airframe development and crew training, and the B-47B embodied numerous structural and equipment changes which were to result in the maximum overload weight of the bomber climbing from the 162,500 lb. of the XB-47 to no less than 202,000 lb. Provision was made for in-flight refuelling and for two 1,250 Imp. gal. auxiliary fuel tanks beneath the wings, the latter raising total fuel capacity to 14,155 Imp. gal., and the first eighty-seven B-47Bs retained the J47-GE-11 engines of the original model, all subsequent B-model Stratojets having J47-GE-23 engines rated at 5,800 lb.s.t. The first production B-47B (49-2642) flew on April 26, 1951, and a total of 406 aircraft was built, twenty-four of these being converted as RB-47Bs with eight cameras and associated equipment in a weapons bay pack, some were converted to weather reconnaissance configuration as WB-47Bs, and fifty-one were converted for crew training as TB-47Bs.

Deliveries of the B-47B to the U.S.A.F. Strategic Air Command began in mid-1951, the 306th (Medium) Bomb Wing being the first unit to receive the type, and in service, the bomber provided the full share of problems that were to be expected of so advanced a

A Boeing B-47E-II Stratojet (52-501). Although scheduled to be phased out by 1966, several hundred remain in service.

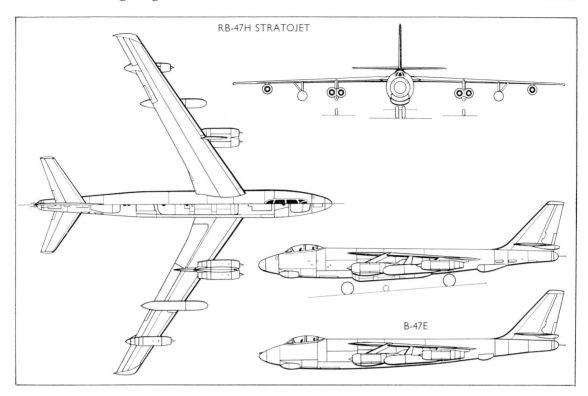

RB-47H STRATOJET

B-47E

warplane. The thin wing of the B-47B flexed as much as 17 ft. at its tip, and while absorbing shocks in turbulence, it also tended to act as an aileron under certain conditions, a loss of lift from one wing and an increase from the other being experienced during yaw with a resultant reduction in stability. A characteristic peculiar to the aircraft during its early service career was aileron reversal, the aileron acting on the flexible wing much as a servo tab acts on an elevator. The deflected aileron caused the trailing edge of the outboard section of the wing to twist in the opposite direction, the wing thus becoming a larger control surface than the aileron, and neutralising its effects at certain speeds and even reversing them at high speeds.

Considerable care had to be taken in limiting and distributing the load during take-off and flight to keep the c.g. within limits, and also to operate within available runway space. Even with a 10,000-ft. runway it was necessary in semi-tropical conditions to restrict the fuel load in order to take-off in safety, and with a 7,000-ft. runway the aircraft was limited to a take-off weight of 154,000 lb. The B-47B had the distinction of introducing a new expression to the bomber pilots' vocabulary—"the coffin corner". This was the altitude at which the airspeeds for low-speed and compressibility stalls coincided. In other words, the altitude at which the aircraft stalled as a result of *either* excessive or insufficient speed, aft stick movement resulting in a slow-speed stall and forward stick movement producing high-speed buffet.

The B-47B was succeeded in production by the B-47E, the first example of which (51-2357) was flown on January 20, 1953, being outwardly indistinguishable from the B-model apart from the new radar-directed General Electric tail barbette housing twin 20-mm. cannon. Built in larger numbers than any other version of the Stratojet, the B-47E was powered by J47-GE-25 or -25A engines each delivering 6,000 lb.s.t. dry and 7,200 lb.s.t. with water injection. Ejection seats were introduced for the crew members, the fixed JATO installation of the B-model was abandoned in favour of a jettisonable nineteen- or thirty-three-rocket pack, and a 16 ft.-braking chute was provided. The maximum overload weight of the B-47E was raised from 202,000 to 220,000 lb., and production continued until February 15, 1957, 1,359 being built, and the Strategic Air Command attaining its peak utilization of the Stratojet in that year when some eighteen hundred were on strength. In addition to the standard B-47E, the S.A.C. received 255 examples of the RB-47E, the first of which (51-5258) flew on July 3, 1953. The RB-47E featured an extended fuselage nose which increased overall length to 112 ft. 8 in., and accommodated a heated and air-conditioned camera compartment. The weapons bay was also occupied by photographic equipment, mounting seven cameras of various types and sizes.

B-47E-II STRATOJET: In 1958 a programme was initiated in which major structural strengthening of the wings of all service Stratojets was undertaken to boost their active life by some three thousand hours and to increase their operational flexibility. Begun in April and completed in December, the programme, which was known as "Project Milk Bottle", covered the modification of eighteen hundred B-47Bs and B-47Es which were subsequently known unofficially as B-47B-IIs and E-IIs, permitting the use of LABS (Low Altitude Bombing System) and other low-

(*Above*) *An RB-47H Stratojet (53-4297) reconnaissance aircraft which carries both optical and non-optical reconnaissance equipment, including Side Looking Aircraft Radar.*

(*Above*) *A WB-47B Stratojet (51-2115) weather reconnaissance aircraft converted from a B-47B bomber, and (below) a B-47E-II (52-352).*

(*Below*) *A B-47E-75-LM-IV (53-1843), a late production example of the final bomber version of the Stratojet.*

(*Below*) *One of the last production RB-47E Stratojet photo-reconnaissance aircraft (53-4262).*

altitude weapons delivery techniques for "under-the-radar" penetration flights. The forward wing longerons were strengthened, doubler plates were added near the wing roots, and the wing/fuselage attachments were modified.

EB-47H STRATOJET: A specialised electronic reconnaissance version of the Stratojet was evolved primarily for monitoring radio and radar transmissions during fringe flights along the borders of Communist countries, and received the designation EB-47H. Thirty-five Stratojets of this type were built for special missions with Strategic Air Command reconnaissance units, some being completed as RB-47H aircraft. Whereas the EB-47H carries five crew members, three of these being electronics operators housed in a pressurized capsule in the weapons bay, the RB-47H has a crew of six and carries both optical and non-optical reconnaissance equipment, including SLAR (Side Looking Aircraft Radar). An aircraft of this type was shot down by Soviet fighters over the Bering Sea on July 1, 1960 during a reconnaissance mission.

One other reconnaissance version of the Stratojet, the RB-47K, is a conversion of the B-47E for both photographic and weather reconnaissance, fifteen conversions of this type being delivered to the U.S.A.F.

B-47E-II STRATOJET SPECIFICATION

Power Plants : *Six General Electric J47-GE-25A turbojets each rated at 6,000 lb.s.t. dry and 7,200 lb.s.t. with water injection.*
Armament : *Two 20-mm. M-24A1 cannon with 350 r.p.g. in radar-directed tail barbette, and up to 20,000 lb. of bombs for short-range missions. Normal bomb load (typical): Ten 1,000-lb. general-purpose bombs.*
Performance : *Max. speed, 606 m.p.h. at 16,300 ft. (Mach 0.84), 557 m.p.h. at 38,550 ft. (Mach 0.842); max. cruise, 495 m.p.h. at 38,550 ft. (Mach 0.75); initial climb (at 160,000 lb.), 4,660 ft./min., (at 206,700 lb.), 2,300 ft./min.; service ceiling, 40,500 ft.; range (with 10,000-lb. bomb load), 4,000 mls.*
Weights : *Empty, 80,756 lb.; loaded, 206,700 lb.; max. overload, 220,000 lb.*
Dimensions : *Span, 116 ft. 0 in.; length, 109 ft. 10 in.; height, 27 ft. 11 in.; wing area, 1,428 sq. ft.*

BOEING B-52 STRATOFORTRESS

Currently equipping fourteen Heavy Bomb Wings of the Strategic Air Command, the B-52 Stratofortress provides a major part of the U.S.A.F.'s strategic deterrent, and will continue to do so until the late 'sixties, constant refinement of equipment and tactical techniques having maintained the aircraft as a valuable retaliatory weapon.

Following the basic concept of the smaller Stratojet, the Stratofortress heavy bomber resulted from a specification issued by the U.S.A.F. in January 1946 for an intercontinental bomber. The Boeing project envisaged a 360,000-lb. aeroplane powered by six 5,500 e.s.h.p. Wright T35 turboprops mounted on 20° swept wings, and two prototypes were ordered in July 1948 under the designation XB-52. Two months later, however, the Boeing design team concluded that a pure jet configuration offered greater potentialities, and redesign of the bomber began, eight turbojets being suspended in pods from a 35° swept wing. In this form, the first prototype (49-230) was flown on October 2, 1952, being, in fact, preceded into the air by the second prototype (49-231) which, redesignated YB-52, had flown on April 15, 1952. Each powered by eight YJ57-P-1 turbojets rated at 8,700 lb.s.t., these aircraft followed the formula of the Stratojet, with thin, flexible wings, fuselage-mounted main undercarriage members, lateral outriggers, and tandem seating for the crew members.

The first production order for the Stratofortress, placed in February 1951, called for thirteen aircraft, the first three of which were completed as B-52As and differed from the prototypes in having J57-P-9W turbojets, a new cockpit accommodating the pilot and co-pilot side-by-side, a cross-wind landing gear, provision for flight refuelling and 833 Imp. gal. underwing auxiliary tanks, the latter increasing total internal fuel capacity to 29,145 Imp. gal. The first B-52A (52-001), which eventually flew at gross weights up to 415,000 lb., was flown on August 5, 1954, and the three Stratofortresses of this model were followed by fifty B-52Bs, the first seventeen of which were originally designated RB-52Bs, the change of designation signifying reconnaissance capability, provision being made for the installation of a photographic or electronic reconnaissance pod with two operators in the weapons bay. In the event, these aircraft reverted to plain B-52Bs. The first B-52B (52-004) flew on January 25, 1955, and five months later, on June 29, 1955, the Stratofortress entered service with the 93rd (Heavy) Bomb Wing.

Powered by J57-P-19W, -29W or -29WA turbojets, the B-52B differed from the A-model primarily in being equipped to operational standards. Six crew members were carried, an MA-2, or BRANE (Bombing Radar Navigation Equipment), replaced the Sperry K system at an early stage, and defensive armament was provided by four 0.5-in. guns in a Bosch Arma MD-9 tail barbette providing fully automatic radar detection and tracking. The B-52C, which first flew on March 9, 1956 (53-399), was essentially similar to the late production B-model, but the size of the auxiliary underwing tanks was substantially increased, each tank accommodating 2,498 Imp. gal. of fuel, and gross weight rose from 420,000 to 450,000 lb. Thirty-five

A B-52G Stratofortress (58-0210) with two AGM-28A Hound Dog stand-off missiles inboard of the engines.

(Above) A B-52F Stratofortress (57-065), and (below) a B-52D (55-093), both featuring the taller vertical tail surfaces standard prior to the development of the G-model.

B-52C Stratofortresses were built, followed by 170 B-52Ds which differed solely in that they lacked provision for the installation of interchangeable reconnaissance packs in the weapons bay.

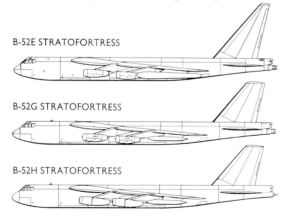

B-52E STRATOFORTRESS

B-52G STRATOFORTRESS

B-52H STRATOFORTRESS

Improvements in the electronics, bombing and navigational systems resulted in a change in designation to B-52E, the first of one hundred examples of which flew on October 3, 1957, and with a switch from the J57-P-29W turbojet which offered 10,900 lb.s.t. dry and 12,500 lb.s.t. with water injection to the J57-P-43W rated at 11,200 lb.s.t. dry and 13,750 lb.s.t. wet, the designation became B-52F. Eighty-eight B-52F Stratofortresses were built for the Strategic Air Command, the first flying on May 6, 1958, and the last being completed in November 1958 to bring Stratofortress production to 448 machines. In the meantime,

a major weight-saving programme had been initiated, the aim being to extend the Stratofortresses' non-refuelled range to increase the Strategic Air Command's targeting capability, the first model that this programme affected being the B-52G.

B-52G STRATOFORTRESS: Although resembling earlier models of the Stratofortress superficially, and retaining the J57-P-43W turbojets of the F-model, a programme of major structural redesign resulted in a major increment in overall performance, including a twenty-five per cent increase in range. Some 10,000 lb. was shaved off the structural weight, but the most important change was to be seen in the wing which had been entirely redesigned, being composed of 80-ft. extruded aluminium panels which, covering two-thirds of the overall span, permitted fuel storage in nearly the entire in-spar area out to the external underwing tanks. The external tanks themselves were reduced in capacity to 583 Imp. gal. to cut drag, and were no longer jettisonable.

Weight-saving measures included the simplification of the fuselage structure, the provision of new vertical tail surfaces of substantially reduced height—overall height being reduced from 48 ft. 3 in. to 40 ft. 8 in.—and broader chord, and the replacement of the ailerons by a system of spoilers for lateral control. Additional weight was saved by moving the gunner forward from the tail to the crew compartment where he monitored his weapons by television, eliminating the need for pressurization, oxygen, communication and other services in the tail area.

The first B-52G (57-6468) was flown on September 26, 1958, and in the following year, when deliveries began to the Strategic Air Command, a major improvement was made in the effectiveness of the aircraft by its adaptation to carry a pair of AGM-28A Hound Dog stand-off missiles. Deliveries of the missile to the U.S.A.F. began on December 21, 1959, and the first unit to operate Hound Dog-equipped B-52G Stratofortresses, the 4135th Strategic Bomb Wing, flew a twenty-two-hour mission in the following April in which 10,800 miles were covered with two Hound Dog missiles underwing, one of these being launched near the end of the mission.

The Hound Dog is carried under each wing of the B-52G on a pylon between the fuselage and inner engine pod, this pylon housing stellar monitoring and launching equipment. The Hound Dog itself carries a four-megaton warhead, possesses a launching weight of 9,600 lb., and cruises at Mach 2.0 over a range exceeding 600 mls., being guided by a self-contained inertial system. Two missiles of this type account for less than half the weight of the total weapons load of the B-52G which can also carry some 20,000 lb. of conventional or thermonuclear free-falling stores in its internal weapons bay, together

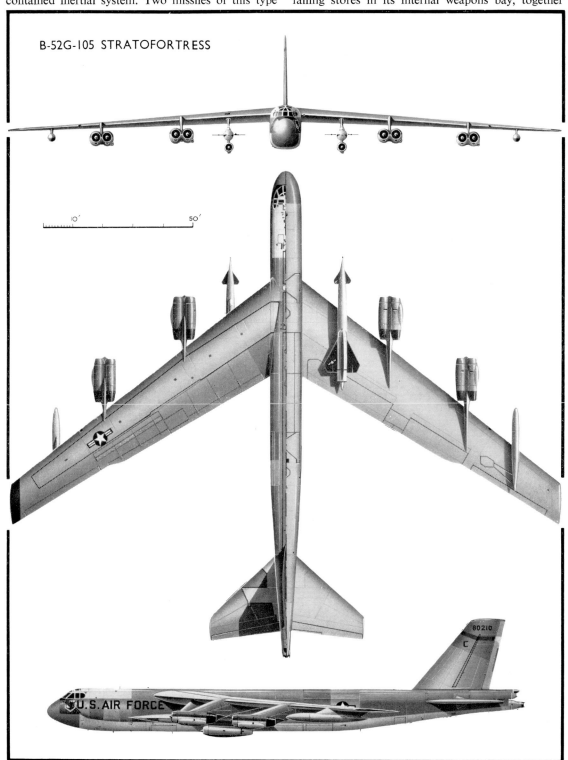

B-52G-105 STRATOFORTRESS

(Above) A Hound Dog-equipped B-52G (58-0210) and (below, left) a close-up view of a Hound Dog installation on a B-52E (56-631).

B-52H STRATOFORTRESS SPECIFICATION

Power Plants: *Eight Pratt and Whitney TF33-P-3 turbo-jets each rated at 17,000 lb.s.t.*
Armament: *(Defensive) One 20-mm. ASG-21 rotary cannon and (offensive) two AGM-28A or -28B Hound Dog supersonic stand-off missiles and up to 20,000 lb. of conventional or thermonuclear free-falling weapons.*
Performance: *Max. speed, 630 m.p.h. at 40,000 ft. (Mach 0.95), 645 m.p.h. at sea level (Mach 0.85); average cruise, 565 m.p.h. at 36,000 ft.; approx. max. unrefuelled range, 12,000 mls.; service ceiling, 55,000 ft.*
Weights: *Approx. max. loaded, 488,000 lb.*
Dimensions: *Span, 185 ft. 0 in.; length, 157 ft. 6¾ in.; height, 40 ft. 8 in.; wing area, 4,000 sq. ft.*

with a number of ADM-20 Quail diversionary missiles. These missiles can be sent off on different paths from the bomber, providing identical reflectivity on the ground radar to divert interception.

One hundred and ninety-three B-52G Strato-fortresses were delivered to the Strategic Air Command, the last being completed on September 23, 1960 when the model was succeeded in production by the B-52H.

B-52H STRATOFORTRESS: One B-52G (57-6471) was re-engined with Pratt and Whitney TF33-P-1 turbofans for flight test purposes in mid-1960, and these engines, offering some twelve per cent improvement in fuel consumption, were adopted for the next and final production model of the Stratofortress, the B-52H. The change to turbofans permitted the elimination of some 10,000 lb. in water injection, and still more weight was saved by replacing the quartette of 0.5-in. machine guns in the tail barbette by a single

20-mm. ASG-21 rotary cannon. Further improvements were made in the bomber's ECM equipment, underwing pods were provided between the engines for chaff-dispensing target penetration aid rockets, and some idea of the unrefuelled range capabilities of the B-52H was provided on January 11–12, 1962 by a 12,519-mile distance-in-a-straight line record flight in 22 hr. 10 min.

The first of 102 B-52H Stratofortresses built for the S.A.C. flew on March 6, 1961, and was delivered to the 379th Strategic Bomb Wing two months later, on May 9th., the last being completed in June 1962, and together with the B-52G, the B-52H equips six Wings. Further extension of the operational life of the Stratofortress was under consideration during 1964 by the introduction of later electronic countermeasures systems and the provision of later stand-off missiles than the Hound Dog currently providing the principal offensive armament.

A B-52G (58-0159) taking-off with Hound Dog missiles, the turbojets of which may be used for supplementary power.

CONVAIR B-58A HUSTLER

When the remarkable B-58A Hustler attained operational status with the three squadrons of the U.S.A.F. Strategic Air Command's 43rd Bombardment Wing in August 1960, it possessed the distinction of being the world's only service strategic bomber capable of attaining dash speeds of the order of Mach 2.0. Today, more than four years later, the Hustler still retains that distinction. Currently equipping the six squadrons of the 43rd and 305th Bomb Wings at Carswell A.F.B. and Bunker Hill A.F.B. respectively, the Hustler was first conceived in 1949 to compete in a U.S.A.F. contest for a manned supersonic bombing system, a development contract being awarded in August 1952.

The initial contract called for thirteen aircraft for test and evaluation purposes, the first of these (55-660) flying on November 11, 1956, followed by the second (55-661) in February 1957, and shortly afterwards an additional seventeen test and pre-production aircraft were ordered. The B-58A Hustler was unique in many respects. It was the first combat aircraft of delta configuration to have podded power plants; it possessed no internal weapons bay, an area rule-conforming external pod containing weaponry, ECM gear, reconnaissance equipment and fuel in varying ratios from almost total fuel to almost wholly weapon and offering the ultimate in mission flexibility, and the airframe embodied substantial quantities of sandwich-type structural panels—aluminium and steel sheet being bonded to a metal honeycomb core—and was developed side-by-side with its power plants to form one aerodynamic and thermodynamic entity.

The first eleven B-58A Hustlers had J79-GE-1 turbojets but the twelfth aircraft (55-671) had the developed J79-GE-5A turbojets intended for the production model, and after extensive manufacturers' trials, the majority of the pre-production and development B-58As were passed to the Air Research and Development Command's B-58 Test Force which comprised the 6592nd Test Squadron concerned primarily with the evaluation of the system, and the 3958th Operational Evaluation and Training Squadron which, representing the Strategic Air Command, was responsible for planning combat crew training, preparing operational procedures and evolving maintenance techniques. With the delivery of the first B-58As by the ARDC to the 65th Combat Crew Training Squadron, a component of the 43rd Bomb Wing, the B-58 Test Force was dissolved, and by March 15, 1960, when the 43rd was activated as the first B-58A Hustler Wing, eighty-six production aircraft had been ordered. The 305th Bomb Wing also re-equipped with the B-58A in 1961.

The B-58A carries three crew members in tandem,

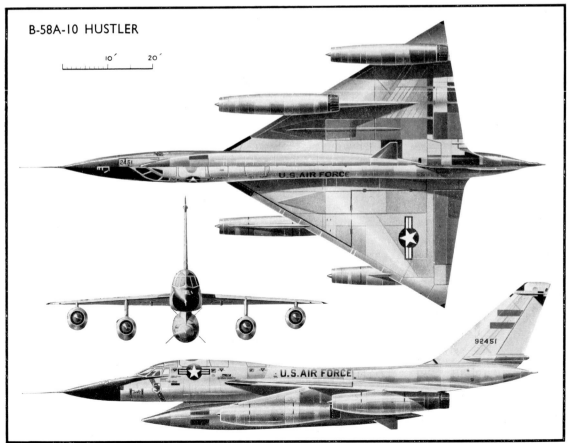

B-58A-10 HUSTLER

The B-58A Hustler currently equips the U.S.A.F.'s 43rd and 305th Bomb Wings at Carswell and Bunker Hill.

individual capsulated cockpits which permit escape at any speed or altitude, and is the first operational aircraft so equipped. The AN/ASQ-42V bombing-navigation system utilises the advantages of Doppler, celestial and inertial navigation, and supplies aircraft position, heading, ground speed and track, true airspeed and wind components, aircraft attitude, altitude, steering data, distance to target, and weapons release information. The rearmost crew member, the defence systems operator, is responsible for the operation of the various ECM equipment, radar chaff dispenser, and the 20-mm. M-61 six-barrel cannon housed in a flexible mounting in the tail cone. This cone is composed of spring-operated plates which permit movement of the cannon in any direction with minimum disturbance of airflow.

Normal fuel capacity, including that housed in the operational pod, exceeds 12,500 Imp. gal., providing

(Above and below) Production B-58A Hustler bombers with different operational pods, that illustrated above lacking the stabilizing fins of that seen below.

an unrefuelled flight range of some 2,500 mls., but by means of three aerial refuellings, a B-58A has flown 5,183 mls. at an average speed of 1,105 m.p.h. However, the B-58A is not intended for sustained supersonic speeds, and on a typical high-altitude mission, the aircraft cruises at approximately Mach 0.9 at 55,000 ft. to within 600 mls. of its target and then accelerates to Mach 2.0 for the run in and escape.

Ten of the pre-production B-58A Hustlers have been brought up to full production standards to augment the eighty-six genuine production machines, the last of which was completed in the Autumn of 1962, and eight other pre-production aircraft have been converted as TB-58A dual-control trainers, the first of these flying on May 10, 1960. The bombing-navigation system is deleted from the TB-58A, together with ECM and other defence systems, but flight refuelling capability is retained, and transparent glazing has been extended so that the aircraft can be flown from either of the forward cockpits. Several developments of the basic Hustler design were proposed during the bomber's production life, including the B-58B which was to have had a lengthened fuselage and J79-GE-9 engines; the B-58C with Pratt and Whitney J58 turbojets for a sustained speed of Mach 2.4; the B-58D long-range all-weather interceptor with two J58 engines for the Air Defence Command, and the similarly-powered B-58E for Tactical Air Command. None of these was proceeded with.

B-58A HUSTLER SPECIFICATION

Power Plants: *Four General Electric J79-GE-5B turbojets each rated at 10,000 lb.s.t. and 15,600 lb.s.t. with afterburning.*
Armament: *One 20-mm. M-61 Vulcan rotary-cannon, and one detachable mission pod housing various combinations of nuclear store and fuel, or ECM and reconnaissance equipment.*
Performance: *Max. speed, 1,385 m.p.h. at 55,000 ft. (Mach 2.1), 700 m.p.h. at sea level (Mach 0.92); cruise, 595 m.p.h. at 40,000–55,000 ft.; approx. tactical radius (Mach 0.9 to 500 mls. of target, Mach 2.0 to target and Mach 0.9 return), 1,200 mls.; typical unrefuelled mission endurance (high altitude), 2.7 hr.; service ceiling 60,000 ft.*
Weights: *Max. loaded, 163,000–165,000 lb.*
Dimensions: *Span, 56 ft. 10 in.; length, 96 ft. 9 in.; height, 31 ft. 5 in.; wing area, 1,542 sq. ft.*

CONVAIR F-102A DELTA DAGGER

Possessing the distinction of having been the first manned interceptor designed from the outset as the principal component of a weapons system, the F-102A Delta Dagger was also the first supersonic aircraft of delta wing planform to attain service status, and currently serves primarily with the U.S.A.F.E., the P.A.C.A.F., and the Air National Guard in the all-weather intercept rôle.

The development phase of the Delta Dagger's career was singularly chequered, and during the proto-type test stage when the transonic drag rise proved too much for the aircraft to hurdle, its performance being decidedly subsonic, the project appeared to be an abysmal failure, its cancellation hanging in the balance. In the event, major redesign was undertaken as a crash programme to result in a highly effective inter-ceptor which, for several years, was appreciably in advance of any contemporary, and provided the back-bone of the U.S. Air Defence Command. Furthermore, in service it has confounded the dire prognostications current during the early stages of its career and prompted by its somewhat exotic appearance in that it is well liked by its pilots.

The Delta Dagger stems directly from the MX1179 design contest held by the U.S.A.F. in 1950 for a complete interceptor fire control system and won by Hughes Aircraft. The system included homing AAMs, and when, in 1951, the characteristics of these missiles and their associated fire control equipment could be predicted with some certainty, the U.S.A.F. requested

proposals for a suitable interceptor to carry this radical armament, a prime requirement being the ability to attain supersonic speeds in level flight. Some years earlier, Convair had built and flown the XF-92A, a flying mock-up of a previous fighter proposal, the Model 7 which drew heavily on wartime German research into the delta wing configuration and had attained speeds up to Mach 0.95. In view of this success, it was hardly surprising that Convair's new

(Above) F-102A-20-CO 53-1810 in its original production form and (below) after intake, tail and brake modifications.

(Below) F-102A Delta Daggers of the U.S.A.F.'s 86th Fighter Wing which comprises four squadrons based at Ramstein, Hahn, and Bitburg in Germany, and Soesterberg in the Netherlands.

interceptor submission should be to all intents and purposes a 1.22 : 1 scale-up of the experimental delta.

The projected interceptor, the Model 8, was selected by the U.S.A.F. under the designation F-102, and from the outset it was decided to adopt the radical Cook-Craigie production plan which called for a slow initial rate of production parallel to an intensive test programme, the intention being to eliminate the faults in a basic design before hundreds of aircraft had been built and yet drastically cut the prototype-to-service time period. The first two machines completed (52-7994 and 5) were designated YF-102 and known by the parent company as the Model 8-80, and the flight test programme commenced with the first of these on October 24, 1953. Eight days later, however, a flame-out during take-off resulted in the loss of the aircraft. The test programme was resumed with the first flight of the second YF-102 on January 11, 1954, but it was soon all too obvious that the results of wind tunnel tests had been misleading, for the transonic drag rise exceeded appreciably the thrust available from the engine, a Pratt and Whitney J57-P-11 of 10,900 lb.s.t. and 14,500 lb.s.t. with afterburning. It was plain that the YF-102 would *never* go supersonic on the level, and a Mach 1.0 plus performance was one of the basic requirements of the U.S.A.F. specification.

The Convair team, therefore, had no alternative but to virtually scrap the existing design and start work on a new airframe conforming to the area rule formula which, evolved by Richard Whitcomb at the NACA (later NASA), offered the possibility of a drastic reduction in transonic drag. The application of the formula necessitated a major revision of the fuselage profile to reduce the cross sectional area over the wing, and the bulging of the aft fuselage to fill in the channel section between the wing, fuselage and vertical tail in order to delay flow breakaway. The overall length of the fuselage was substantially increased to give a higher fineness ratio, and the cockpit canopy was redesigned to reduce drag, although this had an unfortunate effect on visibility only partially compensated for by the drooping of the nose radome. The wing leading edges were partially cambered to improve the behaviour of the thin aerofoil at high attack angles, the engine air intakes were revised, and the opportunity

was taken to install a more powerful version of the J57 turbojet, the -P-41. These changes were coupled with equally drastic revision of the structure and relocation of the systems, and 117 days after the completion of this transformation, the first YF-102A (53-1787), or Model 8-90, was wheeled out, flying on December 20, 1954, and exceeding Mach 1.0 on its second flight.

In the meantime, a further eight YF-102s (53-1779 to -1786), which had attained an advanced stage of construction before the first aircraft had flown, had been completed for various test purposes, and three further YF-102As (53-1788 to -1790) were built, followed closely by the first production F-102A-5 (53-1791) which was handed over to the U.S.A.F. in June 1955, this aircraft, like most Delta Daggers, having a J57-P-23 engine rated at 11,700 lb.s.t. dry and 17,200 lb.s.t. with afterburning. Four F-102A-5s were followed by three -10s, five -15s, nine -20s and seven -25s to complete the initial contract for forty aircraft, all of which were employed for research and development, and flight testing dictated a number of other modifications which were introduced on the sixty-sixth production Delta Dagger, an F-102A-41 (55-3357), these including redesigned and enlarged vertical tail surfaces intended to safe-guard against roll-coupling, an increase in the size of the air brakes, and some revision of the air intake duct configuration. Finally, in mid-1956, the 327th Fighter Interceptor Squadron became the first unit to convert to the Delta Dagger which, at the peak of its operational deployment, was to equip more than twenty-five U.S.A.F. Air Defence Command squadrons. During the early stages of the Delta Dagger's career, between fifty and sixty aircraft were engaged in research and development, these later being brought up to definitive production standards for issue to operational squadrons, and production finally terminated in April 1958 with the 873rd F-102A (57-909).

The F-102A was the first U.S.A.F. interceptor to dispense entirely with fixed gun armament, and initially the aircraft was equipped with the Hughes MG-3 fire control system used in conjunction with a primary armament of three AIM-4A beam-riding and three AIM-4C infra-red homing Falcon AAMs, with

F-102A Delta Daggers of the 32nd Fighter-Interceptor Squadron based at Soesterberg, Netherlands. The general-arrangement drawing on the opposite page illustrates an F-102A of the 68th Fighter-Interceptor Squadron.

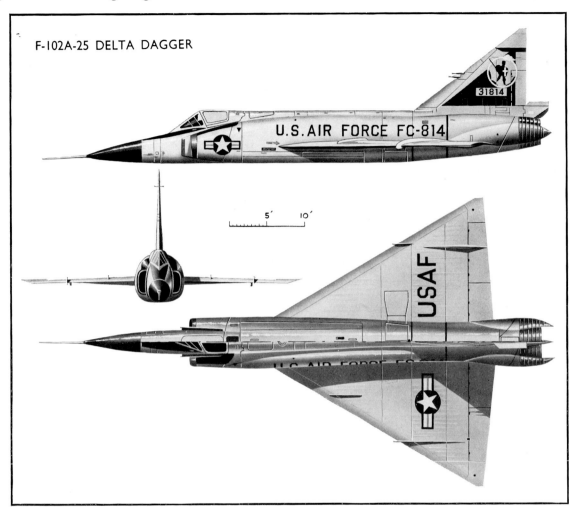

F-102A-25 DELTA DAGGER

a secondary armament of twenty-four 2.75-in. folding-fin rockets. The F-102A was subsequently subjected to a number of modernisation programmes, the first of which resulted in the installation of the more effective MG-10 fire control system and the provision of pick-up points for two 191.5 Imp. gal. drop tanks underwing, supplementing the 891 Imp. gal. internal tankage. When fitted, these tanks limit the F-102A to subsonic performance. Subsequently, further up-dating included the provision of full infra-red capability for target acquisition, lock-on and completion of run, the scanner for a special infra-red sighting system being housed in a transparent dome immediately in front of the pilot's windscreen. The unguided folding-fin rockets were deleted, and provision was made for later versions of the Falcon AAM, such as the AIM-4E radar homing and AIM-4F infra-red homing weapons. Data link is fitted so that the F-102A can be flown by remote control from the ground, feeding course and height directions directly into the autopilot.

TF-102A: In mid-1954, twenty examples of a two-seat combat proficiency trainer variant of the F-102A were ordered. The airframe was essentially similar to that of the single-seat model apart from a new forward fuselage providing side-by-side seating for pupil and instructor. Designated TF-102A, the first two-seater (54-1351) was flown on November 8, 1955, but severe buffet problems resulted from the new canopy, necessitating its redesign and structural strengthening, and the provision of a series of vortex generators to smooth flow over the cockpit. These modifications were tested on the first aircraft and subsequently applied to all production TF-102As, 111 examples of which were ordered under three contracts, although, in the event, these contracts were cut back to sixty-three machines.

The TF-102A retains the weapons capability of the F-102A, although the Hughes MG-10 fire control system is not carried, and at a normal loaded weight of 27,778 lb., attains a maximum speed of 646 m.p.h. at 38,000 ft. (Mach 0.97), the trainer being unable to exceed Mach 1.0 in level flight, although this may be exceeded in a five degree dive. An altitude of 32,800 ft. is attained in 2 min. 50 sec., and a full operational mission may be performed, each F-102A squadron normally including two TF-102As on strength. Overall dimensions are similar to those of the single-seater apart from the length which is 63 ft. 4½ in., including nose probe.

(Above) An F-102A (55-3392) and (below) a TF-102A (54-1360) of the 40th F.I.S. at Yokota A.F.B., Japan.

F-102A DELTA DAGGER SPECIFICATION

Power Plant: *One Pratt and Whitney J57-P-23 turbojet rated at 11,700 lb.s.t. and 17,200 lb. with afterburning.*

Armament: *Three AIM-4C Falcon infra-red homing AAMs and one AIM-26A Nuclear Falcon AAM, or three AIM-4A or -4E beam-riding and three AIM-4C or -4F infra-red homing AAMs.*

Performance: *Max. speed (clean), 825 m.p.h. at 40,000 ft. (Mach 1.25), (with two 191.5 Imp. gal. drop tanks), 630 m.p.h. at 36,000 ft. (Mach 0.95); normal cruise, 540 m.p.h. at 35,000 ft. (Mach 0.8); time to 40,000 ft., 4.25 min.; service ceiling, 54,000 ft.; tactical radius (with two 191.5 Imp. gal. drop tanks and full armament), 500 mls. at 540 m.p.h.; max. range, 1,350 mls.; max. endurance, 2.5 hr.*

Weights: *Normal loaded (clean), 27,700 lb.; max., 31,500 lb.*

Dimensions: *Span, 38 ft. 1½ in.; length (including probe), 68 ft. 4⅔ in.; height, 21 ft. 2½ in.; wing area, 661.5 sq. ft.*

CONVAIR F-106A DELTA DART

Development of an improved version of the Delta Dagger, the F-102B, began in 1955, but as the new interceptor evolved, with progressive changes in systems, armament, and power plant, what was virtually a new aircraft began to emerge, with the result that the designation was changed to F-106A (Model 8-24). As the Delta Dart, the F-106A entered service with the U.S.A.F. Air Defence Command in June 1959, and remains the most sophisticated all-weather interceptor extant.

The F-106A is equipped with the extremely advanced Hughes MA-1 electronic guidance and fire control system designed to operate with the SAGE (Semi-Automatic Ground Environment) defence system. The basis of the MA-1 is a compact digital computer, the "Digitaire", translating data fed into it from ground control intercept stations and issuing commands to the AFCS (Automatic Flight Control System), the pilot acting principally as a monitor with the ability to override the MA-1 in case of emergency. Once within combat radius, the F-106's own radar detects the target and locks on, the missiles being launched automatically.

The initial production contract for the F-106A, which called for seventeen aircraft, was placed in April 1956, the first machine (56-451), which was to all intents and purposes an aerodynamic shell without any operational equipment, flying on December 26, 1956, by which time a contract for an additional eighteen aircraft had been placed. By comparison with the earlier F-102A, the F-106A possessed some fifty per cent more power and differed externally in having swept, angular vertical tail surfaces, repositioned engine air intakes further aft on the fuselage, and in the optimum waisting of the fuselage which eliminated the need for the large fairings built onto the rear fuselage of the earlier interceptor to conform to area rule demands. Most of the F-106As produced under the two initial production contracts were retained for development purposes, the first unit to receive this interceptor, the Air Defence Command's 539th Fighter Interceptor Squadron, becoming operational in June 1959. Approximately half the manned interceptor force of the Air Defence Command had re-equipped with the F-106A by 1961, the last aircraft being delivered to the Command on July 20th of that year.

Since its service début, the F-106A has been progressively up-dated in successive modernisation programmes, the first of which brought all aircraft up

An F-106A Delta Dart of the 94th Fighter-Interceptor Squadron, U.S.A.F. Air Defence Command.

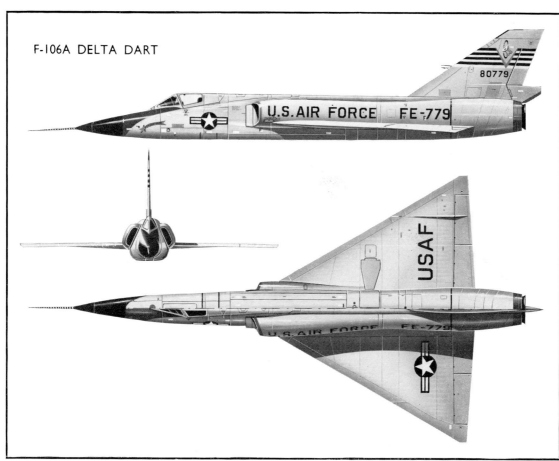

F-106A DELTA DART

to the final production standard. This programme included the fitting of a completely new forward fuselage, and introduced an improved version of the MA-1, supersonic ejector seats and vertical display instrument panels. Subsequently, the F-106A underwent a modification programme designed to increase overall effectiveness at low altitudes and against enemy countermeasures, and a recent addition to its equipment is a special infra-red search and tracking system, the scanner for which is mounted in a bulged housing immediately ahead of the windscreen.

The F-106A carries some 1,200 Imp. gal. of fuel in two integral tanks in each wing and in the fuselage aft of the missile bay, and for ferry purposes this may be supplemented by two 191.5 Imp. gal. drop tanks. Several armament combinations may be carried in the missile bay, including the AIM-4E and -4F Super Falcons, and the attack course may be either lead collision or pursuit, according to the tactical situation. The maximum steady-state altitude of the F-106A is about 57,000 ft., but zoom capability is such that targets flying at an altitude of up to 70,000 ft. can be

The eighth production F-102B Delta Dart (57-2514) tandem two-seat dual-purpose model.

destroyed by a snap-up attack. Maximum level speed is of the order of Mach 2.3, stabilised speed being Mach 1.9, and the aircraft can be flown entirely automatically from wheels-up to flare-out before touchdown.

F-106B DELTA DART: A tandem two-seat dual-purpose version of the Delta Dart, the F-106B, was ordered in June 1957, and the first example of this model (57-2507) flew initially on April 9, 1958. Differing solely from the F-106A in having a second seat inserted immediately aft of the standard seat at some expense of fuselage fuel capacity, the F-106B possesses an identical performance envelope apart from slightly reduced range capability, and carries a similar MA-1 electronic guidance and fire control system, and missile armament, thus retaining full operational potential. Each U.S.A.F. Air Defence Command Delta Dart squadron has several two-

seaters on strength, these being used for normal intercept missions and for combat proficiency training and checks.

F-106A DELTA DART SPECIFICATION

Power Plant: *One Pratt and Whitney J75-P-17 rated at 17,200 lb.s.t. and 24,500 lb.s.t. with afterburning.*
Armament: *Four AIM-4E semi-active radar homing or AIM-4F infra-red homing Super Falcon AAMs and one AIR-2A Genie or AIR-2B Super Genie nuclear AAM.*
Performance: *Max. speed, 1,525 m.p.h. at 40,000 ft. (Mach 2.31); max. stabilised speed, 1,255 m.p.h. (Mach 1.9); combat radius (internal fuel), 575 mls.; ferry range (with two 191.5 Imp. gal. drop tanks), 2,700 mls. at 610 m.p.h. at 41,000 ft. (Mach 0.92); service ceiling, 57,000 ft.*
Weights: *Approx. empty, 26,000 lb.; normal loaded (clean), 35,000 lb.; max. overload, 38,250 lb.*
Dimensions: *Span, 38 ft. 3½ in.; length (including probe), 70 ft. 8¾ in.; height, 20 ft. 3⅓ in.; wing area, 661.5 sq. ft.*

DOUGLAS A-1 SKYRAIDER

Rescued from relative obscurity by the Korean conflict, the A-1 Skyraider has undertaken during its service career every task from troop-carrying to target-towing, from airborne early warning to anti-submarine attack, from close-support to electronic countermeasures. In fact, rarely has one basic aero-

plane fulfilled such a multitude of rôles, and when the last of 3,180 Skyraiders was delivered on February 18, 1957, after twelve years of continuous production, no fewer than twenty-eight variants of this aircraft had appeared. Although out of production for eight years, late in 1964 thirteen U.S. Navy shipboard attack squadrons were still operating the Skyraider as a result of delays in the delivery of its turbojet-powered successor, and the aircraft had embarked upon a new career as a COIN (Counter-Insurgency) warfare type, serving with the 1st Air Commando Group of the U.S.A.F. Tactical Air Command and with the Vietnam Air Force. Others were serving with Armée de l'Air light attack squadrons.

When North Korean forces crossed the 38th parallel in June 1950, the phasing out of production of the Skyraider and its replacement aboard U.S. Navy

(Above left) A-1D Skyraiders of the Armée de l'Air, and (below) A-1H Skyraiders of the Vietnam Air Force.

An A-1H Skyraider of VA-176. Some ten U.S. Navy first line attack squadrons were still operating the A-1H late in 1964.

carriers by jet attack aircraft appeared imminent. During subsequent operations, however, it was discovered that no turbojet-powered attack aircraft could orbit on station during close-support missions for a comparable length of time, or carry the large and varied offensive load of the piston-engined warplane. The result was a new lease of life for the aircraft,

concerning which Rear Admiral John W. Hoskins, commander of Task Force 77 during the Korean War, said: "I am convinced that the Skyraider is the best and most effective close-support aircraft in the world!"

Development of the Skyraider had begun early in 1944 as a replacement for the SBD Dauntless ship-

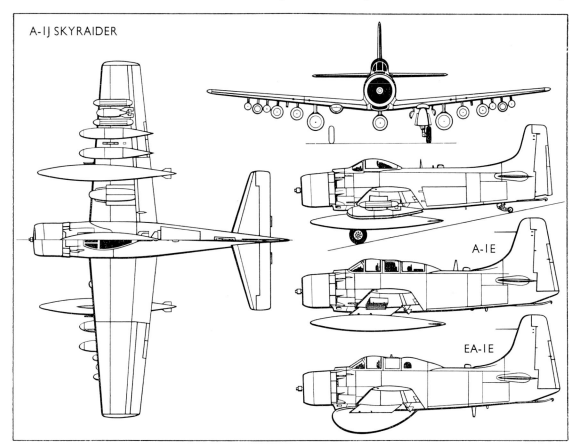

A-1J SKYRAIDER

A-1E

EA-1E

141

(Above) An A-1E of the U.S.A.F.'s 1st Air Commando Group, and (below) EA-1F countermeasures aircraft of VAW-33.

board scout and dive-bomber, and twenty-five production examples had been ordered on July 6, 1944 under the designation XBT2D-1, the first of these flying on March 18, 1945. One month later, on April 18th, an order was placed for 548 production aircraft, although this order was destined to be cut back to 277 machines in the post V-J Day cancellations, and these were to enter service as AD-1 Skyraiders. After some development vicissitudes, the AD-1 was deployed aboard the U.S.S. *Midway* with VA-1B late in 1947. The potential versatility of the Skyraider had been appreciated at an early stage, and one prototype had been fitted with an immense, mushroom-like ventral housing for search radar as the XAD-1W airborne early warning and control post prototype. Bereft of armament, the XAD-1W accommodated two radar operators within the fuselage. Two other prototypes were converted under the designation AD-1N for night attack, these carrying underwing radar pods, two radar operators and a searchlight. The last thirty-five of the 277 AD-1s were completed as AD-1Q radar countermeasures aircraft with a countermeasures operator in the fuselage aft of the pilot in charge of the equipment intended to identify and jam hostile radar.

Failures of the undercarriage attachment points resulted in the introduction of a greatly strengthened inner wing structure, additional skin doublers being applied to the wheel well, a strengthening of the wing flanges and the beefing up of the centre section nose skin in the next production model, the AD-2, which made its début in 1948. In addition to the strengthening, the AD-2 differed from the AD-1 in having a Wright R-3350-26W which could provide 3,020 h.p. for take-off at maximum overload, normal take-off power being 2,700 h.p. as compared with 2,500 h.p. for the -24W engine of the earlier model. Internal fuel capacity was raised from 304 to 316 Imp. gal., and hinged doors were added to the undercarriage main members to seal them off when retracted. One hundred and fifty-six AD-2s were delivered, together with twenty-two AD-2Q countermeasures aircraft.

Production of the AD-2 gave place to the AD-3 featuring minor additional structural strengthening, an increase in the undercarriage oleo strut travel, and a redesigned cockpit canopy. A total of 125 standard AD-3s was produced, two of these being modified as AD-3E Skyraiders with special electronic equipment, others being equipped for ASW under the designation AD-3S. Twenty-three AD-3Q countermeasures aircraft, fifteen AD-3N night attack aircraft, and thirty-one AD-3W early warning aircraft brought total production of the "dash three" model to 194 machines, the type being supplanted on the assembly lines by the AD-4 in mid-1949.

The AD-4 brought to an end the long series of structural modifications that had marked every Skyraider variant. Equipment included new APS-19A radar, a P-1 automatic pilot, further improvements of the windscreen and instrument panel, and a modified arrester hook. The AD-4 remained in production until the late summer of 1953, a total of 1,032 examples of this model being delivered, many of these being AD-4N night attack aircraft, AD-4Q countermeasures aircraft, and AD-4W shipboard early warning aircraft. Forty examples of the last-mentioned variant were supplied to the Royal Navy under the MDAP

(Mutual Defence Assistance Programme), and designated Skyraider A.E.W.Mk.1 in British service, were operated by No. 849 Squadron from 1953. The standard AD-4 retained the built-in armament of two 20-mm. cannon, but the AD-4B special weapons version that appeared in 1953 had provision for carrying tactical nuclear stores and four wing-mounted cannon. Eighty-eight AD-4s were supplied to the Armée de l'Air, being operated by the light ground-attack squadrons manned by reserve and permanent personnel, but this and all previous models have been phased out of the U.S. Navy inventory.

A-1E SKYRAIDER: While production of the AD-4 was proceeding, a new and even more versatile Skyraider variant was under test, the AD-5, later to be redesignated A-1E, which flew for the first time on August 17, 1951. This was perhaps the most remarkable of all Skyraider variants in that, by means of packaged conversion kits, the basic aeroplane could be converted in a few hours aboard a carrier for many different rôles. Much of the structure was interchangeable with that of earlier models, but the forward fuselage was widened to permit side-by-side seating in the cockpit. Overall length was increased from 38 ft. 2 in. to 40 ft. 1 in., the vertical fin and rudder area was increased by fifty per cent, a single dive brake surface replaced the multiple surfaces of earlier Skyraiders, new weapons racks were introduced and the wing armament of four 20-mm. cannon was adopted as standard. New navigational instruments were added, including a radio compass and marker beacon receiver, and numerous maintenance improvements were made.

The A-1E started down the San Diego assembly line as a common chassis, emerging at the other end as the basic A-1E day attack aircraft, EA-1E early warning aircraft, EA-1F countermeasures aircraft, or A-1G night attack version. The kits supplied with these aircraft enabled them to be converted rapidly as VIP transports with four rear facing seats, as a twelve-seat transport with bench-type seats, as a cargo aircraft accommodating a 2,000-lb. freight load, as an ambulance aircraft with four casualty stretchers, and as a target tug.

A total of 670 Skyraiders of this multi-purpose model was produced, and the A-1E currently serves in the training rôle with U.S. Navy Squadrons VA-44

and VA-122, and for the COIN warfare rôle with the U.S.A.F. Tactical Air Command's 1st Air Commando Group. It also serves with the Vietnam Air Force which has received some fifty aircraft of this type, and with a number of U.S. Navy Air Reserve Training Units, and in its EA-1E and EA-1F versions with VAW-11, -13 and -33.

A-1H SKYRAIDER: Produced in parallel with the A-1E, the single-seat A-1H (formerly AD-6) differs from the AD-4 primarily in having special equipment for low-level attack bombing, and late in 1954 served with ten first-line U.S. Navy shipboard attack squadrons (VA-35, 52, 65, 85, 115, 145, 152, 165, 176 and 196), and also with two squadrons of the Vietnam Air Force, this service having received thirty aircraft. Production of the A-1H, deliveries of which had commenced in 1953, terminated in 1956 with the 713th aircraft, Skyraider production finally drawing to a close with seventy-two examples of the A-1J (AD-7).

The A-1J was essentially similar to the A-1H apart from having the improved R-3350-26WB engine in place of the -26WA, and strengthened wings and undercarriage to prolong low-level service life with increased tactical loads. Three U.S. Navy first-line shipboard attack squadrons were operating the A-1J late in 1964, these being VA-25, VA-95 and VA-215. The following specification relates to the A-1J Skyraider but is generally applicable to the A-1H.

A-1J SKYRAIDER SPECIFICATION

Power Plant: *One Wright R-3350-26WB eighteen-cylinder two-row radial engine rated at 2,700 h.p. for take-off and 3,050 h.p. with water injection.*
Armament: *Four 20-mm. cannon and up to 8,000 lb. of ordnance on fifteen external pylons. Loads include eight 1,000-lb. general-purpose bombs or mines, or eight Aero-7D rocket launchers each housing nineteen 2.75-in. rockets.*
Performance: *Max. speed, 318 m.p.h. at 18,500 ft.; econ. cruising, 188 m.p.h. at 6,000 ft.; normal range, 900 mls.; max. range (max. external fuel), 3,000 mls.; initial climb rate, 2,380 ft./min.; service ceiling, 32,000 ft.*
Weights: *Empty, 10,550 lb.; normal loaded, 19,000 lb.; max. overload, 25,000 lb.*
Dimensions: *Span, 50 ft. 9 in.; length, 38 ft. 10 in.; height, 15 ft. 8¼ in.; wing area, 400.33 sq. ft.*

An A-1J of VA-122, a training unit based at Naval Air Station Lemoore, California.

DOUGLAS A-4 SKYHAWK

Evolved to meet a U.S. Navy requirement issued in 1950 for a shipboard attack aircraft capable of delivering tactical nuclear weapons and performing non-nuclear interdiction missions, the Skyhawk represented an attempt to reverse the trend towards increased weight and complexity in combat aircraft. The specification included a maximum permissible loaded weight of 30,000 lb., but by placing design accent on structural simplicity and exercising rigid weight control, the Douglas team, led by E. H. Heinemann, offered an aircraft weighing exactly half the permissible maximum yet fulfilling, and in most cases exceeding, all the U.S. Navy's demands.

The first mock-up board inspection of the proposed attack aircraft took place in February 1952, and four months later, on June 21st., a contract was placed for two prototypes and a pre-production batch of aircraft. The first YA-4A prototype (BuA.No.137814—at that time designated Y/A4D-1) was flown on June 22, 1954, only eighteen months after design had begun, and the first pre-production A-4A (BuA.No.137816) followed on August 14, 1954. On October 15, 1955, an A-4A, powered by a 7,200 lb.s.t. Wright J65-W-2 engine, established an international speed record over a 500-km. closed-circuit course with an average speed of 695.127 m.p.h., and on October 26, 1956, the type entered service with the U.S. Navy's Attack Squadron VA-72.

The production A-4A switched from the J65-W-2 to the up-rated J65-W-4 of 7,800 lb.s.t., and carried 641 Imp. gal. of fuel in a fuselage tank and integral wing tanks. This could be augmented by a pair of 208 Imp. gal. drop tanks mounted beneath the wings or one 250 Imp. gal. tank beneath the fuselage. The three pick-up points had a total capacity of 5,000 lb., 3,000 lb. of this being carried on the fuselage centreline. Several hundred combinations of stores could be carried, including various types of bombs on multiple racks, a tactical kiloton weapon, 2.75-in. rocket pods, AGM-12 Bullpup ASMs, Mk.11 double-barrel 20-mm. cannon packs, and various other weapons.

On March 26, 1956, five months before the A-4A had entered service with the U.S. Navy, a modified version of the Skyhawk had flown for the first time, the A-4B (BuA.No.142095) with a 7,700 lb.s.t. J65-W-16A engine. The A-4B introduced a new powered rudder with dual hydraulic control, a single-point pressure fuelling system, a new gun sight, and changes in the cockpit layout. In addition, the rear fuselage was strengthened, and later machines featured a flight refuelling probe on the starboard side of the forward fuselage. Six A-4B Skyhawks were delivered in 1956, and this model was produced in parallel with the A-4A until it entirely supplanted the earlier model on the assembly line early in 1957.

Late in 1964 the A-4B remained operational with three U.S. Navy Attack Squadrons (VA-163, 164, and 212) and with U.S. Marine Corps Squadrons VMA-324 and -533. It is also operated by the U.S. Naval Air Reserve Training Units at Alameda, New York, Norfolk, and South Weymouth.

In the meantime, consideration had been given to replacing the Wright-built engine with a Pratt and Whitney J52, although, in the event, this power plant was not to be installed in the Skyhawk until 1961, four prototypes with the J52-P-2 being cancelled. The next production model was the A-4C which, flown on August 21, 1959, carried terrain-avoidance radar and was equipped for limited all-weather operation. An autopilot was installed together with a low-level ejection seat, the pilot oxygen system was improved, and further revisions were made to the cockpit layout, the net result of these changes being increases in empty and normal loaded weights to 9,559 lb. and 17,294 lb. from 8,526 lb. and 15,500 lb. respectively. Currently the most widely-used version of the Skyhawk, the A-4C serves with twenty-three U.S. Navy Attack Squadrons (VA-12, 22, 34, 46, 55, 64, 66, 72, 76, 83, 86, 93, 106, 112, 113, 144, 146, 153, 155, 172, 192, 195, and 216) and nine Marine Corps Squadrons (VMA-121, 211, 214, 223, 224, 225, 242, 332, and 343).

The 1,000th Skyhawk, an A-4C, was delivered in

An A-4C Skyhawk of VA-66 (Bu.No.148455). Currently the most widely used version of the Skyhawk, the A-4C serves with twenty-three U.S. Navy attack squadrons.

A-4E SKYHAWK SPECIFICATION

Power Plant: *One Pratt and Whitney J52-P-6A turbojet rated at 8,500 lb.s.t.*

Armament: *Two 20-mm. MK-12 cannon and a maximum external ordnance load of 8,200 lb. A typical offensive load for short-range interdiction mission could comprise an AGM-12 Bullpup ASM on each outboard pylon, six 250-lb. bombs on each inboard pylon, and six 500-lb. bombs on the centreline pylon.*

Performance: *Max. speed (clean), 685 m.p.h. at sea level (Mach 0.9), (high drag configuration, i.e., five pylons and stores), 576 m.p.h. at sea level (Mach 0.8), 578 m.p.h. at 30,000 ft. (Mach 0.85); range (clean, internal fuel), 920 mls.; ferry (one 250 Imp. gal. centreline tank and two 208 Imp. gal. tanks on inboard pylons), 1,800 mls.; service ceiling (clean), 49,000 ft., (with 6,000 lb. external load), 45,000 ft.*

Weights: *Empty, 9,284 lb.; loaded (clean), 14,647 lb.; max. overload, 24,500 lb.*

Dimensions: *Span, 27 ft. 6 in.; length, 42 ft. 10¾ in.; height, 15 ft. 2 in.; wing area, 260 sq. ft.*

(Above) An A-4E aboard the U.S.S. Coral Sea (CVA-43).

the Pratt and Whitney J52-P-6A turbojet of 8,500 lb.s.t. with which range was increased by twenty-seven per cent. The maximum external stores load was raised to 8,200 lb. by the provision of two additional underwing pylons, and the catapult launching gear was strengthened to permit carrier take-offs at appreciably higher gross weights. Deliveries to the U.S. Navy began in November 1962, and in December 1963, the 1,500th Skyhawk, an A-4E, was delivered. Late in 1964 the A-4E was operational with U.S. Navy Squadrons VA-23, 56, 81 and 94, and with Marine Corps Squadron VMA-331. Production of the A-4E is expected to continue into the last quarter of 1965, and it is anticipated that the type will remain in first-line service with the U.S. Navy and Marine Corps until 1973.

February 1961, and a few months later, on July 12th, yet another version of the aircraft flew for the first time, the A-4E (BuA.No.148613). Retaining the wing root-mounted 20-mm. Colt-Browning cannon, the A-4E was completely re-engineered and switched to

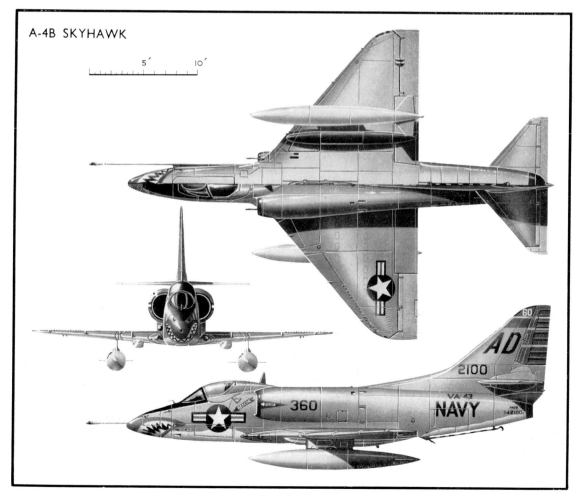

A-4B SKYHAWK

DOUGLAS A-3 SKYWARRIOR

Scheduled to remain in the U.S. Navy's first-line aircraft inventory throughout the 'sixties to provide *Essex* and *Midway* class carriers with long-range nuclear capability, the Skywarrior currently equips eight Heavy Attack Squadrons and two Heavy Photographic Squadrons, and has done more to change carrier warfare concepts than any other shipboard aircraft.

In the immediate post-war years with the prospect of larger carriers, the U.S. Navy began to think in terms of shipboard aircraft capable of undertaking missions of a more strategic nature than those to which previous carrier-based warplanes had been restricted. A requirement was formulated for an attack bomber which, although fully "navalized" and permanently carrier-based, could carry a heavy load of conventional or nuclear weapons over strategic distances at speeds comparable with those of corresponding land-based aircraft. Discussions regarding this requirement took place between the U.S. Navy Bureau of Aeronautics

A-3B SKYWARRIOR

EA-3B SKYWARRIOR

RA-3B SKYWARRIOR

TA-3B SKYWARRIOR

and Douglas in 1947, and after initial difficulties in formulating even the basic specification, the U.S. Navy's ideas crystallized in what was easily the largest and heaviest aircraft ever planned for carrier operation.

Douglas's optimum solution to the exacting specification was a three-seat aircraft with an internal weapons bay, a shoulder-mounted wing swept 36° and folding for carrier stowage, two podded turbojets, pressurized crew accommodation, a radar bombing system in the nose, and a tail-mounted remotely-controlled gun barbette, and a contract for the construction of two prototypes was awarded on March 31, 1949.

Designated XA3D-1, the first prototype (BuA. No. 129412) was flown on October 28, 1952 with two 7,000 lb.s.t. Westinghouse XJ40-WE-3 turbojets. Original proposals had called for the installation of 7,500 lb.s.t. J40-WE-12 engines in the production model, but before the first prototype had joined the flight test programme, the unsatisfactory development of the Westinghouse power plant had led to a decision to switch to the Pratt and Whitney J57, and only eleven months elapsed before the first J57-engined YA3D-1 (BuA. No. 130352) joined the test programme, its first flight taking place on September 16, 1953. The production A3D-1 Skywarrior entered service with the U.S. Navy in 1956, VAH-1 commencing re-equipment with the type on March 31st of that year. A compact, straight-forward aircraft of conventional construction, the A3D-1 had a gross weight of 70,000 lb., and was powered by two J57-P-6 engines each rated at 9,700 lb.s.t. for take-off and 11,600 lb.s.t. with water injection. Almost the entire nose was occupied by the elaborate ASB bombing radar, the box-like, 15-ft. weapons bay which had dictated the fuselage cross section could accommodate a wide variety of ordnance loads totalling up to 12,000 lb., and defensive armament was provided by a radar-directed Westinghouse tail barbette housing twin 20-mm. cannon.

From an early stage, the A3D-1 was considered as an interim production model for indoctrination, the development of shipboard procedures and operational techniques, etc., and only fifty examples of this version were built before production switched to the definitive A3D-2. Redesignated A-3A in 1962, the

The A-3A Skywarrior currently serves in the training rôle with VAH-3 and VAH-123, an aircraft from the latter unit being illustrated.

An A-3B Skywarrior (Bu.No.138973) of VAH-13, a component of the U.S. Navy's Heavy Attack Wing 2. The A-3B equips eight Heavy Attack Squadrons.

initial production model is currently operated in the training rôle by VAH-3 and VAH-123, alongside a dual-control trainer conversion, the TA-3A.

A-3B SKYWARRIOR: The definitive attack model of the Skywarrior, the A-3B (originally designated A3D-2), is externally similar to the initial production model but embodies a number of equipment changes and the more powerful J57-P-10 turbojet. Intended for all-weather operation, the A-3B can be based aboard carriers down to the size of the *Essex* class (800 ft.) and has been launched at weights in excess of 80,000 lb. The internal weapons bay can house a variety of 2,000-lb., 1,000-lb., and 500-lb. bombs, mines or depth charges carried on individual ejector racks to ensure separation, a spoiler or anti-buffet rake

deflecting ahead of the weapons bay automatically as soon as the bomb doors are opened to avoid buffeting. The bombing-navigation system permits a wide range of bomb modes and approach patterns including LABS (Low Altitude Bombing System) attacks with automatic, semi-automatic or manual techniques, and the A-3B may be adapted for the rôle of flight-refuelling tanker by means of a special weapons bay pack comprising a 1,082.5 Imp. gal. tank and a hose-reel assembly. All A-3Bs were initially delivered with the standard Westinghouse twin-20-mm. cannon radar-directed tail barbette, but this has now been deleted from many aircraft which employ the space previously occupied by this armament for radar chaff dispensers and other ECM equipment.

The A-3B first entered service with Heavy Attack

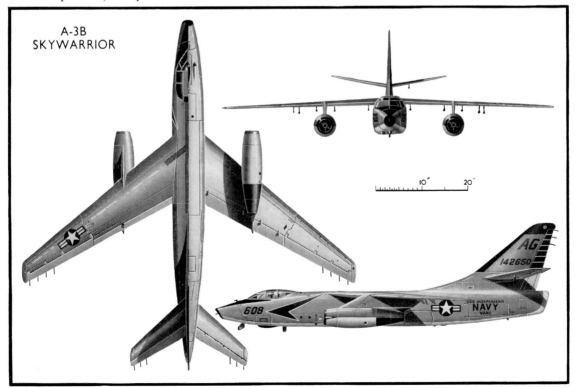

A-3B
SKYWARRIOR

(Above) An EA-3B Skywarrior seven-seat radar countermeasures and electronic reconnaissance aircraft of VQ-1.

(Above) A TA-3B Skywarrior (Bu.No.144860) of VAH-123 at Whidbey Island Naval Air Station, Washington.

Squadron VAH-2 in 1957 and, at the time of closing for press, equipped eight Heavy Attack Squadrons (VAH-2, 4, 6, 8, 9, 10, 11 and 13), two of these—to be redesignated RVAH-9 and RVAH-11 to indicate their additional reconnaissance capability—being scheduled for re-equipment with the RA-5C Vigilante during 1965.

RA-3B SKYWARRIOR: Serving with U.S. Navy Heavy Photographic Squadrons VAP-61 and VAP-62 which deploy detachments with the various Carrier Air Wings, the RA-3B is a five-seat photographic reconnaissance aircraft which features a redesigned, fully-pressurised fuselage, the space occupied by the weapons bay in the A-3B being utilised by a photo-navigator and photo technician, and various camera stations, some of which have provision for alternate cameras. Dual view finders and a master control in the cockpit permit single or multiple operation of all cameras by the pilot or photo-navigator, and a small bay aft of the pressurised photographic compartment houses photoflash bombs for night illumination. The prototype of the photographic reconnaissance Skywarrior, the YRA-3B, flew for the first time on July 22, 1958, and deliveries to the U.S. Navy began in August 1959. A maximum of twelve oblique and vertical cameras, including framing strip and panoramic types for low-, medium-, and high-altitude photography may be carried.

EA-3B SKYWARRIOR: A seven-seat radar counter-measures and electronic reconnaissance development of the Skywarrior with forward- and side-looking radar, infra-red scanner and other non-photographic reconnaissance and ECM equipment. With a generally similar fuselage to that of the RA-3B, the EA-3B flew for the first time on December 10, 1958, production deliveries to the U.S. Navy commencing in November 1959, and the type currently serves with Fleet Reconnaissance Squadron VQ-1. Possessing a fully pressurised fuselage with stations for four electronics operators and additional fuel cells, the EA-3B is intended primarily for the long-range reconnaissance of enemy electronic installations. The SLAR (Side-Looking Aircraft Radar) is housed in a long ventral fairing, and a probe is attached to the port side of the fuselage for in-flight refuelling.

TA-3B SKYWARRIOR: The TA-3B bombardier trainer embodies a pressurised fuselage providing accommodation for a pilot, instructor and six pupils with individual radar bomb sights and navigational equipment. First flown on August 29, 1959, the TA-3B enables pupils to be instructed in LABS bombing techniques, and is operated by training squadrons VAH-3 and VAH-123.

A total of sixty-seven examples of the TA-3B, EA3B, and RA-3B aircraft had been delivered when Skywarrior production terminated in January 1961.

A-3B SKYWARRIOR SPECIFICATION

Power Plants: *Two Pratt and Whitney J57-P-10 turbojets each rated at 10,500 lb.s.t. for take-off and 12,400 lb.s.t. with water injection.*
Armament: *Four 2,000-lb., twelve 1,000-lb., or twenty-four 500-lb. bombs and (some aircraft only) twin 20-mm. cannon in Westinghouse radar-directed tail barbette.*
Performance: *Max. speed, 610 m.p.h. at 10,000 ft. (Mach 0.83), 560 m.p.h. at 36,000 ft. (Mach 0.85); tactical radius (standard internal fuel), 1,050 mls.; max. range, 2,900 mls.; service ceiling, 41,000 ft.*
Weights: *Empty, 39,409 lb.; normal loaded, 70,000 lb.; max. overload 82,000 lb.*
Dimensions: *Span, 72 ft. 6 in.; length, 76 ft. 4 in.; height, 22 ft. 9½ in.; wing area, 812 sq. ft.*

DOUGLAS B-66 DESTROYER

Evolved from the U.S. Navy's A-3 Skywarrior as a light bomber and reconnaissance aircraft for the U.S.A.F. Tactical Air Command, the Destroyer did not attain large-scale production, 209 being manufactured between 1954 and 1958, these serving primarily in the tactical reconnaissance rôle, and the Destroyer is currently being phased out of Tactical Air Command's active reconnaissance squadrons.

The first Destroyer, the RB-66A (52-2828) flew for the first time on June 28, 1954 with 9,700 lb.s.t. Allison YJ79-A-9 turbojets, but only five examples of this initial version were produced, being confined to the type development rôle, and the first variant to enter Tactical Air Command service was the RB-66B, the first of which (53-409) flew on January 4, 1955. The RB-66B carried a crew of three and was intended for the all-weather night photographic reconnaissance rôle. Early production machines had the 9,700 lb.s.t. J79-A-9 turbojets, but these quickly gave place to the 10,200 lb.s.t. J79-A-13. Cameras and photo-flash bombs were stowed in a central fuselage bay, three K-46 night cameras and a K-38 being initially carried. AN/APS-27 search radar was mounted in the fuselage nose, and twin 20-mm. cannon were carried by a General Electric remotely-controlled tail barbette surmounted by the MD-1 scanner. Basic internal fuel capacity was 3,871 Imp. gal., and this could be supplemented by two 375 Imp. gal. underwing tanks to result in a maximum overload weight of 79,000 lb.

The RB-66B bore little more than an external resemblance to the U.S. Navy's A-3 Skywarrior. The U.S.A.F. had originally anticipated buying the A-3 "off-the-shelf" with a minimum of changes but, during the course of development, more than four hundred alterations had been made, including a two-degree change in wing incidence, a reduction in the sweep angle of the inboard wing trailing edge to decrease thickness/chord ratio and minimise pitch-up, and a

completely new fuselage layout, and these changes, added to the specialised equipment demanded for the various Destroyer versions, had resulted in a full-scale development project. Contracts called for 175 RB-66Bs and seventy-two examples of a tactical bomber version, the B-66B, although, in the event, these were to be cut back substantially. The RB-66B entered service with the 1st, 19th, and 30th Tactical Reconnaissance Squadrons in 1957, and the B-66B, the first example of which (53-482) followed the initial RB-66B production batch on the assembly line, was delivered to the 17th and 47th Bombardment Wings. The B-66B was essentially similar to its reconnaissance counterpart, the camera bay being replaced by a weapons bay capable of housing free-falling conventional or nuclear stores.

Thirty-six Destroyers, thirty of these originally ordered as RB-66Bs, were completed as RB-66Cs for all-weather electronics reconnaissance, equipped to gather intelligence by analysing and identifying signals emanating from enemy electronic equipment. A pressurized ECM compartment between the fore and aft fuel cells supplanted the camera bay and housed two ECM observers, increasing the total crew to four members, small ECM housings were mounted at the wingtips and, at a later stage, chaff dispensers supplanted the tail gun barbette and its fire control system. The first RB-66C was flown on October 29, 1955, and the last example of this model was followed by yet another reconnais-

(Above right) An RB-66B Destroyer (53-433), and (below) an RB-66C (54-478). The Destroyer is currently being phased out of first line operational service with the Tactical Air Command.

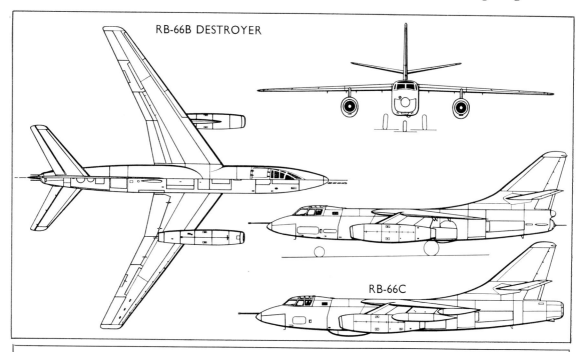

RB-66B DESTROYER

RB-66C

RB-66B DESTROYER SPECIFICATION

Power Plants: *Two Allison J79-A-13 turbojets each rated at 10,200 lb.s.t.*

Armament: *Some aircraft retain twin 20-mm. cannon in remotely-controlled tail barbette. (B-66B): Up to 15,000 lb. of free-falling weapons in internal bay.*

Performance: *Max. speed, 620 m.p.h. at 10,000 ft. (Mach 0.85), 594 m.p.h. at 36,000 ft.; tactical radius (normal internal fuel), 800 mls. at 42,000 ft. at 460 m.p.h. (Mach 7.0); max. range (internal fuel), 1,650 mls., (with two 375 Imp. gal. drop tanks), 1,900 mls.; service ceiling, 45,000 ft.*

Weights: *Empty, 39,686 lb.; normal loaded, 70,000 lb.; max. overload, 79,000 lb.*

Dimensions: *Span, 72 ft. 6 in.; length, 75 ft. 1¼ in.; height, 23 ft. 7 in.; wing area, 779 sq. ft.*

sance variant of the Destroyer, the WB-66D, the primary function of which was to obtain accurate weather data in combat areas. The WB-66D carried five crew members and thirty-six examples were delivered before production terminated in June 1958, total contracts having been cut back by eighty-five aircraft. Some B-66B Destroyers with modified equipment have been redesignated B-66E.

GENERAL DYNAMICS F-111

The first tactical fighter to be designed from the outset for use by both the U.S.A.F. and the U.S. Navy, the side-by-side two-seat F-111 bi-service multi-purpose aircraft has been evolved to meet the requirements of the TFX (Tactical Fighter Experimental) specification formulated in February 1960. The TFX requirement called for Mach 2.5 high-altitude dash and Mach 1.2 interdiction at zero altitude; the ability to take-off and clear 50 feet and descend from this height and land within 3,000 feet; suitability for operation from short, rough strips in forward areas for the support of ground forces, and a range exceeding 4,000 miles to enable the aircraft to fly between any two airfields in the world in one day. In addition, the U.S. Navy demanded five-six hour loiter capability and take-off and landing speeds not exceeding 115 and 90 knots respectively. Furthermore, a high degree of "commonality" was demanded between versions for the two services.

It was apparent from the outset that an aircraft capable of fulfilling *all* these requirements could only be produced if a practical variable-geometry wing could be evolved, and the development of such a wing possibly represents the greatest advance of the past decade in the field of airframe design.

The Fort Worth Division of the General Dynamics Corporation was announced the winner of the closely-contested TFX competition on November 24, 1962, with Grumman Aircraft as an associate, the latter being responsible for the design and manufacture of the undercarriage, aft fuselage, tailplane and arrester gear for both U.S.A.F. and U.S. Navy versions, as well as for the assembly and flight testing of the shipboard model. The initial contract calls for the delivery of twenty-three development aircraft, eighteen of which will be U.S.A.F. F-111As, the remaining five being U.S. Navy F-111Bs, and the first F-111A (63-9766) was rolled out on October 15, 1964, this being essentially complete, with the wingsweep mechanism installed and operative, and only sub-systems remaining to be installed. This aircraft was expected to commence flight testing late in 1964, with the first F-111B following in the late spring of 1965.

The U.S. Defence Department has stated that the F-111 will surpass in cost any U.S. fighter programme since the Second World War, with total production eventually exceeding seventeen hundred aircraft of which the U.S. Navy anticipates receiving three hundred and fifty. The F-111A is scheduled to enter service with the U.S.A.F. Tactical Air Command in October 1966, with the F-111B entering U.S. Navy service in May 1968.

The most revolutionary feature of the F-111 is, of course, its variable-geometry wing. Such wings were used experimentally by the Bell X-5 and Grumman XF10F-1 Jaguar, but satisfactory behaviour was achieved only by moving the wing roots forward as sweep was increased and, in consequence, the operating mechanism was unacceptably complex and heavy. A practical lightweight scheme was eventually evolved by NASA and adopted for the F-111, and apart from increasing subsonic range through the reduction of induced drag, this variable-geometry wing offers the advantages of improved airfield performance through the use of high lift coefficients, supersonic dash capability at ground level through minimized wave

drag and gust response, increased loiter in combat patrol, and the elimination of wing folding for shipboard stowage. The hinges are positioned well out from the fuselage sides so that a substantial part of the gross wing area is fixed. In extended configuration the wing is cambered and twisted towards the tip, and uses conventional leading edge slats and full-span trailing edge double-slotted flaps, the former having an intermediate drooped position for long-endurance cruise or loiter. In the fully swept condition the wing has no camber or twist effect, and there is no physical overlap of the wing and tail. The tail surfaces are large in order that, as wing sweepback increases and its downwash reduces the contribution of the tailplane to stability, there is a forward shift of the aerodynamic centre, restoring the stability to its low speed value.

The two Pratt and Whitney TF30 (JTF10A-20) turbofans are mounted side-by-side in the aft fuselage and are fed by quarter-cone, multi-shock, external-internal compression intakes set back beneath the wings to minimize wetted area and incidence effects. Large rectangular splitter plates divert the boundary layer down the sides of the fuselage in the low-level

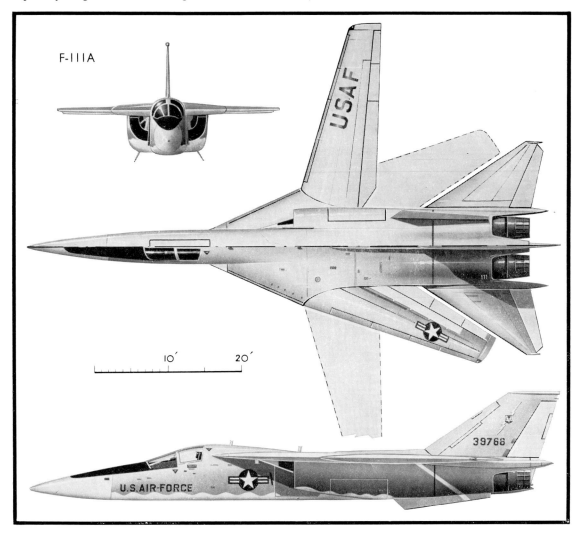

F-111A

10′   20′

U.S. AIR FORCE

39766

supersonic flight regime. High speed directional stability is aided by two strakes beneath the rear fuselage, and the long fairings at the tailplane roots may house the actuators, keeping them clear of the heat of the afterburners.

Side-by-side seating for the two crew members results from carrier restrictions on overall length, but although this arrangement is used at some cost in wave drag, a worthwhile gain in internal fuel volume results. The crew members of the F-111A are considered as pilot and co-pilot, but as the U.S. Navy considers its F-111B as primarily a missile platform, its two crew members are pilot and missile operator. In the first fourteen aircraft conventional ejector seats are provided for the crew members pending the availability of a McDonnell-developed escape system currently under test. Escape will be achieved by ejecting the entire cabin section of the fuselage which will be initially stabilized by the front part of the wing stub which will be built integral. The enormous development programme demanded by such an escape capsule suggests that it is necessitated by the F-111's ability to fly at Mach 1.2 at sea level where the air loads may be too great for a simple ejector seat.

The crew will be able to control the ejection sequence manually, but normally the entire operation will be automatic with the pulling of the escape system handle by either crew member. When this handle is pulled, a shaped charge will cut through the supporting structure and, simultaneously, the escape capsule's rocket motor will ignite to complete separation and propel the capsule clear of the aircraft. During separation and descent, the capsule's emergency support systems will provide oxygen for the crew and, to assist retrieval, will automatically dispense radar chaff. An emergency transceiver radio and a flashing beacon will also function automatically. After separation, a drogue parachute will be deployed almost immediately to decelerate the capsule and stabilize it during the descent, the main chute lowering it to the ground. Beside escape from any altitude and speed condition, the capsule's capability will include zero altitude and zero speed escape.

The mission requirements of the U.S.A.F. and the U.S. Navy are fundamentally different, as has already been indicated, and thus two versions of the aircraft are being developed simultaneously, "commonality" in the equipment and structures of the two versions being claimed to exceed eighty per cent, non-commonality apparently predominating in the armament systems.

F-111A: The U.S.A.F. version of the aircraft, the F-111A, has the primary rôle of supersonic low-altitude penetration for interdiction or tactical reconnaissance, secondary tasks being the provision of air superiority over ground forces and high-altitude reconnaissance. It is intended to carry a wide variety of conventional or nuclear bombs or rockets beneath the fuselage and fixed portion of the wing, a typical attack load comprising four AGM-12 Bullpup ASMs. Sidewinder infra-red homing AAMs will be carried for the intercept rôle.

In maximum extended condition, the movable portion of the wing has 16° of sweep and overall span is 63 ft., but when fully swept with leading edge sweep angle becoming 72.5°, overall span is reduced to 31 ft. 11½ in. The design is based on a manoeuvre load

factor of 7.33 g, ensuring outstanding manoeuvrability at zero altitude. The original target gross weight was 69,000 lb., but weight escalation during development has resulted in a gross weight of some 77,000 lb., the target empty weight having risen from 36,700 lb. to just under 42,000 lb.

The U.S.A.F. Tactical Air Command anticipated receiving some 1,350 F-111A tactical fighters, and it was announced on October 24, 1963 that twenty-four F-111As had been ordered for the R.A.A.F. In R.A.A.F. service the F-111A will supplant the Canberra currently equipping Nos. 1, 2 and 6 Squadrons, but delivery to Australia will not be effected until 1968, and it is estimated that the aircraft will not attain operational status with the R.A.A.F. until late 1969 or early 1970.

F-111B: The U.S. Navy's F-111B will differ from the F-111A in a number of respects, and its prime rôle will be that of affording air superiority over the fleet, its endurance enabling it to loiter at the outer defensive perimeter for appreciably longer periods than current U.S. Navy interceptors. The F-111B differs markedly from the U.S.A.F. model in systems and equipment, and the weight of avionics is approximately one-third greater than that of the F-111A because of the chosen armament. The radar, intended primarily for the air intercept mode, results in a shorter fuselage nose, and overall length is 66 ft. 9 in., some five feet less than the U.S.A.F. aircraft. By comparison with the F-111A, the F-111B will have a greater overall wing span in maximum extended condition, this being approximately 70 ft., the higher aspect ratio being intended to improve low-speed ferry and loiter performance. An enlarged ventral fin houses the carrier arrester hook.

The primary armament of the F-111B will comprise six AIM-54A Phoenix AAMs, two semi-recessed under the fixed portion of each wing and two under the fuselage, but provision is presumably made for ASMs, bombs or napalm tanks as alternative loads for the attack mission. The original target weight of the F-111B was 55,000 lb., empty weight being 39,000 lb., but by late 1964 these had risen to 69,000 lb. and 46,000 lb. respectively. It is anticipated that 3,000 lb. will be pared from the empty weight and 2,000 lb. from the loaded weight of later F-111Bs, but doubts have been expressed that the eventual gross weight of 67,000 lb. will permit the aircraft to operate from carriers smaller than the *Forrestal* class, raising the key question of whether the Defence Department's insistence on commonality between the U.S.A.F. and U.S. Navy F-111s has led to an aircraft too heavy for carrier use.

F-111 SPECIFICATION

Power Plants: *Two Pratt and Whitney TF30 (JTF10A-20) turbofans rated at approximately 11,500 lb.s.t. and 19,000 lb.s.t. with afterburning.*

Armament: *Various combinations of bombs, napalm tanks or rockets under fixed portions of wing and fuselage.*

Performance: *Design max. speed, 1,650 m.p.h. at 40,000 ft. (Mach 2.5), 865 m.p.h. at sea level (Mach 1.2); service ceiling, 60,000 (plus) ft.; ferry range (internal fuel), 3,300 mls., (with maximum external fuel), 4,500–5,000 mls.*

Weights: *Empty, 41,780 lb.; loaded, 69,000 lb.*

Dimensions: *Maximum span, 63 ft. 0 in.; minimum span, 31 ft. 11½ in.; length, 72 ft. 1½ in.; height, 17 ft. 1½ in.*

GRUMMAN A-6A INTRUDER

Scheduled to be deployed operationally for the first time with VA-75 in March 1965 aboard the U.S.S. *Independence*, the Intruder two-seat shipboard low-level strike aircraft is the U.S. Navy's counterpart of the Hawker Siddeley Buccaneer, and was designed specifically for sorties against targets obscured by weather or darkness. Selected from eleven proposals submitted by eight manufacturers to meet a U.S. Navy requirement formulated in 1956, and combining the requirements of limited "brushfire" war missions with extended, low-altitude nuclear missions, the Intruder was awarded a development contract in March 1959. This, together with a supplementary contract placed one year later, called for eight aircraft for evaluation and development purposes, and designated A-6A, the first of these (BuA.No.147864) flew on April 19, 1960.

Production orders were subsequently placed for sixty-seven A-6As and twelve examples of an electronics countermeasures version, the EA-6A, and deliveries to the U.S. Navy began in 1963, the production model differing from the development aircraft primarily in having a fixed, in-flight refuelling probe mounted centrally in front of the cockpit, and non-swivelling jet pipes, these having been arranged to tilt through 23° in early Intruders to reduce stalling speed by six knots. The hydraulically-actuated hinging tail-pipes were considered by the U.S. Navy to be an unnecessary complication in view of the aircraft's already low (90 knot) stalling speed. The tailpipes of the production A-6A are angled downwards 7° from the mean aerodynamic chord.

The A-6A is equipped with DIANE (Digital Integrated Attack System) which includes Norden AN/APQ-92 search radar, AN/APQ-88 tracking radar, inertial and Doppler navigators, a communications, navigation and identification package, automatic flight control system, integrated cockpit displays, and a high-speed AN/ASQ-61 digital computer. The system enables the pilot to pre-select a course of action, approaching the target, discharging the weapons and

leaving the target area automatically. The DIANE can accomplish all basic mission manoeuvres for the pilot, except take-off and landing, can automatically perform all conventional weapons delivery manoeuvres, and is designed to have the capability of launching and directing AGM-12 Bullpup and similar ASMs automatically. The bombardier-navigator is seated to starboard and slightly aft of the pilot, and approximately 2,000 Imp. gal. of fuel is carried internally. This, at best range consumption, is sufficient for three-and-a-half hours' low-level flight, but may be supplemented by up to five 250 Imp. gal. drop tanks, increasing ferry endurance to approximately five-and-a-quarter hours cruising at approximately 345 m.p.h. in high-drag configuration.

The moderately swept high-mid wing features hydraulically-operated full-span leading and trailing edge flaps, with inset spoilers for lateral control, rigged permanently 3° up, forward of the trailing edge flaps. The outer panels of the wing fold upward and inward immediately outboard of the stores pylons, reducing overall span for shipboard stowage to 25 ft. 2 in. All weapons are carried externally on five pylons each having a 3,600-lb. capacity.

EA-6A INTRUDER: The EA-6A electronics countermeasures version of the Intruder is intended to accompany A-6As on low-level, long-range missions, and its countermeasures capability is derived from replacing the bombing and navigational system by ECM equipment intended to confuse radar-controlled anti-aircraft weapons and detecting devices. The EA-6A carries more than thirty different antennae to analyse signals received and produce active countermeasures, but retains partial attack capability. Externally evident changes from the A-6A include redesigned vertical tail surfaces which, increasing overall length and height to 55 ft. 6 in. and 16 ft. 7 in. respectively, are surmounted by an avionics package, antenna housings under the wingtips, and a housing under the rear fuselage for the Doppler radar antenna. There are five

An A-6A Intruder (Bu.No.149941) of VA-42, the Intruder training unit, aboard U.S.S. Forrestal for carrier qualification.

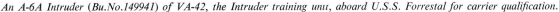

A-6A Intruders of VA-75 which is scheduled to be deployed operationally aboard the U.S.S. Independence in March 1965.

external stations for ECM pods or fuel tanks. The prototype EA-6A was flown for the first time in 1963, and production deliveries were scheduled to commence during 1965.

A-6A INTRUDER SPECIFICATION

Power Plants: *Two Pratt and Whitney J52-P-6 turbojets each rated at 8,500 lb.s.t.*
Armament: *A maximum external load of 15,000 lb., typical offensive loads including four AGM-12B Bullpup ASMs, five 1,000-lb. Mk.83 or 2,000-lb. Mk.84 general-purpose bombs, thirty 500-lb. bombs, four packs each containing four 5-in. Zuni unguided rockets, or four nineteen-rocket Aero 7D launchers.*
Performance: *Max. speed (clean), 685 m.p.h. at sea level* *(Mach 0.9); max. cruise, 575 m.p.h. at 28,000 ft.; low-level range cruise (high drag configuration), 345 m.p.h.; low-level range (internal fuel), 1,250 mls., (with five 250 Imp. gal. drop tanks), 1,950 mls.; max. range (at 28,000 ft). 2,600 mls.*
Weights: *Loaded (clean), 30,000 lb.; normal loaded, 43,000 lb.; max. overload, 54,000 lb.*
Dimensions: *Span, 53 ft. 0 in.; length, 54 ft. 7 in.; height, 15 ft. 10 in.*

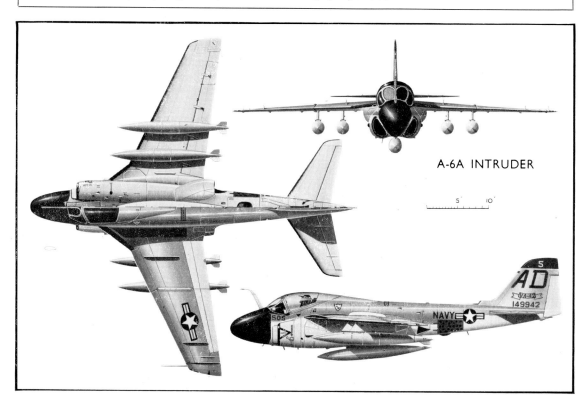

A-6A INTRUDER

GRUMMAN S-2 TRACKER

The first carrier-based aircraft capable of performing all the phases of the anti-submarine warfare mission—detection, classification and destruction—as a self-contained system, the Tracker is the mainstay of the U.S. Navy's shipboard ASW operations, is based aboard Argentine, Brazilian, Canadian and Dutch carriers, and serves with shore-based ASW elements of the Italian Air Force and the Japanese Maritime Self-Defence Force. The ASW mission does not demand remarkable high-speed performance, but pre-requisites are good patrol endurance, low-speed manoeuvrability, and the ability to carry substantial loads of detection equipment and offensive stores. That these attributes are possessed in good measure by the Tracker may be gauged from the fact that this ASW aircraft has been in continuous production for no less than twelve years.

Prior to the development of the Tracker, the search and attack rôles had been performed by two aircraft operating in "hunter-killer" pairs, and Grumman's G-89 design combining both functions was awarded a prototype contract on June 30, 1950, the prototype (BuA. No. 129137), designated XS2F-1, flying twenty-nine months later, on December 4, 1952. A shoulder-wing monoplane powered by two 1,525 h.p. Wright R-1820-82WA radial engines, the XS2F-1 was noteworthy for its capacious fuselage with internal weapons bay and retractable radome. The basic design subsequently proved amenable to adaptation for a variety of defensive and supporting rôles, and for its primary ASW mission has been found capable of accommodating the wide variety of new devices developed over a dozen years to locate and kill submarines.

S-2A TRACKER: The first production version of the Tracker, the S-2A (originally designated S2F-1), entered service with the U.S. Navy's Anti-Submarine Squadron VS-26 in February 1954, and is currently operated alongside the later S-2D by eight first-line squadrons (VS-21, 22, 23, 27, 28, 29, 31 and 32), by replacement training units VS-30 and -41, and by the majority of U.S. Navy Air Reserve Training Units. It has been manufactured under licence in Canada as the CS2F-1 and, with modified equipment, as the CS2F-2,

serving with VS 880 aboard H.M.C.S. *Bonaventure*, and with utility squadrons VU 32 and 33, some of the one hundred aircraft built by de Havilland Canada also serving with the Brazilian Air Force's 1° Grupo de Aviacao Embarcada which operates thirteen Trackers from the carrier *Minas Gerais*. The R.Neth. N.A.S. was another recipient of Canadian-built CS2F-1s, seventeen being supplied to equip No. 1 Squadron at Curacao, twenty-four Grumman-built S-2A Trackers equipping Nos. 2 and 4 Squadrons of that service for operation from the carrier *Karel Doorman*. Forty-eight S-2A Trackers equip the Italian Air Force's 86°, 87° and 88° Gruppi, sixty delivered to the Japanese Maritime Self-Defence Force are operated by the 11th, 12th, 13th, and 14th Squadrons, and by the 204th Air Training Squadron, and six S-2As of Patrol Squadron I are employed by Argentine Naval Aviation from the light fleet carrier *Independencia*.

The S-2A normally carries four crew members, consisting of pilot, co-pilot/navigator and two radar

(Below) S-2A Trackers of VS-22 based at Naval Air Station Quonset Point, and (above) an S-2A of training unit VS-30.

(Above) S-2A *(Bu.No.133264) of the Naval Air Reserve Unit, Grosse Ile, Michigan, and (below) an S-2C (Bu.No.133349) originally operated by VS-36.*

operators. Night identification is aided by a 70-million candlepower searchlight mounted in the leading edge of the starboard wing, APS-38 search radar is installed in a retractable ventral radome, an ASQ-10 MAD (Magnetic Anomaly Detection) boom retracts into the rear fuselage and has permanent-magnetic compensation, ALD-3 electronic countermeasures DF is provided to pinpoint radar or radio signals emanating from underwater craft, and other equipment includes TACAN, Doppler radar, etc.

The rear of the engine nacelles each house eight sonobuoys, and the weapons bay can accommodate two Mk. 101 depth bombs or homing torpedoes. There are six underwing attachment points for 5-in. HVARs, torpedoes or depth charges, and internal fuel tanks provide a total capacity of 2,598 Imp. gal. which is sufficient for a time on station of some five hours at a range of 230 mls. The wings have fixed leading-edge slots and almost full-span flaps—to which the S-2A owes its fine low-speed characteristics—and large span spoilers on the upper wing surfaces augment the small ailerons. For carrier stowage the wings fold upward and inward hydraulically from outboard of the engine nacelles, reducing overall span

---

S-2A TRACKER SPECIFICATION

Power Plants: Two Wright R-1820-82WA nine-cylinder radial engines each rated at 1,525 h.p. for take-off.
Armament: (Internal) Two electric acoustic homing torpedoes, two Mk.101 depth bombs. or four 385-lb. depth charges, and (external) six 5-in. HVARs, Zuni rockets, or 250-lb. bombs.
Performance: Max. speed, 287 m.p.h. at sea level; econ. cruising, 172 m.p.h. at 5,000 ft., patrol speed (with MAD boom and radome extended), 150 m.p.h. at 1,500 ft.; initial climb rate, 1,920 ft./min.; max. range, (standard tankage), 900 mls.; endurance, 6 hr.; service ceiling 23,000 ft.
Weights: Empty, 17,357 lb.; loaded (carrier operation), 24,500 lb.; max. overload, 26,300 lb.
Dimensions: Span, 69 ft. 8 in.; length, 42 ft. 0 in.; height, 16 ft. 3½ in.; wing area, 485 sq. ft.

---

to 27 ft. 4 in. Several variants of the basic S-2A have been developed as follows:

S-2A (MAP Mod) Tracker: A proposed modification of the basic S-2A for supply to Allied nations under the Military Assistance programme has wing-folding mechanism and all carrier equipment deleted, being intended for operation from shore bases. Internal fuel capacity is increased to 3,762 Imp. gal. (as in the later S-2D), and this may be supplemented by an 833 Imp. gal. auxiliary tank in the weapons bay. Normal range (with ten per cent reserves) is 1,352 mls. on standard fuel, and empty and maximum loaded weights are increased to 17,674 lb. and 26,300 lb. respectively.

TS-2A Tracker: Serving with U.S. Navy Training Squadrons VT-27, 28 and 31, the TS-2A is an ASW training version of the Tracker. Equipment is similar to that of the S-2A, and a typical load for a long-range training mission comprises twenty-five Mk. 15 Mod. 8 practice depth charges in the weapons bay, plus practice rockets underwing and sonobuoys in the engine nacelle bays.

S-2B Tracker: The S-2B is the S-2A modified to carry AQA-3 Jezebel passive long-range acoustic search equipment and a fuselage dispenser for sixty underwater sounding charges for echo ranging with the automatic target computing and plotting of the Julie localization equipment.

S-2C TRACKER: Originally known as the S2F-2, the S-2C Tracker was an interim development of the basic design intended to carry larger homing torpedoes in a weapons bay featuring an asymmetrical extension on the port side. To compensate for the increased weight, the tail surfaces were increased in area, but only sixty examples of this version of the Tracker were built, and these have mostly been converted as US-2C utility aircraft for use by U.S. Navy Utility Squadrons VU-2 and VU-7. A few others were converted as RS-2C photographic aircraft.

S-2D TRACKER: Major changes in the basic Tracker design were introduced by the S-2D (originally designated S2F-3) which flew for the first time on May 21, 1959. Physically, the overall dimensions were increased, an eighteen-inch extension of the forward fuselage permitting the lengthening of both pilots' and radar operators' accommodation, this being accompanied by a three-and-a-quarter-inch widening of the fuselage, and wing span was increased by thirty-five inches. The tail surfaces were enlarged, internal fuel capacity was increased to 3,762 Imp. gal., modified engine nacelle configuration permitted an increase in sonobuoy stowage from eight to sixteen per nacelle bay, and ECM antennae were mounted at the wingtips.

The S-2D is operated by fifteen ASW squadrons, eight of these operating the aircraft alongside the earlier S-2A, and seven (VS-26, 33, 34, 35, 36, 37 and 39) being equipped exclusively with the S-2D. The increased fuel capacity of the S-2D permits twice the endurance on station of the S-2A at a range of 230 mls. the AC electrical power system has fifty per cent greater capacity, a Ground Track Plotter eliminates the computing and plotting duties previously required of the crew, providing the pilot with an instantaneous picture of the tactical situation, a more

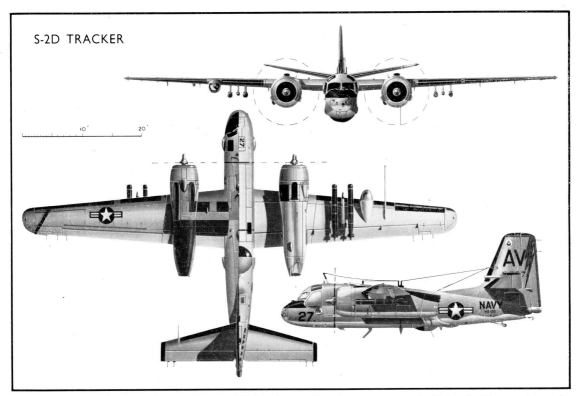

S-2D TRACKER

powerful (85-million candlepower) searchlight is carried, the MAD gear has a longer retractable boom,

S-2D TRACKER SPECIFICATION

Power Plants: *Two Wright R-1820-82WA nine-cylinder radial engines each rated at 1,525 h.p. for take-off.*
Armament: *As for the S-2A Tracker.*
Performance: *Max. speed, 280 m.p.h. at sea level; econ. cruising, 166 m.p.h. at 5,000 ft.; max. range (standard internal fuel), 1,352 mls.; endurance (10% reserves), 9 hr.; service ceiling, 22,000 ft.*
Weights: *Empty, 18,315 lb.; max. loaded (long-range), 26,147 lb.*
Dimensions: *Span, 72 ft. 7 in.; length, 43 ft. 6 in.; height 17 ft. 6 in.; wing area, 499 sq. ft.*

and other equipment includes Sniffer passive submarine exhaust trail detector and instantaneous ECM direction finder with automatic cockpit read-out.

S-2E TRACKER: When fitted with AQA-3 Jezebel passive long-range acoustic search equipment and its associated Julie active (explosive) echo ranging equipment with sixty charges in a fuselage dispenser, the S-2D is redesignated S-2E, and this variant currently serves with VS-24, 25 and 38.

The amenability of the basic Tracker design to adaptation for various defence and support rôles has been referred to earlier, and derivatives are as follows:

C-1A TRADER: A general utility shipboard transport and trainer evolved from the S-2A, the C-1A employs

An early production S-2D Tracker (Bu.No.147869), this type now serving with some fifteen U.S. Navy ASW squadrons.

(Above) AC-1 A Trader (Bu.No.136778) of the U.S. Navy Logistics Support and Transport Squadron VR-24.

many of the components of the ASW aircraft, including the power plants and outer wings which, together with the enlarged tail surfaces of the S-2D, are married to a new fuselage which can accommodate a 3,500-lb. load of freight or a maximum of nine passengers. Possessing a maximum loaded weight of 27,000 lb., the C-1A has a maximum speed of 290 m.p.h. at 4,500 ft., and a range of 800 mls. at 205 m.p.h. at 10,000 ft. Used to supply carriers while at sea, the C-1A is operated by the U.S. Navy's Fleet Logistics Support and Transport Squadrons VR-21, 24 and 40, and the EC-1A is a specialised ECM version.

E-1B TRACER: Derived from the C-1A Trader for airborne early warning and fighter direction duties, the E-1B carries APS-82 radar to detect surface vessels and high- and low-flying aircraft, and extensive operational electronic gear for all-weather operation, including TACAN, IFF, interphone and radio control systems, direction finders and radar altimeter. The oval radome, which measures 32 ft. by 20 ft., houses a 17.5-ft. antenna which sweeps at 6 r.p.m., and two of the four crew members monitor identical 10-in. screens. An aerodynamic prototype of the E-1B flew on March 1, 1957, and the first of sixty-four production machines flew in February 1958, currently serving with Airborne Early Warning Squadrons VAW-11 and VAW-12 which deploy detachments with the various Carrier Air Wings. VAW-11 began re-equipment with the more advanced E-2A Hawkeye in 1964, and VAW-12 is expected to receive the later aircraft during the course of 1965.

(Below) An E-1B Tracer (Bu.No.148913) early warning aircraft of VAW-12, and (above, left) a close-up of the E-1B's radome housing a 17.5-ft. antenna which sweeps at 6 r.p.m. Detachments of VAW-12 are deployed with various Carrier Air Wings, and the unit is scheduled to re-equip with the E-2A Hawkeye during 1965.

LING-TEMCO-VOUGHT (CHANCE VOUGHT) F-8 CRUSADER

The first shipboard combat aircraft capable of attaining speeds greater than Mach 1.0 in level flight, the Crusader is unique among current operational aircraft in having a variable-incidence wing, and remarkable for the rapidity with which it was developed. Equipping fourteen U.S. Navy fleet fighter squadrons and nine U.S. Marine Corps fighter squadrons, the Crusader was being phased out of production during the summer of 1964 with forty-two aircraft for France's Aéronavale, these having been preceded by some 1,200 aircraft for the U.S. Navy and Marine Corps.

The Crusader was first projected in September 1952 by the Chance Vought Corporation—now a component of Ling-Temco-Vought Incorporated—to meet a U.S. Navy request for design proposals for a single-seat shipboard day "air superiority" fighter capable of exceeding Mach 1.0 in level flight. Competing with seven proposals from other manufacturers, the Chance Vought project was awarded a development contract in May 1953, and the prototype flew for the first time twenty-two months later, on March 25, 1955, exceeding Mach 1.0 on its first flight. Originally designated XF8U-1 and subsequently redesignated XF-8A, the prototype was powered by a Pratt and Whitney J57-P-11 turbojet rated at 10,900 lb.s.t. dry and 14,500 lb.s.t. with afterburning, and its most unusual feature was its variable-incidence wing. Mounted on top of the slab-sided fuselage, this was arranged to hinge upwards around the rear spar by some 7°, providing the pilot with good forward visibility for deck landing despite a high angle of attack. When the incidence of the wing was increased, the ailerons, a section of the flaps, and the leading edges were all drooped automatically, further increasing effective camber.

F-8A CRUSADER: The initial production model of the Crusader, the F-8A, made its service début on March 21, 1957, a second prototype having joined the test programme on September 30, 1955, and the first production aircraft having appeared late in 1956. This carried a built-in armament of four 20-mm. Colt-Browning MK-12 cannon with 144 r.p.g., backed by a fuselage rocket pack for thirty-two 2.75-in. missiles and later supplemented by a pair of AIM-9A Sidewinder AAMs mounted externally on the sides of the forward fuselage, this installation leaving the wing clean to maintain performance and offering improved accuracy in weapons release. Internal fuel capacity was 1,165 Imp. gal., and power was provided by a J57-P-12 engine which, after delivery of the first few dozen aircraft, was supplanted by the J57-P-4A providing an afterburning thrust of 16,200 lb. At a normal loaded weight of 27,000 lb., this engine endowed the F-8A with a maximum speed of Mach 1.67 which was accompanied by a maximum range on internal fuel of approximately 1,400 mls.

The first squadron to operate the F-8A was the U.S. Navy's VF-32 which embarked on the U.S.S. *Saratoga* towards the end of 1957, and 318 Crusaders of this model had been manufactured by September 3, 1958 when production switched to the F-8B. The F-8A is now employed only by training squadrons, but in 1964

the Lebanese Air Force was negotiating the purchase of eighteen refurbished F-8As, the airframes, engines and equipment of which were to be brought to zero time, and the original wings replaced by F-8E wings to provide for underwing loads.

RF-8A CRUSADER: Consideration to the adaptation of the basic Crusader for the photographic reconnaissance rôle had been given at an early stage in the development of the aircraft, and the conversion involved the replacement of the cannon and fire control equipment by a camera bay of squared-off section, this accommodating three CAX-12 trimetrogen cameras plus two K-17 vertical cameras. To compensate for the increased cross-sectional area resulting from the introduction of this bay, the upper portion of the fuselage was area-ruled to result in a slightly humped-back profile. Provision was made for

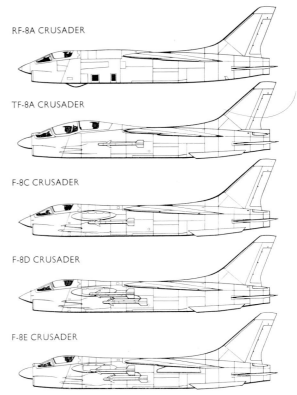

RF-8A CRUSADER

TF-8A CRUSADER

F-8C CRUSADER

F-8D CRUSADER

F-8E CRUSADER

internally-stowed photo-flash bombs, and powered by a similar J57-P-4A turbojet to that of the F-8A, the first photo-reconnaissance RF-8A flew on December 17, 1956, 144 Crusaders of this type being built. Twin ventral fins for improved directional stability, particularly at high speeds, were added retrospectively to a number of RF-8As.

The RF-8A is currently operated by U.S. Navy Photographic Squadrons VFP-62 and -63 which send detachments to the various Carrier Air Wings, and with Marine Corps Squadrons VMCJ-1, -2 and -3.

F-8B CRUSADER: Whereas the F-8A was a pure day

(Above) An F-8C Crusader of VF-142 which re-equipped with the F-4B in 1963, and (below left) an RF-8A of VFP-62.

interceptor, the F-8B, which flew on September 3, 1958, was given limited all-weather intercept capability with a small scanner in a plastic nose cone. Power plant and armament were similar to those of the F-8A, and 130 examples were built before the type was phased out of production in 1959 in favour of the more powerful F-8C. A photo-reconnaissance version, the RF-8B, was projected for limited all-weather surveillance but not proceeded with. Like the F-8A, the B-model has now been relegated to the training rôle.

YTF-8A CRUSADER: One tandem two-seat training version of the Crusader was built and flown as the YTF-8A. This aircraft began life as the seventy-fourth production F-8A, subsequently serving as the proto-

type F-8E before being fitted with a new forward fuselage as the YTF-8A. Powered by a de-rated J57-P-20 engine, the YTF-8A flew for the first time on February 6, 1962, and its performance was within Mach 0.05 of that of the single-seat F-8A. Two of the 20-mm. cannon were removed to permit the installation of the second cockpit aft of the original pilot's position, and provision was made for the installation of additional equipment, such as LABS or TABS weapon delivery, Litton LN-3 inertial guidance, Ryan APN-122 or LFE APN-131 Doppler navigation, APN-149 terrain avoidance radar, NASARR, and low-pressure tyres for rough-field operation.

Six TF-8A trainers were ordered for France's Aéronavale, but following the refusal of appropriations for the two-seat Crusader in the U.S. Fiscal 1964 Budget, the French order was cancelled.

F-8C CRUSADER: The prototype of an improved day "air superiority" version of the Crusader, the F-8C powered by a J57-P-16 offering an afterburning thrust of 16,900 lb., flew initially in December 1957, this merely being a re-engined F-8A. A second prototype more representative of the production model followed in January 1958, and the first production F-8C flew on August 20, 1958, entering service with VF-84 during the following January, and, late in 1964, serving operationally with this squadron and with VF-24, VF-103, VF-194, and VF-211, and with

An F-8B (Bu.No.145456) formerly operated by VF-33 which currently operates the F-8E version of the Crusader.

(Top, right) The Sidewinder AAM installation of an early production F-8E, and (below, right) Zuni rockets and a Bullpup on a late F-8E. Note "hump" on fuselage accommodating the Bullpup electronic equipment

Marine Corps squadrons VMF-212, -232, -235 and -333.

Externally, the F-8C was distinguished from its predecessors by two small air intakes above the tail cone for afterburner cooling, and twin ventral strakes beneath the rear fuselage. The Crusader is limited to about Mach 1.7 by stability characteristics, but the additional power resulted in an improved rate of climb which exceeded 25,000 ft./min. A total of 187 F-8C Crusaders was built, the last of these being delivered on September 20, 1960.

F-8D CRUSADER: Successor to the F-8C, the F-8D introduced further improvements in its electronic equipment, plus installation of a "push-button" autopilot for a higher degree of automaticity in defensive sorties. Still more power was provided by the installation of a J57-P-20 engine developing 10,700 lb.s.t. dry and 18,000 lb.s.t. with afterburning, this permitting the gross weight to be raised from the normal clean figure of 27,550 lb. to a maximum of 32,000 lb. for shipboard operation or 34,000 lb. for shore-based operation. The basic cannon armament

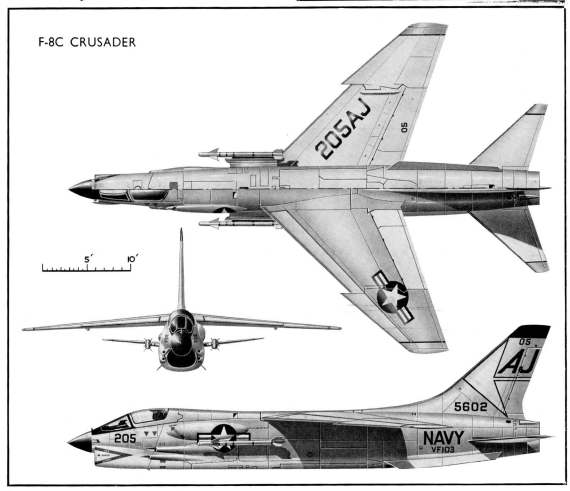

F-8C CRUSADER

(Above and below, left) The second production F-8E(FN) Crusader for France's Aéronavale. Forty-two aircraft of this type will equip flottilles aboard the carriers Clémenceau and Foch.

was retained, but the ventral missile pack was deleted and provision for AIM-9 Sidewinder stowage on the fuselage sides was doubled to four missiles. The first F-8D flew on February 16, 1960, deliveries to the U.S. Navy commencing during the following June, the last of the 152 Crusaders of this type being completed in

January 1962, and these serve with U.S. Navy squadrons VF-32 and VF-31, and with Marine Corps squadrons VMF(AW)-334 and -451.

F-8E CRUSADER: The final production variant of the Crusader for the U.S. Navy, the F-8E, was the first to introduce underwing attachment points for external ordnance loads. The prototype of the F-8E, a conversion of the seventy-fourth production F-8A, flew on June 30, 1961, followed by the first production F-8E three months later, in September. The F-8E received improved all-weather intercept capability by the installation of the APQ-94 search and fire control radar, the larger scanner of which resulted in an enlarged and slightly extended nose cone which was surmounted by a separate housing for the infra-red scanner for use with the Sidewinder AAMs.

At an early stage in the F-8E production run, two underwing attachment points were standardised to increase the ground attack capability of the fighter, this change being accompanied by a "hump" on the wing centre section to house the electronic equipment demanded by AGM-12 Bullpup ASMs, two of which could be mounted on detachable underwing pylons. The F-8E can carry the full range of attack weapons up to a maximum of 5,000 lb., a typical ground attack load comprising four 1,000-lb. bombs and eight Zuni rockets. Production of the F-8E was completed in the summer of 1964 with the 286th aircraft. Late in 1964

(Above, left) The sole tandem two-seat YTF-8A trainer (Bu.No.143710), and (below) an F-8E (Bu.No.145548) of the Naval Air Test Centre.

the F-8E was serving with U.S. Navy squadrons VF-11, -33, -51, -62, and -191, and with Marine Corps squadrons VMF(AW)-122 and -312.

F-8E(FN) CRUSADER: Selected to succeed the Aquilon as a standard Aéronavale shipboard interceptor, the F-8E(FN) is basically similar to the late production F-8E for the U.S. Navy but embodies a number of modifications to suit it for operation from the carriers *Clémenceau* and *Foch*. The principle changes embodied by the F-8E(FN) are the chordwise separation of the drooping wing leading edges into two sections to increase the camber, the introduction of flap-blowing, double the aileron and flap deflection, and a 2° reduction in wing incidence travel. The net result is a reduction in landing approach speed of about 17 m.p.h. These modifications were first tested in flight on a converted F-8D on February 27, 1964, but this aircraft was destroyed in a crash on April 11, 1964, and the first production F-8E(FN), which flew on June 26, 1964, was consequently assigned the task of completing the test programme.

The F-8E(FN) possesses multi-mission capability, and for the intercept mission will normally carry two MATRA R.530 AAMs in addition to the standard cannon armament. Tests with the R.530 installation have been carried out with a U.S. Navy F-8E. The F-8E(FN) is scheduled to enter service with the Aéronavale early in 1965, and forty-two aircraft have been ordered to equip two flottilles.

F-8E CRUSADER SPECIFICATION

Power Plant: One Pratt and Whitney J57-P-20A turbojet rated at 10,700 lb.s.t. and 18,000 lb.s.t. with afterburning. *Armament:* Four 20-mm. MK-12 cannon with 144 r.p.g. plus four AIM-9 Sidewinder 1 infra-red homing AAMs, or (attack) twelve 250-lb. bombs, eight 500-lb. bombs or four 1,000-lb. bombs plus eight Zuni ASMs, or two AGM-12A or AGM-12B Bullpup ASMs. *Performance:* Max. speed, 1,120 m.p.h. at 40,000 ft. (Mach 1.7); time to 57,000 ft., 6 min.; service ceiling, 59,000 ft.; tactical radius (unrefuelled), 600 mls.; max. range, 1,400 mls. at 560 m.p.h. at 36,000 ft. (Mach 0.85). *Weights:* Loaded (clean), 28,000 lb.; max. overload, 34,000 lb. *Dimensions:* Span, 35 ft. 2 in.; length, 54 ft. $5\frac{3}{4}$ in.; height, 15 ft. 9 in.; wing area, 350 sq. ft.

LING-TEMCO-VOUGHT A-7A

Scheduled to fly for the first time in October 1965, with first deliveries to the U.S. Navy being effected one year later, the A-7A was announced, on February 11, 1964, as the winner of the VAL (V for heavier-than-air, A for attack and L for lightweight) contest to provide a successor for the Douglas A-4 Skyhawk. The VAL operational requirements were established on May 17, 1963, Douglas, Grumman, North American, and Ling-Temco-Vought submitting their design and cost proposals, and the last-mentioned company was awarded an initial contract on March 19, 1964. This calls for seven research and development aircraft with provision for initial purchases totalling 160 production articles, although the U.S. Navy anticipates procuring the A-7A throughout the late 'sixties, total purchases eventually amounting to approximately one thousand aircraft.

Essentially a subsonic derivative of the F-8 Crusader series, the A-7A is smaller than the earlier aircraft, has slightly reduced wing sweepback, outboard ailerons, a non-afterburning turbofan engine, and lacks the two-incidence wing. Claimed to offer twice the effectiveness of the A-4E Skyhawk for short-range missions and four times the effectiveness for longer-ranging missions,

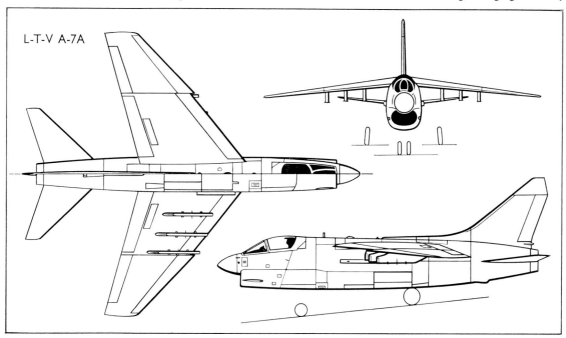

L-T-V A-7A

(Above) A detailed mock-up of the A-7A attack aircraft.

the A-7A will have eight external stores stations, the four outboard stations each having a 3,500 lb. capacity, the two inboard wing stations having a 2,500 lb. capacity, and those on each side of the fuselage having a 500 lb. capacity. Built-in armament will comprise two 20-mm. MK-12 cannon, and for the "limited war" rôle more than 10,000 lb. of ordnance may be carried. Each stores station will be equipped with its own integral hoist for rapid loading.

The electronic equipment installed in the A-7A will differ markedly from that to be installed in the A-7B scheduled to succeed the initial model in production in 1967. The A-7B will feature ILAAS (Integrated Light Attack Avionics System) which will incorporate a digital central computer, Doppler-inertial navigation and high-frequency communications, and will employ microcircuitry and miniaturization to reduce size and weight.

Internal fuel capacity is approximately 1,260 Imp. gal., which is sufficient for a ferry range in clean condition of 3,050 mls., and internal fuel may be supplemented by four 250 Imp. gal. drop tanks to extend

maximum ferry range to 4,100 mls. At a take-off weight of 25,969 lb. with full internal fuel and no external stores, the A-7A will clear a 50-ft. obstacle within 1,257 yds., catapult take-off and minimum usable power approach speeds will be 154 m.p.h. and 139 m.p.h. repectively, and landing distance from 50 ft. will be 1,565 yds.

Approximately six months after the first A-7A delivery to the U.S. Navy, six aircraft will be selected for a demonstration of fleet suitability, being subjected to some 800 flight hours with all maintenance undertaken by U.S. Navy personnel. The contract with Ling-Temco-Vought calls for the attainment of an eighty per cent probability of mission success plus less than twenty maintenance manhours per flying hour during this demonstration.

A-7A SPECIFICATION

Power Plant: *One Pratt and Whitney TF30-P-6 turbojet rated at 11,350 lb.s.t.*
Armament: *Two 20-mm. MK-12 cannon and four AGM-12 Bullpup ASMs or (limited warfare rôle) twelve 500-lb. and twelve 250-lb. general-purpose bombs plus two AIM-9 Sidewinders or Zuni rockets. Maximum ordnance load, 10,000 lb.*
Performance (Design): *Max. speed, 578 m.p.h. at sea level (Mach 0.8); tactical radius (with 4,000-lb. ordnance load), 715 mls.; ferry range (clean), 3,050 mls. at 542 m.p.h. at 40,000 ft. (Mach 0.82), (with four 250 Imp. gal. drop tanks) 4,100 mls. at 518 m.p.h. (Mach 0.785).*
Weights: *Empty, 14,857 lb.; loaded (clean, with max. internal fuel), 25,969 lb., (with four 250 Imp. gal. drop tanks) 35,649 lb.; des'gn catapult, 32,500 lb.*
Dimensions: *Span, 38 ft. 8¾ in.; length, 45 ft. 7⅓ in.; height, 15 ft. 11¼ in.*

LOCKHEED P-2 NEPTUNE

Currently the most widely used of land-based maritime reconnaissance aircraft, serving with nineteen U.S. Navy first-line patrol squadrons, and operational units of the Argentine, Australian, Brazilian, Canadian, French, Japanese, Dutch and Portuguese forces, the Neptune possesses the distinction of having been the first land-based aircraft to be designed from the outset for the maritime rôle, all previous types employed for this task having been adaptations of "off-the-shelf" machines. The Neptune was manufactured continuously for no fewer than nineteen years; nineteen years in which there was an astonishing increase in the quantity and complexity of electronic devices designed to locate and kill submarines. The Neptune succeeded in accommodating each new development in this field, and no fewer than 838 aircraft of this type were produced to U.S. Navy contracts, additional contracts for export and under the MDAP (Mutual Defence Assistance Programme) raising this total to substantially more than a thousand.

Design work on the Lockheed Model 26, which was eventually to emerge as the Neptune, began in September 1941, but owing to the exigencies of war which necessitated concentration on production of the interim PV-2 Harpoon, it was not until April 4, 1944 that the U.S. Navy placed a contract for two prototypes and fifteen production aircraft. Designated

XP2V-1, the first of these prototypes (BuA. No 48237) flew on May 17, 1945. Weighing 32,651 lb. empty and grossing 54,527 lb., the XP2V-1 was powered by two 2,300 h.p. Wright R-3350-8 Cyclones and was intended primarily for anti-submarine and anti-surface vessel patrol work, with rocket and night torpedo attack, mine laying, level bombing and reconnaissance as secondary missions. A crew of seven was carried, defensive armament comprised six 0.5-in. machine guns with 466 r.p.g. in nose, dorsal and tail positions, and the weapons bay could house two 2,000-lb. torpedoes or twelve 325-lb. depth charges. Performance included maximum speeds of 231 m.p.h. at sea level and 289 m.p.h. at 15,600 ft., an initial climb rate of 1,120 ft./min., a service ceiling of 23,200 ft., and a maximum range of 4,210 mls.

The empty and gross weights of the production P2V-1, the first example of which (BuA. No. 89080) was delivered to the U.S. Navy in December 1945, rose to 33,720 lb. and 61,153 lb. respectively, combat weight being 47,115 lb. The third production P2V-1 was modified during 1946 for long-range flights, fuel tankage being substantially increased, all armament being deleted, and an extended, streamlined nose being fitted. First flown on August 29, 1946, and dubbed *Truculent Turtle*, this aircraft established a straight-line distance record of 11,236 miles.

A P-2E Neptune (Bu.No.131444) of Patrol Squadron VP-6 based at Barber's Point Naval Air Station, Hawaii.

A second production order for 151 examples of an improved version, the P2V-2, placed on December 16, 1944, was reduced by 100 aircraft in the post V-J Day cancellations, but a supplementary order for a further thirty machines raised the total quantity of this variant produced to eight-one. Featuring similar nose contours to the *Truculent Turtle* but mounting a battery of six fixed forward-firing cannon of 20-mm. calibre, the P2V-2 was powered by R-3350-24W engines rated at 2,500 h.p. for take-off and 2,800 h.p. with water injection. The prototype XP2V-2 flew on January 7, 1947, the first production P2V-2 following four months later, on May 20th., this and the next seven aircraft having twin 0.5-in. guns in the dorsal and tail positions but the ninth P2V-2 (Model 126) substituting twin 20-mm. cannon for the 0.5-in. weapons in the tail, all subsequent aircraft being similarly armed.

The P2V-2 had an empty weight of 33,962 lb., combat and maximum gross weights being 49,040 lb. and 63,078 lb., and performance included a maximum speed at combat weight of 320 m.p.h. at 13,500 ft., an initial climb rate of 810 ft./min., and a maximum range of 3,985 mls. The eighty-first and last P2V-2 was delivered to the U.S. Navy in July 1948.

Continued development led to the P2V-3 in which more elaborate ASW systems resulted in empty and normal loaded weights of 34,875 lb. and 64,100 lb., and necessitated the installation of R-3350-26W engines offering 2,700 h.p. for take-off or 3,200 h.p. with water injection, these being equipped with jet augmentation exhaust stacks. The first P2V-3 (Model 326) flew on August 6, 1948, and two of the fifty-three ordered were completed as armoured special transports under the designation P2V-3Z, while eleven others were equipped for carrier operations as P2V-3Cs, one of these taking-off from the U.S.S. *Coral Sea* at a gross weight of 74,000 lb. with a dummy 10,000-lb. nuclear weapon, and subsequently flying 4,000 mls., dropping the weapon at mid-point. A further thirty were built under the designation P2V-3W, these carrying APS-20 search radar, the scanner of which was housed in a large radome under the forward fuselage and formed a characteristic of all subsequent production models of the Neptune. The crew included two radar operators, and the first P2V-3W flew on August 12, 1949.

The P2V-4 (Model 426), first flown on November 14, 1949, also carried the APS-20 search radar and embodied further revisions of electronic equipment. Maximum fuel capacity was raised from 2,790 Imp. gal. to 3,503 Imp. gal. by means of fixed wingtip tanks,

A P-2G Neptune (Bu.No.131494), a conversion of the P-2F to similar standards to the P-2H Neptune. The P-2F currently equips Flottilles 21F and 22F of France's Aéronavale.

and empty and gross weights rose once more—to 42,021 lb. and 67,500 lb. The maximum overload weight was 74,129 lb., and the R-3350-30W Turbo-Compound engines offered 3,250 h.p. with water injection for take-off. The P2V-4 attained a maximum speed of 352 m.p.h. at 9,500 ft. and 312 m.p.h. at sea level, maximum range being 4,200 mls., and fifty-two Neptunes of this type were built. When, in 1962, the designations of many U.S. Navy aircraft were revised, the P2V-4 became the P-2D, despite the fact that, together with all earlier versions of the Neptune, it had already been supplanted in U.S. Navy service by later variants of the aircraft.

P-2E NEPTUNE: Built in larger numbers than any other version of the Neptune, the P2V-5 (BuA. No. 124865), or Lockheed Model 426, was first flown on December 29, 1950, and under the impetus of the Korean War, successive orders brought total production of this variant to 424 aircraft, the last being delivered in September 1954.

As initially produced, the P2V-5 featured an Emerson ball turret mounting twin 20-mm. cannon in the nose, the fixed guns being deleted. Enlarged wingtip tanks were centrally mounted, and the starboard tank incorporated a searchlight controlled automatically by movement of the nose turret, total fuel capacity being raised to 3,913 Imp. gal., and maximum gross weight rising to 76,152 lb. The power plants were similar to those installed in the P2V-4, and initial production orders called for forty-five aircraft for the

U.S. Navy, the first of these entering service in 1951, and twelve for the R.A.A.F. for operation by No. 11 Squadron. Thirty-six were supplied to the R.A.F. under the MDAP in 1952 for operation by four squadrons of Coastal Command. These remained in R.A.F. service for some four years, twelve being subsequently transferred to the R.Neth.N.A.S. for operation by that service's No. 320 Squadron and, later, being passed on to the Portuguese Air Force with which they still serve. Six other ex-R.A.F. P2V-5s were transferred to the Argentine Navy, currently serving with Patrol Squadron I of the Escuadra Aeronavale No. 2, and fourteen were delivered to the Brazilian Air Force.

As initially produced, the P2V-5 attained a maximum speed of 341 m.p.h. at 9,500 ft., and had a maximum range of 4,750 mls. In addition to the Emerson nose turret, built-in armament comprised two 0.5-in. guns in a dorsal turret and twin 20-mm. cannon in the tail. A total weapons load of 8,000 lb. could be carried, including sixteen 5-in. HVARs carried underwing. However, the P2V-5 was progressively modified during its production life, the most noteworthy changes being the deletion of the nose turret which was supplanted by an elongated, glazed observation position, and the provision of a MAD (Magnetic Anomaly Detection) tail extension.

Post-production modification programmes included the up-dating of ASW systems, the deletion of the ventral turret, and the fitting of two 3,400 lb.s.t. Westinghouse J34-WE-34 turbojets in underwing pods. These auxiliary turbojets were first fitted on a

The Julie/Jezebel-equipped SP-2H Neptune of Patrol Squadron VP-1 (above) and VP-2 (below).

(Above and below, right) The P-2H Neptune equips four flottilles of France's Aéronavale, 23F, 24F, 25F and 28F.

P2V-5 as a test-bed for the later P2V-7 (P-2H), but later all U.S. Navy P2V-5s were fitted with two J34-WE-34 or -36 turbojets to supplement the power of the R-3350-30W engines for take-off and increase dash and over-target performance, and aircraft so modified were designated P2V-5F. A further modification programme making provision for Julie active explosive echo-sounding and the complementary Jezebel passive detector system, together with associated electronic equipment to interpret the information pro-

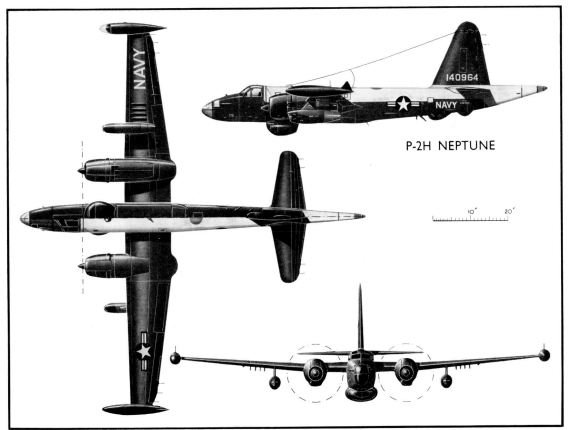

P-2H NEPTUNE

A P-2H Neptune of No. 407 Squadron of the R.C.A.F.'s Maritime Air Command.

vided by these systems, resulted in the P2V-FS, and in 1962 these variants were redesignated P-2E and SP-2E respectively.

At the beginning of September 1964, the P-2E and SP-2E were serving with nine of the U.S. Navy's first-line patrol squadrons (VP-5, 6, 7, 10, 16, 21, 22, 26 and 28), and with fourteen U.S. Naval Air Reserve Training Units. The Neptunes operated by the R.A.A.F.'s No. 11 Squadron have been brought up to the latest P-2E standards, and modified mission versions include the DP-2E drone director and EP-2E with special electronics equipment.

P-2F NEPTUNE: Originally known as the P2V-6, the P-2F Neptune differed from its predecessor in being equipped for mine laying and in having modified electronic equipment. Stainless-steel engine nacelles were introduced for the first time, together with pressure fuelling, reduced-capacity wingtip tanks were fitted, and secondary missions included night torpedo attack, photo reconnaissance and high- and low-level bombing. The first of eighty-three aircraft of this type (BuA. No. 126514) flew on October 16, 1952, and a number were supplied under the MDAP to France's Aéronautique Navale, currently equipping Flottilles

21F and 22F. A small number of aircraft modified to carry Fairchild AUM-N-2 Petrel missiles are designated MP-2F, a training conversion being known as the TP-2F, and with auxiliary J34-WE-36 jet pods the designation is changed to P-2G, but no aircraft of this type remain in first-line U.S. Navy service.

P-2H NEPTUNE: The final production variant of the Neptune, the P-2H (formerly P2V-7) embodies all the improvements progressively introduced by earlier models, and variants include the SP-2H Julie/Jezebel-equipped version serving with U.S. Navy Air Development Squadron VX-1, and the LP-2J with the Antarctic Exploration Squadron VX-6. The P-2H was equipped with auxiliary turbojets from the outset, and the first YP-2H (Model 726) flew on April 26, 1954. Improvements incorporated in this model included the introduction of the more powerful R-3350-32W Turbo-Compound engines, a bulged cockpit canopy for increased all-round view, revised crew accommodation, simplified multi-function control systems, a modified nosewheel unit, and redesigned wingtip tanks. Initial production aircraft retained the dorsal turret mounting twin 0.5-in. guns, but this was replaced at an early stage by a new Emerson turret with two 20-mm.

A Kawasaki-built P-2H Neptune of the Japanese Maritime Self-Defence Force. The J.M.S.D.F. has received sixty-four Neptunes.

cannon and, eventually, the dorsal turret was omitted entirely.

Twenty-five P-2H Neptunes were supplied to the R.C.A.F. These first entered service without the auxiliary turbojets, but power pods were fitted retrospectively, and these aircraft currently equip No. 407 Squadron and No. 2 Maritime Operational Training Unit of the R.C.A.F.'s Maritime Air Command. Twelve P-2H Neptunes were delivered to the R.A.A.F. in mid-1962 to equip No. 12 Squadron, four flottilles of France's Aéronautique Navale, 23F, 24F, 25F and 28F, received the P-2H, and the last fifteen aircraft of this type built were for the R.Neth. N.A.S. The Dutch P-2H Neptunes were originally delivered with an unglazed nose housing four 20-mm. cannon, but these weapons were later removed and the standard P-2H nose reintroduced. The aircraft serve with the R.Neth.N.A.S.'s No. 320 Squadron in the NATO Channel Command, and have been modified to carry Nord AS.12 ASMs underwing.

Sixteen P-2H Neptunes were supplied by the parent company to the Japanese Maritime Self-Defence Force and, in 1959, the Japanese Kawasaki company received a contract for the licence manufacture of forty-two P-2H Neptunes, later supplemented by a further six aircraft, bringing the total quantity for the J.M.S.D.F. to sixty-four aircraft. The first Kawasaki-built P-2H was delivered on December 11, 1959, and the type equips the J.M.S.D.F.'s 1st, 2nd, 3rd, and 4th Squadrons. Seven P-2H Neptunes were supplied to the U.S.A.F. for the training of electronic counter-measures operators under the designation RB-69.

At the beginning of September 1964, the P-2H equipped ten of the U.S. Navy's first-line patrol squadrons (VP-1, 2, 4, 9, 11, 17, 18, 23, 24 and 56). Seven crew members are normally carried, comprising pilot, co-pilot, navigator-bombardier, radar/MAD-operator, radio-operator, sonobuoy-operator, and ordnanceman, and normal fuel capacity is 1,832 Imp. gal., although there is also provision for a 583 Imp. gal. ferry tank in the weapons bay. Production of the P-2H by the parent company was completed in April 1962, and the last Kawasaki-built P-2H was expected to be delivered late in 1964.

P-2H NEPTUNE SPECIFICATION

Power Plants: Two Wright R-3350-32W Turbo-Compound eighteen-cylinder two-row radial engines each rated at 3,500 h.p. for take-off with water injection, and two Westinghouse J34-WE-36 turbojets each rated at 3,400 lb.s.t.
Armament: Weapons bay may accommodate two 2,165-lb. torpedoes, two 2,000-lb. Mk.55 mines, eight 1,000-lb. Mk.52 mines, twelve 500-lb. mines, twelve 325-lb. depth charges, or sixteen 500-lb., eight 1,000-lb., or four 2,000-lb. bombs. Provision for sixteen 5-in. HVARs externally.
Performance: Max. speed, 356 m.p.h. at 10,000 ft., (piston engines only), 305 m.p.h. at 8,500 ft., 262 m.p.h. at sea level; patrol speed, 173–207 m.p.h. at 1,000 ft.; normal range, 2,200 mls.; max. range (with 583 Imp. gal. ferry tanks), 3,685 mls.; service ceiling, 22,000 ft.
Weights: Empty, 49,935 lb.; max. loaded, 79,895 lb.
Dimensions: Span, 103 ft. 10 in.; length, 91 ft. 8 in.; height, 29 ft. 4 in.; wing area, 1,000 sq. ft.

LOCKHEED P-3A ORION

When the U.S. Chief of Naval Operations issued Type Specification No. 146 in August 1957, calling for a land-based maritime reconnaissance aircraft to succeed the P-2 Neptune, all participants in the contest to fulfil this requirement based their proposals on existing production aircraft in order to meet its cost and delivery demands. Only Lockheed's proposal met all the requirements, and on April 24, 1958, this was awarded a Research and Development Contract. The Lockheed proposal was based on the commercial Electra transport, and to serve as an aerodynamic prototype, the third Electra prototype (N1883) was fitted with a mock-up of a MAD (Magnetic Anomaly Detection) tail extension and a shallow ventral fairing over what was to be the weapons bay in the operational aircraft. In this form, the aircraft flew for the first time on August 19, 1958. Less than two months later, on October 7, 1958, a pre-production contract was awarded and, on February 19, 1959, funds were allocated for the conversion of a commercial Electra airframe as a flight test vehicle under the designation YP-3A (originally Y/P3V-1), this aircraft (BuA. No. 148276) flying for the first time on November 25, 1959.

Eleven months later, on October 25, 1960, a production contract was placed for the P-3A, shortly afterwards christened "Orion", and on March 2, 1961, the first pre-production P-3A (BuA. No. 148883) was rolled out, flying six weeks later, on April 15th. The only really major change in design from the Electra

found desirable was the shortening of the forward fuselage by some seven feet. The commodious transport fuselage provided ample room for the multifarious equipment required for ASW, and the deletion of the forward cabin both saved weight and improved the aerodynamics of the aircraft. Five of the pre-production P-3As were delivered to the Naval Air Test Centre at Patuxent River, and the sixth was sent to the Naval Weapons Evaluation Facility at Albuquerque. On June 8, 1962, it was announced that the U.S. Navy Patrol Squadrons VP-8 and VP-44 of Fleet Air Wing 5 would be the first recipients of the P-3A, and the former had its full complement of twelve P-3As by the end of the year. A third FAW-5 squadron, VP-49, was subsequently re-equipped with the P-3A, and by September 1964, squadrons VP-19 and VP-46 of FAW-10, VP-30 and VP-45 of FAW-11, and VP-31 of FAW-14 had converted to the P-3A.

The P-3A adds a vastly improved degree of versatility to the basic capabilities of its predecessor, the P-2 Neptune, both within and outside the basic maritime rôles. For instance, for the extended low-altitude coastal reconnaissance mission, two engines may be shut down during the patrol to extend remaining time-on-station by some forty per cent, enough power being available on two engines even at combat weight to climb when required. For offshore patrol, escort, task force protection and general ASW surveillance, *en route* operations can be conducted at high altitudes

P-3A Orions of Patrol Squadron VP-8, the first U.S. Navy unit to operate this successor to the P-2 Neptune.

where fuel economy is improved, and radar, ECM and communications ranges are extended, the P-3A, unlike its predecessor, being fully pressurized. The flexibility of the P-3A permits it to fulfil the barrier monitoring rôle which demands an aircraft capable of long range at intermediate altitudes and speeds to effect a proper revisit interval to each sector. Outside the ASW spectrum, the P-3A has provision for a

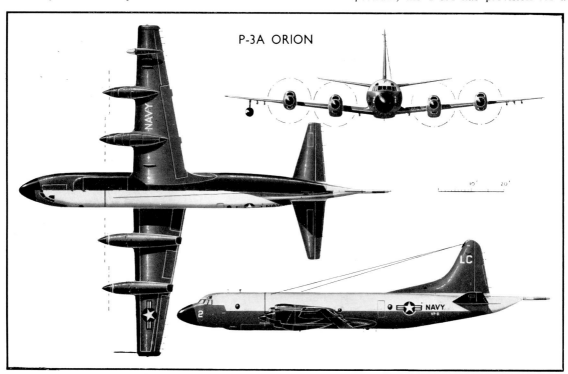

P-3A ORION

substantial load of mines, as well as the ability to carry a wide range of other weapons for attacks on ground and shipping targets, and by removal of the sonobuoy stowage racks and with combat seats installed it can be rapidly converted into an emergency troop carrier, accommodating fifty combat troops and 4,000 lb. of equipment. Its long range and extensive communications equipment lend the P-3A for employment in Command and Control missions, acting as a signals centre or airborne headquarters for the commander of a fleet or task force.

Compared with the P-2 Neptune, the P-3A offers some sixty per cent increase in ferry range and almost twice the speed. Outstanding low-speed handling characteristics permit tight circles during submarine attacks, and at combat weight the P-3A can be manoeuvred within a turning circle of 600 yds. radius—180° in only twenty seconds. Some two-and-a-half times the floor area of the Neptune and a total interior volume of 6,900 cu. ft. permits optimum location of the equipment and a comfortable crew environment. Normally, a crew of ten is carried, and the maximum ASW stores load is 10,909 lb., the weapons bay being situated ahead of the wing centre section. This has sufficient capacity for three or four conventional or nuclear homing torpedoes, Lulu nuclear depth charges and other stores, all of which can be jettisoned in twenty seconds. There are also four underwing stations for additional stores on each side, the outboard starboard pylon carrying a powerful anti-shipping searchlight. Some 8,400 Imp. gal. of JP-4 or JP-5

fuel is housed in the completely "wet" wing, seventy-one per cent of the fuel being contained in four integral tanks stretching from the wingtips to the centre section, the remaining tank, which is divided between the centre section and a fuselage bladder cell forward of the wing, being utilised only for extra-long flights.

The Royal New Zealand Air Force is to acquire five P-3A Orions for service with No. 5 Squadron, and a more advanced version of the basic design, the P-3B with Allison regenerative turboprops offering comparable fuel consumptions to the most economical piston engines, and the latest ASW systems and weapons, is being developed for 1967-68 service.

P-3A ORION SPECIFICATION

Power Plants: *Four Allison T56-A-10W turboprops each rated at 4,050 e.s.h.p. for take-off, and 4,500 e.s.h.p. with water-alcohol injection.*

Armament: *(Internal) Three or four nuclear or conventional torpedoes and Lulu depth charges, and (external) five Mk.52 or Mk.55 mines, depth bombs or Zuni rockets.*

Performance: *Max. speed (at 70,000 lb.) 460 m.p.h. at 24,000 ft., (at 100,000 lb.) 440 m.p.h. at 20,000 ft., (at 130,000 lb) 437 m.p.h. at 15,000 ft.; average cruise, 403 m.p.h. at 20,000 ft.; patrol speed, 207–437 m.p.h.; initial climb (combat weight), 2,820 ft./min.; time to 20,000 ft., 15 min.; service ceiling, 30,000 ft.; max. range, 5,000 mls.*

Weights: *Design loaded, 127,500 lb.; max. overload, 130,000 lb.*

Dimensions: *Span, 99 ft. 8 in.; length, 116 ft. 10 in.; height, 33 ft. 8 in.; wing area, 1,300 sq. ft.*

LOCKHEED U-2

The U-2 strategic reconnaissance aircraft has possibly achieved more notoriety during its career than any modern military aeroplane and, operationally, has certainly proved the most controversial. Conceived in 1954, allegedly at the request of the U.S. Central Intelligence Agency, the aircraft was developed under conditions of the utmost secrecy and, in order to disguise its intended rôle, it was categorised as a *utility* aeroplane and, accordingly, allocated the official designation "U-2".

The intended task of strategic reconnaissance and other clandestine missions over Communist territory demanded exceptional altitude capability to render the aircraft immune to interception. The primary aim of the Lockheed design team headed by Clarence L. Johnson was, therefore, the evolution of an aeroplane optimized for the attainment of what were then considered to be extreme altitudes and their sustentation for protracted periods, and all design features were subordinated to this goal.

The optimization of the design for maximum altitude necessitated considerable sacrifice in structural strength, and with its light airframe and a wing possessing the extremely high aspect ratio of 14.3 : 1, the U-2 was virtually a powered sailplane. The wing loading was barely 25 lb./sq. ft., the fuselage employed a fineness ratio of almost 10 : 1, and the aircraft was, to all intents and purposes, hand built, possessing an exceptional external finish. All fuel was housed in wing tanks which, in the initial model, had a total capacity of 653.5 Imp. gal., and when the tanks were

fully fuelled, the wings required support on the ground, necessitating provision of small wheels on flexible outrigger struts designed to fall away from the aircraft under their own weight after take-off.

The undercarriage itself comprised a retractable dual-wheel main member slightly forward of the c.g., and a small, steerable aft member with dual, solid-rubber wheels. During landing, the aircraft was intended to balance on these, sinking onto a wingtip skid as the aircraft slowed down. The wingtip skids were so designed as to serve as partial end plates, reducing the strength of wingtip vortexes and improving the efficiency of the wing when operating at the high lift coefficients of high altitude cruise.

The U-2 was flown for the first time in 1955, and the first three examples of the initial production model, the U-2A, were accepted by the U.S.A.F. in mid-1956, by which time some ten other U-2As were being operated ostensibly on behalf of NASA (National Aeronautics and Space Administration) from Lakenheath, United Kingdom, and Wiesbaden, Germany. The U-2A was powered by a Pratt and Whitney J57-P-37A turbojet rated at 11,200 lb.s.t. at sea level and, in view of the exceptionally light structure, endowing the aircraft with a very favourable power-to-weight ratio. Special low-volatility fuel (MIL-F-25524A) was used to prevent losses due to evaporation at high operational altitudes, resulting in approximately two per cent greater range than had standard JP-4 been used. Internal fuel tankage could be supplemented by two 87 Imp. gal. pinion tanks which increased loaded

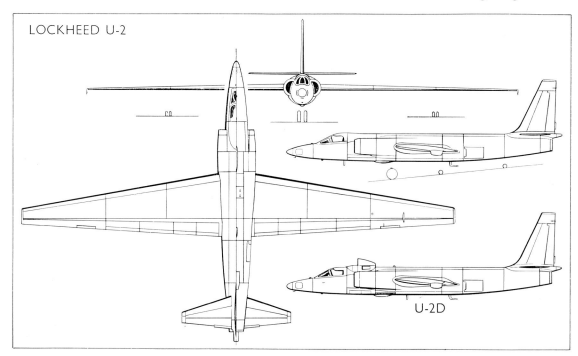

LOCKHEED U-2

U-2D

weight from 15,850 lb. to 17,270 lb., stretching high-altitude range from some 2,200 to 2,600 mls. with

ten per cent reserves. Initial climb rate was approximately 7,500 ft./min., and operational technique included climb to a cruising altitude of some 65,000 ft., a constant angle of attack being maintained, and the aircraft drifting up to its maximum altitude of 75,000 ft. as fuel was burned off. Range could be stretched by gliding between intermittent bursts of power.

Later U-2A aircraft featured a "wet" wing, integral tanks stretching from wingtip to wingtip and offering a total capacity of 1,112 Imp. gal., and similar tankage was provided the U-2B which, introduced in 1959, featured a Pratt and Whitney J75-P-13 engine offering 17,000 lb.s.t. at sea level, although no changes were made in the basic airframe. The U-2B offered a substantially improved performance over the U-2A, despite an increase in maximum loaded weight to some 19,750 lb., maximum attainable ceiling approaching 90,000 ft., and ranges of the order of 4,000 mls. being possible.

(Below and above, left) A Lockheed U-2D (56-6954), one of five two-seat examples of this high-altitude aircraft

(Above) Lockheed U-2A (56-6701) employed for research at Edwards A.F.B., and (below) U-2A (56-6708) of the 4080th Strategic Wing at Laughlin A.F.B.

The pilot of the U-2 was housed in a small, pressurized cockpit ahead of the air intakes, and equipped with a partial pressure suit. In an emergency, this suit was capable of maintaining an equivalent altitude of 29,000 ft., permitting a gradual descent in the event of sudden cockpit depressurization. The standard control surfaces were actuated through direct mechanical linkage, and a gust control system automatically deflected flaps and ailerons to reduce loads on the structure when gusts were encountered. Equipment included an inertial navigation system, receivers for monitoring and recording radio and radar transmissions, and various cameras, including a panoramic camera with a ventral periscopic sight.

CIA aircraft operated by civilian contract pilots and carrying no national markings, officially being assigned to NASA, began clandestine reconnaissance sorties over Communist territory in 1956, and continued such missions successfully until, on May 1, 1960, a U-2B flying across the Soviet Union from Adana, Turkey, to Bodo, Norway, was intercepted and shot down near Sverdlovsk, the CIA pilot surviving. The international repercussions of this incident led to the U-2's subsequent notoriety. Another U-2, this time flown by a U.S.A.F. pilot from the 4080th Strategic Wing, was shot down by an SA-2 Guideline SAM over Cuba in 1962, after descending to get below high cirrus cloud cover, and two U-2B aircraft supplied to the Chinese Nationalist Air Force have both been lost during reconnaissance sorties over the mainland.

Although designed primarily for the strategic reconnaissance rôle, the high altitude capabilities of the U-2 render it an ideal research vehicle. In consequence, the U-2 has been employed by NASA for high altitude gust research, and by the U.S.A.F. Strategic Air Command and Research and Development Command for radar calibration and other tasks. Under the designation WU-2A, the U-2A is employed for high altitude air sampling, the purpose being to determine the type, distribution and overall amount of

radio active dust in the upper atmosphere, and others monitor missile launchings, gathering data on the infrared characteristics of the missiles' exhausts. A two-seat version of the U-2B, the U-2D, is employed for missile monitoring, a second seat being inserted aft of the standard cockpit, its occupant monitoring infra-red radiometers or spectrometers, an external housing above the cockpit having apertures to admit radiation.

Only fifty-five Lockheed U-2s were built, five of these being two-seat U-2Ds and the remainder single-seaters, and a number of these remain in service with the U.S.A.F. Technically, the U-2 is a very interesting aircraft, and the success of Clarence Johnson in meeting the CIA's requirements can be gauged from the fact that for more than three years the aircraft repeatedly penetrated Communist territory, its altitude capabilities affording it immunity from interception by manned aircraft or missile.

U-2B SPECIFICATION

Power Plant: *One Pratt and Whitney J75-P-13 turbojet rated at 17,000 lb.s.t.*
Performance: *Max. speed, 528 m.p.h. at 60,000 ft (Mach 0.8), 200 m.p.h. at sea level; range cruise, 460–480 m.p.h.: normal operational ceiling, 75,000–80,000 ft.; max. ceiling, 90,000 ft.; approx. max. range, 4,000 mls.*
Weights: *Approx. loaded, 19,750 lb.*
Dimensions: *Span, 80 ft. 0 in.; length, 49 ft. 7 in.; height, 13 ft. 0 in.; wing area, 565 sq. ft.*

LOCKHEED A-11 (SR-71 AND YF-12A)

Designed originally as a successor to the U-2 in the long-range strategic reconnaissance rôle, the Lockheed A-11 was first revealed in February 1964, and is scheduled to be evaluated by the U.S.A.F. Strategic Air Command during 1965 under the designation SR-71. Under development since late 1959, the designation "A-11" being that allocated to the project by the manufacturer, this extremely advanced aircraft was the winner of a design contest which, held in 1958 and in which projects by Boeing, General Dynamics and North American competed, called for an aircraft combining the survival potential of sustained Mach 3.0 cruise at extreme altitudes with a range capability sufficient for deep penetrations of Communist territory. The A-11 was developed largely with funds provided via the U.S. Central Intelligence Agency, and the first of an initial quantity of twelve development aircraft allegedly flew late in 1961.

The A-11's design was optimized for maximum performance at extreme altitudes, and employs a relatively light structure in which extensive use is made of titanium alloys. The design team, headed by Clarence Johnson, went to considerable lengths to minimize the wave drag due to lift by extending the lifting surfaces forward along the fuselage and nacelles, thus spreading lift over the greatest possible length. The basic wing planform selected was a 60° delta with rounded tips and cut-outs at the engine afterburner

nozzles, and, at the current gross weight of approximately 136,000 lb., wing loading is moderately high, and take-off would appear to be normally facilitated by starting with only a nominal proportion of the 6,000–7,500 Imp. gal. total fuel, flight refuelling being employed.

The nacelles of the 32,500 lb.s.t. Pratt and Whitney J58 (JT11D-20B) single-spool turbojets are canted downwards several degrees, enabling the forward fuselage to operate at a higher incidence than the main wing for maximum lift while allowing symmetrical ram air compression during cruise. The engines have circular intakes with limited-travel conical centre-bodies. Large-area radial slot intakes around the nacelles provide cooling ram air for the afterburner nozzles which are of variable-orifice petal type. The twin slab-type vertical tail surfaces pivot on fixed stub-fins on the engine nacelles, and are canted inwards about 15° from the vertical to place them in a favourable position in relation to the vortices shed by the nacelles, and in addition to the fixed lower fins which are canted outwards, a large ventral fin folds to port when the undercarriage is extended to provide adequate ground clearance. The two crew members are seated in tandem ejector seats beneath clamshell-type hoods.

SR-71: The designation "SR-71" was first applied to the version of the A-11 for the Strategic Air Command

in July 1964. The A-11 was designed from the outset to carry advanced camera, electronic and infra-red reconnaissance systems, and it may be assumed that a number of examples of the SR-71 version of the A-11 are included in the initial quantity of twelve development and research aircraft. The first SR-71 is scheduled to be delivered to Beale Air Force Base during 1965 for evaluation, and will carry the bulk of its equipment in a streamlined ventral mission pod. This detachable pod will permit systems to be changed rapidly, and has already been tested in its operational environmental conditions of extreme altitudes and speeds by a North American X-15 research aircraft.

It has been stated that the SR-71 will operate at altitudes in excess of 80,000 feet at speeds exceeding Mach 3.0, although it may be assumed that such speeds are greater than the normal range cruise of the aircraft, acceleration to speeds approaching Mach 3.5 being reserved for specific penetrations and escape. An enlarged version of the basic aircraft, the SR-71A, attained the mock-up stage during 1964, and proposals have been made for the purchase of some thirty examples of this variant, but it would seem likely that the entire SR-71 programme may be overtaken by events. The growth of anti-ICBM defences will ultimately rule out the use of high-flying aircraft whose infra-red emissions broadcast their presence over enormous distances, and, in any case, advances in the quality of satellite reconnaissance data are likely to nullify the value of a manned reconnaissance system.

YF-12A: During 1964 three examples of the A-11 (60-6934, 6935 and 6936) were modified for evaluation in the intercept fighter rôle under the designation YF-12A, despite the fact that the relatively light structure of the basic A-11, optimized for maximum speed, maximum altitude operation and probably having a design load factor of only 2.5–3 g as compared with a fighter's normal 6.67–8 g, would seem unsuited for flight manoeuvres demanded by the intercept rôle.

Admittedly the really high loads are normally encountered during low-level sorties rather than during high-altitude interception, and the U.S.A.F. has stated that the YF-12A will take advantage of the exceptional range and manoeuvrability of its missiles in intercepting both low- and high-flying intruders while remaining at its optimum cruise altitude, such interceptors as the F-106A having to manoeuvre much more precisely to get the target within its launch zone before it can fire. But it has also been stated that one advantage offered by the YF-12A is its re-attack ability which demands a high standard of manoeuvrability, and thus it would seem probable that *should* the funds reportedly requested by the U.S.A.F. for the quantity production of the F-12A be granted, some structural strengthening will be undertaken.

Reportedly possessing a 1,200-mile combat radius, the YF-12A has been married to the Hughes pulsed-Doppler AN/ASG-18 fire control radar originally developed for the now defunct North American F-108A Rapier Mach 3.0 interceptor, and armament comprises four Hughes AIM-47A Falcon missiles stowed in tandem bays in the wing extensions along the fuselage sides, two infra-red detectors being mounted in cut-outs at the forward ends of these extensions. The missiles, which carry either nuclear or conventional warheads, are explosively ejected downwards from the YF-12A's weapons bays prior to the ignition of their solid rocket motors. Overall dimensions of the YF-12A include a length of approximately 102 ft. and a span of some 55 ft.

It has been suggested that two hundred F-12A interceptors will cost $5,000M (£1,714M), or $25M (£9M) each, and there is some doubt that funds of this magnitude will be granted failing fresh evidence that the Soviet Union is continuing the development of supersonic cruise manned bombers, as all known existing types can presumably be intercepted satisfactorily by the F-4C or F-111A.

LOCKHEED F-104 STARFIGHTER

One of the most controversial combat aircraft ever to enter service and one of the most significant developments of the 'fifties, the Starfighter was, in its original form, something of a disappointment, and fewer than three hundred examples of this warplane were delivered to the U.S.A.F. The design then underwent an amazing metamorphosis from a short-range day superiority weapon to an all-weather tactical strike and reconnaissance aircraft. This transformation resulted in the selection of the Starfighter by the

Luftwaffe, a choice which triggered a chain reaction of production plans which crystallized in the largest international aircraft manufacturing programme ever undertaken.

By the beginning of 1952, shortcomings in the first generation of U.S.A.F. jet fighters had resulted in a requirement for a day superiority fighter in which all criteria were subordinated to flight performance. The Lockheed design team began preliminary investigations aimed at fulfilling this requirement in March

One of twelve Lockheed F-104A Starfighters (56-804) supplied to the Pakistan Air Force to equip one squadron.

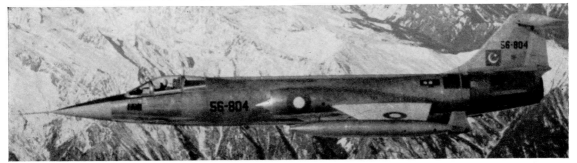

1952, examining delta wings, swept wings, flush cockpits, wingtip-mounted vertical fins, rocket propulsion, and projects with gross weights ranging from 8,000 lb. to 50,000 lb., before, in November 1952, a radical configuration embodying a long, needle-nosed fuselage, exceptionally small anhedralled trapezoidal wings, and a T-tail, was finally selected, and detailed design began. Known as the Lockheed Model 83, two prototypes were ordered in March 1953 under the designation XF-104, the first of these (53-37786) flying on February 7, 1954.

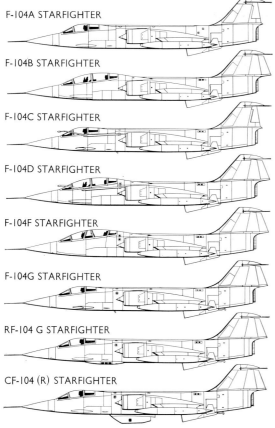

F-104A STARFIGHTER

F-104B STARFIGHTER

F-104C STARFIGHTER

F-104D STARFIGHTER

F-104F STARFIGHTER

F-104G STARFIGHTER

RF-104 G STARFIGHTER

CF-104 (R) STARFIGHTER

The XF-104 was powered by a Wright XJ65-W-6 turbojet of 7,200 lb.s.t. dry and 10,500 lb.s.t. with afterburning and fed by conventional lateral intakes. On March 25, 1955, one of the two XF-104s attained a speed of Mach 1.79, but in the meantime the Lockheed team had set its sights higher, and had introduced major changes in the design which were incorporated in the YF-104A, fifteen examples of which were ordered, the majority of these having joined the flight test programme by the end of 1955. The most important change embodied by the YF-104A was the introduction of the substantially more powerful General Electric YJ79-GE-3 engine which, together with increased internal tankage, necessitated the lengthening of the fuselage by several feet. The new engine was fed by fixed-geometry, multi-shock intakes with a bleed system matching airflow requirements to the flight regime, a forward-retracting nose undercarriage member supplanted the rearward-retracting

unit of the XF-104, and an a.c. electrical system of enhanced capacity was provided. The first YF-104A (55-2955) attained a speed of Mach 2.0 on April 27, 1955, and the first production F-104A (55-2970), which incorporated all the features successively introduced on the YF-104A, was flown for the first time on February 17, 1956.

F-104A STARFIGHTER: The Starfighter's flight test programme had to overcome a number of severe problems and, in consequence, this proved more protracted than had been anticipated, involving no less than fifty-two aircraft which flew some eight thousand missions during its course. One of the most fundamental troubles was super-stalled pitch-up which was not finally rectified until April 1957. Another major problem was provided by the wingtip fuel tanks which tended to hit the fuselage after jettisoning, but finally the F-104A was released for service, and deliveries to the U.S.A.F.'s 83rd Fighter-Interceptor Wing began on January 26, 1958. However, shortly after the F-104A's service introduction, the J79-GE-3A turbojet began to suffer flame-outs, roughness, backfiring and other teething troubles, resulting in a series of accidents, and, early in April 1958, all F-104A Starfighters were grounded.

The F-104A carries a 20-mm. M-61 Vulcan rotary cannon which may be supplemented by two AIM-9B Sidewinder 1A infra-red homing AAMs attached to wingtip shoes. Alternatively, these shoes may each carry a 141.5 or 166.5 Imp. gal. jettisonable fuel tank. The fuselage nose houses the AN/ASG-14TI radar fire control system, and the pilot is equipped with a *downward* ejection seat, the first of its kind to be installed in a fighter. Weights range from 11,660 lb. empty to 17,320 lb. loaded in clean configuration, with a maximum overload of 22,420 lb., and performance includes a short-period maximum speed of Mach 2.28 and a stabilised speed of Mach 1.9, tactical radius with two 166.5 Imp. gal. tip tanks being 580 miles.

As a result of the engine teething troubles experienced early in 1958, all F-104A Starfighters were fitted with J79-GE-3B turbojets before being returned to service with the Air Defence Command, but the safety record of the aircraft continued to compare unfavourably with that of other "Century-series" fighters, and the F-104A's operational effectiveness was marred by its relatively short range in relation to the North American air defence problem, and its lack of all-weather capability which prevented its operation within the SAGE (Semi-Automatic Ground Environment) system. Thus, by the beginning of 1960, the F-104A had been withdrawn from the U.S.A.F.'s active combat inventory, twenty-five later being transferred to the Chinese Nationalist Air Force and twelve to the Pakistan Air Force. Twenty-four were converted to QF-104 target drone configuration, and three, each fitted with a 6,000 lb. thrust Rocketdyne AR-2 auxiliary rocket motor, were converted as NF-104As for use by the Aerospace Research Pilots' School. Most of the remaining F-104As were transferred to the Air National Guard, equipping two squadrons, but early in 1963 these were returned to service with the U.S.A.F. Air Defence Command's 319th and 331st Fighter-Interceptor Squadrons. Production of the F-104A (excluding YF-104As) totalled 155 aircraft.

F-104A Starfighters in Air National Guard service prior to their return to the Air Defence Command. (Above) F-104A 56-834 with the Tennessee Air Guard, and (below, right) F-104A 56-779 with the South Carolina Air Guard.

F-104B STARFIGHTER: The F-104B, the first example of which (56-3719) was flown on February 7, 1957, is a tandem two-seat instrument and transition training variant of the F-104A in which a second cockpit has been inserted immediately aft of the standard cockpit in space occupied in the single-seater by electronics racking, the Vulcan cannon and fuel. Initial flight trials dictated a substantial increase in rudder area and the introduction of a ventral fin similar to that later applied to the F-104A to solve the problem of the blanking out of the upper vertical tail surface by the fuselage and wing at high attack angles. Initially assigned to the Air Defence Command, the F-104B was later reassigned to the Air National Guard, and a few of the twenty-six aircraft of this type built were supplied to the Chinese Nationalist Air Force.

F-104C STARFIGHTER: Serving with the U.S.A.F. Tactical Air Command's 479th Tactical Fighter Wing, the F-104C was the first multi-mission version of the basic Starfighter design. Externally similar to the F-104A, the F-104C is provided with a flight refuelling boom on the port side of the fuselage which, fixed in flight, is removable on the ground, together with its fairing. A J79-GE-7, with a two-inch increase in turbine diameter and improved specific fuel consumption, supplants the earlier J79-GE-3B, this engine offering normal and military dry ratings of 9,700 and 10,000 lb.s.t. as compared with 8,950 and 9,600 lb.s.t. for the -3B, full afterburning thrust being 15,800 lb. as compared with 14,800 lb. Further changes include the introduction of blown flaps and provision for carrying a range of stores underwing. The six-barrel M-61 rotary cannon of the F-104A is retained, and for the intercept rôle a maximum of four AIM-9B Sidewinder AAMs may be carried, two on wingtip shoes and two on underwing pylons. Alternative underwing loads include two LAU-3/A launcher pods each housing nineteen 2.75-in. rockets, or two 750-lb. or 1,000-lb. general-purpose or demolition bombs.

The ASG-14 fire control system is essentially similar to that of the F-104A, and the normal internal fuel capacity of 746 Imp. gal. may be augmented by two 141.5 Imp. gal. wingtip tanks and a 187 Imp. gal. tank pylon-mounted on the fuselage centreline. Normal and maximum loaded weights are 20,500 lb. and 23,590 lb. respectively, and performance includes a short-period maximum Mach number of 2.3, maximum stabilized speed being Mach 2.0. An altitude of 50,000 ft. is attained in 5 min. 40 sec. with Sidewinders mounted at the wingtips, and maximum

operational ceiling with this armament is 55,000 ft.

The first deliveries of the F-104C were made to the 831st Air Division of the Tactical Air Command on October 16, 1958, but only seventy-seven Starfighters of this type were completed, and the 479th Tactical Fighter Wing, scheduled to re-equip with the F-4C Phantom II in 1965, has been the only U.S.A.F. unit to operate this type.

F-104D STARFIGHTER: A tandem two-seat operational training version of the F-104C for Tactical Air Command with similar in-flight refuelling provision, blown flaps, and an enlarged, powered rudder as first

(Below) F-104C Starfighters of the 479th Tactical Fighter Wing.

(Above) An F-104B (57-1294) of the Chinese Nationalist Air Force, and (below) the refuelling probe of F-104D (57-1333).

being assembled in Japan, Mitsubishi being the prime contractor assisted by Kawasaki, delivery to the J.A.S.D.F. being completed in May 1964. Unlike the F-104D, the F-104DJ has upward ejection seats, and power is provided by an Ishikawajima-Harima-built version of the J79 engine, the J79-IHI-11A, which offers similar thrust ratings to the F-104D's J79-GE-7. The F-104DJ two-seaters are distributed among the F-104J-equipped squadrons of the J.A.S.D.F.'s 2nd and 5th Fighter-Interceptor Wings at Chitose and Nyutabaru.

F-104F Starfighter: The F-104F is also basically similar to the F-104D but has Martin-Baker upward ejection seats and generally similar equipment to the F-104G single-seater apart from the NASARR system and M-61 Vulcan cannon. Thirty were built by the parent company and delivered to the Federal German Luftwaffe in 1960–61, these currently serving with the operational training units of the Kommando der Schulen.

fitted to the F-104B, the F-104D followed the Air Defence Command's F-104B on the assembly line, and twenty-two examples were built. The M-61 cannon of the single-seater is deleted but provision is made for full external stores, and power is provided by a J79-GE-7 engine.

Two export versions of the F-104D have been produced as follows:

F-104DJ Starfighter: Twenty tandem two-seat operational trainers essentially similar to the F-104D ordered for the Japanese Air Self-Defence Force are designated F-104DJ. Built by the parent company in California, the first F-104DJ was assembled and flight tested by Lockheed, the remaining nineteen

F-104G STARFIGHTER: Although the F-104G differs little externally from the U.S.A.F. Tactical Air Command's F-104C, it in fact embodies extensive structural redesign, the entire airframe being re-stressed to meet strike fighter strength requirements with full external loads, and to permit close-support and penetration missions at low altitudes without placard restrictions. Furthermore, it is equipped with the extremely sophisticated NASARR F-15A-41B optimized in air-to-air and air-to-ground modes to provide airborne target detection and tracking, guidance data, terrain avoidance, contour mapping for navigation, ground mapping for all-weather bombing, and ranging information for bombing computation in visual bombing modes.

Lockheed began development of the multi-mission version of the Starfighter in 1958 which was to result in the current F-104G. Structural improvements to the fuselage, wing and tail assembly were made, a total of thirty-six new forgings being provided for such major structural items as fuselage main frames, wing fittings and beams, fuselage longerons and joints, fuselage tail frames, tail assembly beams and ribs, plus some fuselage skins. In order to provide the increased

Thirty tandem two-seat F-104F Starfighters have been supplied to the Luftwaffe's Kommando der Schulen.

F-104DJ Starfighter trainers of the J.A.S.D.F.'s 2nd Wing at Chitose. The J.A.S.D.F. has received twenty F-104DJs.

control power demanded by low-altitude operations at increased gross weights, the tailplane servo-mechanism was modified to afford increased hinge moment; the vertical tail surfaces were increased in area by some twenty-five per cent by extending the leading edge of the fin forward and moving the trailing edge aft, providing increased directional stability at high Mach numbers; irreversible hydraulic power was incorporated to drive the rudder, the separate yaw damper tab previously fitted being eliminated, and the control system governing the trailing-edge flaps was modified to permit their employment as manoeuvring flaps, resulting in a thirty-three per cent reduction in turning radius at 5,000 feet. Supplemented by full-span leading-edge flaps for landing, the trailing-edge flaps were fully blown. Electro-thermal de-icing elements were added to the engine air intakes, a runway arrester hook was introduced, together with fully powered brakes and an anti-skid system, and the downward ejection seat of earlier single-seat Starfighters was

supplanted by a Martin-Baker Mk.5 upward ejection seat.

The multi-mission F-104G version of the Starfighter was evolved primarily to meet requirements formulated by the Federal German Luftwaffe, and the Federal Republic's signing of a contract for the development of this aircraft and its subsequent licence manufacture in Germany, on March 18, 1959, was a lead rapidly followed by other countries. Canada signed a licence production contract on September 17, 1959 (see page 10), Japan followed suit on January 29, 1960, the Netherlands on April 20, 1960, Belgium on June 20, 1960 and, finally, Italy on March 2, 1961. Originally, it had been planned to build 210 F-104Gs in Germany by a southern consortium of Messer- schmitt, Dornier, Heinkel and Siebel known as the Arbeitsgemeinschaft 104 (ARGE 104), but later revised plans and the decisions of the Netherlands, Belgium and Italy to participate in a European F-104G manufacturing programme led to the original ARGE

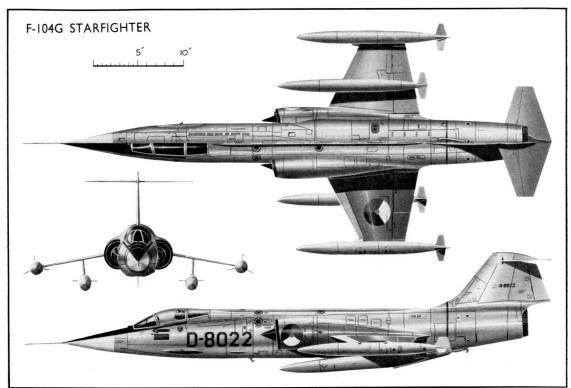

F-104G STARFIGHTER

F-104G Starfighters of Jabo.G.33 at Büchel, the second Federal German Luftwaffe unit to equip with this type.

104 becoming the ARGE Süd, the establishment of the ARGE Nord, comprising Focke-Wulf, Hamburger Flugzeugbau, Weser Flugzeugbau and the Dutch Fokker and Aviolanda concerns, a western group comprising SABCA and Avions Fairey in Belgium, and an Italian Group comprising Fiat, Aerfer, Macchi, Piaggio, SACA, and SIAI-Marchetti, with total orders for 947 aircraft.

The principal recipient of the European-built F-104Gs is Germany, this country being in process of receiving 604 aircraft which, together with ninety-six F-104Gs acquired from Lockheed brings the Federal Republic's orders for the single-seat Starfighter to 700 machines. The Netherlands are receiving 120

European-built F-104Gs, and Belgium and Italy are respectively receiving ninety-nine and 124, each of the last two mentioned countries having also received one Lockheed-built F-104G to bring their total procurement to 100 and 125 aircraft.

Manufacture of the F-104G is also being undertaken by Canadair which company has received orders for 140 machines for supply to NATO countries under the U.S. Military Assistance Programme. Differing from European-built F-104Gs primarily in the type of NASARR installed—this being of the F-15AM-11 variety and is, like the F-15A-41B, optimized in both air-to-air and air-to-ground modes—the first Canadair-built F-104G (as distinct from the CF-104) flew on July 30, 1963, and recipients and the quantities of aircraft that they are scheduled to receive are as follows: Denmark (25), Norway (16), Greece (36), and Turkey (38).

The F-104G flew for the first time on October 5, 1960, and the first of the ninety-six Lockheed-built single-seaters for the Federal German Luftwaffe was delivered to Germany in May 1961. The first German-assembled aircraft (from ARGE Süd) followed on August 10, 1961, and the first Luftwaffe unit to re-equip with the F-104G was Jabo.G.31 at Nörvenich, this being followed by Jabo.G.33 at Büchel, current plans

(Above, left and below) F-104G Starfighters built in the Netherlands by Fokker for the R.Neth.A.F.

An RF-104G of the R.Neth.A.F.'s No. 306 Squadron. The conversion for the photo-reconnaissance rôle is undertaken by Avio Diepen.

calling for seven Geschwader of F-104Gs with a first-line strength of 380 aircraft. The Federal German Kriegsmarine is also to standardise on the F-104G, plans calling for the delivery of 100 aircraft to that service.

In the Netherlands, Nos. 322 and 323 Squadrons of the R.Neth.A.F. have re-equipped with the F-104G, Nos. 311 and 312 Squadrons being scheduled to convert during the course of 1965. In Belgium, the F-104G-equipped 349ème and 350ème Escadrilles are being followed on this type by Escadrilles 23 and 31, and in Italy the first F-104G formation is the IV[a] Aerobrigata.

The F-104G retains the M-61 Vulcan rotary cannon of earlier single-seat Starfighters, and for the intercept rôle missile armament normally comprises two or four AIM-9B Sidewinder AAMs, the NASARR system giving radar search, acquisition and automatic tracking for lead-collision or lead-pursuit attack with the missiles. A director-type gunsight is used for the cannon and gives optical indication of line of sight with the lead angle furnished by the NASARR computer. With two Sidewinders, the F-104G attains an altitude of 35,000 ft. in ninety seconds, and then, after three-and-a-half minutes for acceleration to Mach 2.0, attains 50,000 ft. in a further 140 seconds. Thus, the F-104G requires less than eight minutes from brakes off to a Mach 2.0 interception at 50,000 ft.

The F-104G's bombing computer ties in with the inertial navigator, air data computer and NASARR systems, mechanizing the relationship between the bomb trajectory and the aircraft in space, and there are four basic bomb delivery modes: level release, over-the-shoulder, dive-toss and LABS (Low-Altitude Bombing System). With one 2,000-lb. Mk.84 and two 1,000-lb. Mk.83 general-purpose bombs and two 100 Imp. gal. wingtip tanks, the F-104G has a radius of action for a Hi-Lo-Hi mission of 510 mls. and 334 mls. for a Lo-Lo-Lo mission. With a 2,000-lb. one-megaton store and wingtip tanks, plus two 162 Imp. gal. underwing tanks, the F-104G has a radius of 690 mls. using a Hi-Lo-Lo-Hi mission profile. The F-104G has been flown in a constant 2 g turn at Mach 1.8 at 43,000 ft. without loss of speed, and can be flown at low altitude with wing flaps partly extended at Mach 0.75 to 0.8 in turns of only 3,300 ft. radius.

RF-104G STARFIGHTER: Equipping No. 306 Squadron of the R.Neth.A.F., the RF-104G is a tactical photographic reconnaissance derivative of the basic F-104G which, first flown in October 1963, has the M-61 cannon deleted and a ventral camera bay inserted immediately aft of the nosewheel housing.

TF-104G STARFIGHTER: Possessing a basically similar airframe to the single-seat F-104G, the tandem two-seat TF-104G carries full NASARR equipment, and is intended for pilot training, particularly in low-level navigation. The autopilot and M-61 cannon have been eliminated and electronics equipment and fuel tanks relocated to provide space for the second cockpit. The centreline rack capable of carrying a nuclear store has also been removed, but partial weapons capability is retained, AAMs, ASMs, bombs or fuel tanks being mounted on the two underwing pylons and at the wingtips. Internal fuel capacity is 583 Imp. gal. as compared with 746 Imp. gal. for the single-seater, but apart from range, the performance capabilities of the TF-104G are almost identical to those of the F-104G. Successive orders for the TF-104G have been placed by the Federal German Luftwaffe, a total of 104 machines being purchased by that service, thirty of these being retained in the U.S.A. where, together with fifty European-built F-104Gs, they are being used for Luftwaffe pilot training at Luke Air Force Base. Ten TF-104Gs have been supplied to the R.Neth. A.F., twelve are being delivered to Italy and three to Belgium, and other recipients of the twenty-eight additional TF-104Gs ordered by mid-1964 under the MAP include the R.Dan.A.F. which service anticipated receiving four during 1965.

F-104H STARFIGHTER: A proposed export version of the basic single-seat F-104G without NASARR, an optical gunsight and simplified equipment, the F-104H is intended to fulfil both intercept and fighter-bomber rôles, empty equipped weight being 13,492 lb. and maximum overload weight being 28,440 lb. During 1964 the F-104H was offered to the Saudi Arabian and other governments.

TF-104H STARFIGHTER: A tandem two-seat version of the F-104H retaining operational capabilities and adding conversion training to its repertoire,

An F-104J (36-8555) of the J.A.S.D.F.'s No. 201 Squadron.

the TF-104H has empty and maximum overload weights of 13,750 lb. and 24,800 lb. respectively. The performance envelope of the F-104H and TF-104H is essentially similar to that of the F-104G and TF-104G.

F-104J STARFIGHTER: A licence-manufactured version of the Starfighter for the Japanese Air Self-Defence Force, the F-104J has an essentially similar airframe to that of the F-104G but is limited by U.S. treaty agreements to the intercept rôle although possessing similar air-to-ground capability. The NASARR F-15J-31 installed in the F-104J is optimized in the air-to-air mode, the J79-IHI-11A turbojet is licence-manufactured by Ishikawajima-Harima, the M-61 cannon is retained, and primary armament comprises four AIM-9B Sidewinder AAMs, two mounted underwing and two carried by a rack on the fuselage centreline.

The licence manufacturing agreement was signed by the Japanese government on January 29, 1960, and under this Lockheed built and tested three F-104J Starfighters, the first of which flew on June 30, 1961, these subsequently being disassembled and shipped to Japan for reassembly by Mitsubishi. Current orders call for an additional 177 F-104Js of which the first twenty-nine were produced from knockdown assemblies, subsequent aircraft being manufactured completely by Mitsubishi in association with Kawasaki, 100 having been delivered to the J.A.S.D.F. by

June 1964, with the initial order being scheduled for completion by March 1965 when work on a follow-on batch of fifty additional F-104Js is expected to commence.

The first J.A.S.D.F. units to convert to the F-104J were the 201st and 202nd Fighter-Interceptor Squadrons at Chitose and Nyutabaru, these being followed by the 203rd Squadron at Chitose in June and the 204th Squadron at Nyutabaru in November 1964, with the 205th Squadron being scheduled to have re-equipped with the F-104J at Komatsu in February 1965. Nos. 201 and 202 Squadrons became operational on the F-104J in November and September 1964 respectively. The type has been given the popular name of "Eiko" (Glory) in Japanese service.

F-104G STARFIGHTER SPECIFICATION

Power Plant: *One General Electric J79-GE-11A turbojet rated at 10,000 lb.s.t. and 15,800 lb.s.t. with afterburning.*
Armament: *One 20-mm. M-61 Vulcan rotary cannon and (intercept) two of four AIM-9B Sidewinder infra-red homing AAMs or (attack) two AGM-12A Bullpup ASMs, two LAU-3 pods each with nineteen 2.75-in. rockets, two LAU-10 pods each with seven 5-in. rockets, three 700-lb. MLU-10B land-mines, three 1,000-lb. Mk.83 general-purpose bombs, two 1,000-lb. Mk.83 and one 2,000-lb. Mk.84 bombs, or one 2,000-lb. nuclear store.*
Performance: *Short-period max. speed (clean), 1,550 m.p.h. at 40,000 ft. (Mach 2.35); max. stabilised speed, 1,320 m.p.h. at 40,000 ft. (Mach 2.0); max. low level speed, 915 m.p.h. (Mach 1.2); time to 35,000 ft., 1.5 min.; time to 49,200 ft., 6.5 min.; combat ceiling, 55,000 ft.; tactical radius (patrol mission with two 100 Imp. gal. and two 162 Imp. gal. drop tanks), 690 mls. at 610 m.p.h. (Mach 0.92); max. ferry range (1,455 Imp. gal. fuel), 1,988 mls.*
Weights: *Operational empty, 14,300 lb.; loaded (clean), 19,841 lb.; max. loaded, 25,027 lb.*
Dimensions: *Span, 21 ft. 11 in.; length, 54 ft. 9 in.; height, 13 ft. 6 in.; wing area, 196.1 sq. ft.*

MARTIN B-57

Serving in the reconnaissance-bomber rôle with the U.S.A.F.'s Pacific Air Force, with the Air National Guard, and with the Pakistan Air Force, the B-57 began life as a licence-manufactured version of the Canberra (see pages 90–95), but such has been the evolution of the basic design in the U.S.A. that, in its latest high-altitude RB-57F form, it bears little resemblance to the British light bomber from which it stems.

The only combat aircraft of foreign design to be adopted for operational service by U.S. forces since the Second World War, the B-57 was, in its original form, patterned closely on the Canberra B.Mk. 2. A manufacturing licence for the Canberra had been acquired by the Glenn L. Martin Company on April 19, 1951, after the type had been evaluated by the U.S.A.F., and one Canberra B.Mk.2 (WD940) was flown across the Atlantic on August 31, 1951 to serve as a pattern aircraft. The first eight production aircraft, which received the designation B-57A, differed from their progenitor solely in having engineering

changes dictated by American production techniques and Wright J65-W-1 engines, and the first of these (52-1418) flew on July 20, 1953. The following sixty-seven aircraft housed cameras aft of the bomb-bay, and as the RB-57A, entered service with the 363rd Tactical Reconnaissance Wing late in 1954.

In the meantime, an extensive design modification programme was being undertaken by Martin, the aim being to increase the suitability of the aircraft for the tactical night intrusion rôle. The result was the B-57B, the first example of which (52-1493) flew on June 28, 1954. A new forward fuselage provided tandem seating for two crew members, a rotary weapons-bay door was introduced, and provision was made in the wings for a fixed gun armament of eight 0.5-in. or four 20-mm. weapons, stores pylons being provided beneath the outboard wing sections. In addition to providing more versatility than the Canberra B.Mk.2 in weapons capability, the B-57B offered a marginal improvement in performance first obtained with the B-57A by means of better airframe sealing and the

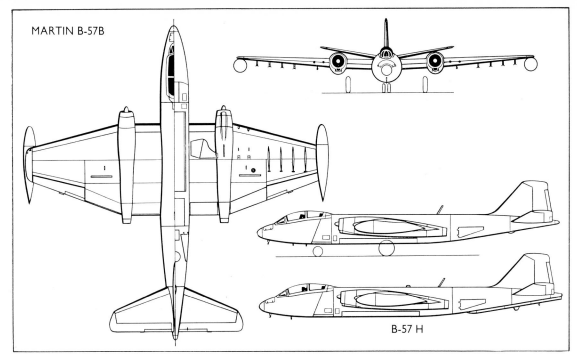

MARTIN B-57B

B-57 H

slightly greater power available from the J65 engines, maximum attainable speed in level flight being raised by Mach 0.09 at altitude.

The B-57B began to enter service with the 461st Bombardment Wing of the Tactical Air Command in January 1955, the 345th Wing also converting in 1956, followed by the 3rd Wing of the P.A.C.A.F. The B-57B was finally withdrawn from Tactical Air Command service in 1959, by which time thirty B-57Bs had been supplied to the Pakistan Air Force with which they currently equip two squadrons. It remained in P.A.C.A.F. service, and ex-T.A.C. B-57Bs were issued to Air National Guard units from 1961, some being converted to RB-57B configuration with a fuselage camera bay.

B-57C: The B-57C, which followed the 202 examples of the B-57B on the production line, differed from its predecessor solely in having provision for dual controls with which, as the TB-57C, it could serve as a transition trainer. The first example of this version (53-3825) was flown on December 30, 1954, thirty-eight being built and serving with the B-57-equipped

T.A.C. wings until transferred to the A.N.G. with which they currently serve.

RB-57D: Evolved from the basic B-57B specifically for strategic electronic and photographic reconnaissance, the RB-57D was built in several versions, a

---

B-57B SPECIFICATION

Power Plants: *Two Wright J65-W-5 turbojets each rated at 7,220 lb.s.t.*
Armament: *Eight 0.5-in. Colt-Browning machine guns and 5,000-lb. bomb load internally, plus eight 5-in. HVARs and two 500-lb. bombs or napalm tanks on underwing pylons.*
Performance: *Max. speed, 582 m.p.h. at 40,000 ft. (Mach 0.88), 534 m.p.h. at sea level (Mach 0.74); initial climb, 3,500 ft./min.; service ceiling, 48,000 ft.; tactical radius, 1,100 mls. at 480 m.p.h.; normal range (clean), 2,300 mls.*
Weights: *Normal loaded, 49,000 lb.; max. overload, 55,000 lb.*
Dimensions: *Span, 63 ft. 11½ in.; length, 65 ft. 6 in.; height, 15 ft. 7 in.; wing area, 960 sq. ft.*

A dual-control B-57C (53-3846), the personal aircraft of the C.-in-C. of the Pakistan A.F. which has two B-57B squadrons.

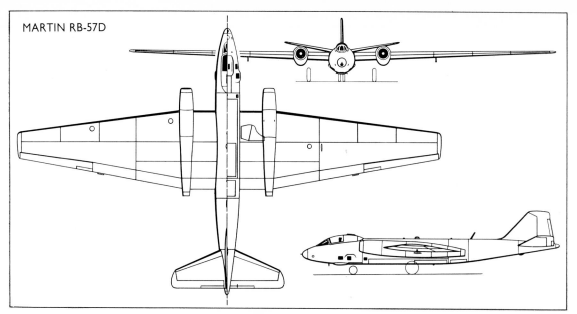

MARTIN RB-57D

(*Above*) *An RB-57A (52-1440) of the Arkansas Air Guard.*

(*Above*) *An RB-57B (52-1589) of the Kentucky Air Guard.*

(*Above*) *An RB-57C (53-3831) of the Nevada Air Guard.*

(*Above*) *A B-57E (55-4248) of the Arkansas Air Guard.*

total of twenty being manufactured of which two were supplied to the Nationalist Chinese. While the fuselage remained essentially similar to that of the B-57B,

an entirely new wing was introduced which, without the tip ECM fairings which characterised one version, had an overall span of 106 ft. Power was provided by two 11,000 lb.s.t. Pratt and Whitney J57-P-37A turbojets, and on strategic reconnaissance missions over Communist territory, the RB-57D cruised at altitudes between 60,000 and 70,000 ft.

Of the twenty aircraft built, six were two-seat photo-reconnaissance RB-57D2s with provision for in-flight refuelling, and the remaining fourteen were single-seaters, several of which, for electronic reconnaissance and referred to as RB-57D(C)s, having bulbous nose and tail radomes increasing overall length to 67 ft. 9¾ in. and wingtip fairings increasing span to 107 ft. 6 in., the RB-57D(D) being similar but lacking the wingtip fairings and in-flight refuelling capability. In addition to its use by the U.S.A.F. Tactical Air Command, the RB-57D served with the P.A.C.A.F. in the strategic reconnaissance rôle, with the Air Defence Command for calibration of the NORAD radar network, and with the Military Air Transport Service for air sampling, but wing structural problems necessitated the grounding of the U.S.A.F.'s RB-57Ds during 1963.

B-57E: The final production version of the B-57 was the multi-purpose B-57E which, in addition to performing the tactical bomber-reconnaissance (RB-57E) task and being suitable for transition training (TB-57E), was equipped for the target-towing rôle, a detachable banner target and cable container being mounted beneath the rear fuselage. A total of sixty-eight B-57Es was built.

RB-57F: The most drastic revision of the basic B-57 is represented by the RB-57F intended for strategic reconnaissance at extreme altitudes, and for weather reconnaissance with the U.S.A.F. Military Air Transport Service. Converted from the B-57B by General Dynamics' Fort Worth Division, the RB-57F has an entirely new long-span wing built up on three spars and incorporating a large number of bonded aluminium honeycomb sandwich panels. In static position, the wing, which has an overall span of 122 ft.,

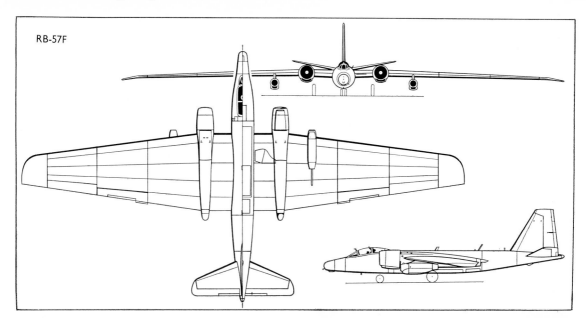

RB-57F

has an anhedral of approximately 1.5° outboard of the main engine nacelles. The fuselage nose is extended by forty inches to accommodate electronic equipment, increasing overall length to 68 ft. 10 in., and power is provided by two Pratt and Whitney TF33-P-11 turbo-fans each rated at approximately 18,000 lb.s.t. dry. These are special high altitude engines, and may be supplemented by two 3,300 lb.s.t. Pratt and Whitney J60-P-9 turbojets which, mounted beneath the wings, outboard of the main engine nacelles, are detachable, depending on mission requirements.

The RB-57F carries two crew members, and endurance exceeds ten hours using the standard integral wing tankage. This may be extended by the addition of auxiliary tanks. Operating altitudes of between 90,000 and 100,000 feet are reportedly attainable, and delivery of the first RB-57F (61-3291) to the Military Air Transport Service's 58th Weather Reconnaissance Squadron took place at the beginning of July 1964. The initial contract called for twelve RB-57F conversions, but it is believed that further contracts for this type have now been placed.

(Below) An RB-57D (53-3977), and (above, right) an RB-57F (61-3291), high-altitude versions of the basic design.

MARTIN P-5 MARLIN

The U.S. Navy's last operational flying boat and, apart from the Beriev Be-10 (see page 46), the last waterborne aircraft to see extensive service in the maritime reconnaissance rôle, the Marlin is being steadily phased out in favour of land-based types and, by the beginning of September 1964, only five squadrons (VP-40, 42, 47, 48 and 50) remained in first-line U.S. Navy service. One Marlin-equipped unit, Flottille 27F, also served with France's Aéronautique Navale.

Preliminary design studies for what was to become the Marlin were initiated in July 1946, design evolution of the wartime Mariner having led to a new and more

(Below) A P-5B Marlin of the French Navy's Flottille 27F.

efficient hull shape which, with a length-to-beam ratio of 8.5:1, had given the flying boat a new lease on life, substantially reducing the performance differential between this type of aircraft and comparable land-based types. The U.S. Navy contract for the construction of a prototype maritime reconnaissance flying boat utilising the new hull had been awarded on June 26, 1946, and as the XP5M-1, this aircraft was flown for the first time on May 4, 1948. The XP5M-1 employed the wing and upper hull of the earlier Mariner, and the production P5M-1, twenty-five examples of which were ordered in July, 1950, embodied a number of major changes.

Powered by two Wright R-3350-30WA engines each rated at 3,250 h.p. for take-off, the P5M-1 flew for the first time on June 22, 1951, and differences from the prototype included a raised flight deck, the replacement of the bow turret by a large radome for the APS-80 search radar, the deletion of the dorsal turret, and the provision of pylons in place of the struts for the stabilising floats. Carrying a crew of eight, the P5M-1 housed two 2,000-lb. bombs or two torpedoes in each engine nacelle, and eight 1,000-lb. bombs could be mounted on underwing stations. Defensive armament comprised twin 20-mm. cannon in the tail. The first P5M-1 was delivered to the U.S. Navy in December 1951, the first squadron, VF-44, being equipped with the flying boat on April 23, 1952, and a total of 114 aircraft of this type had been completed

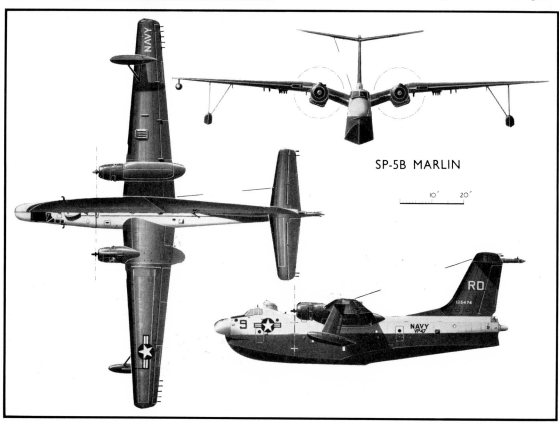

SP-5B MARLIN

10'　20'

An SP-5B Marlin of Patrol Squadron VP-47, one of the last U.S. Navy flying boat-equipped maritime reconnaissance units.

when the P5M-1 was phased out of production in favour of the P5M-2 in 1954.

The P5M-1 was progressively up-dated, AN/ASQ-8 MAD (Magnetic Anomaly Detection) equipment and other ASW systems were installed and, in 1962, the designation of this initial production version of the Marlin was changed to P-5A. Introduction of the Julie active explosive echo-sounding and complementary Jezebel passive detector system, together with their associated electronic equipment, resulted in a change of designation to SP-5A, a training variant being known as the TP-5A.

P-5B MARLIN: The P-5B Marlin began life as the P5M-2, and this is the only model now serving with the U.S. Navy. Considerable redesign of the Marlin had been undertaken during 1951-52, and the improved P5M-2 (later to be redesignated P-5B) was flown for the first time on April 29, 1954, deliveries to the U.S. Navy commencing two months later and continuing until December 20, 1960. By comparison with its predecessor, the P-5B featured an increase in internal fuel tankage from 1,003 Imp. gal. to 1,686 Imp. gal. which, with jettisonable 670 Imp. gal. tanks in each weapons bay, gave a total fuel tankage of 3,027 Imp. gal. Tail surfaces of T-configuration were fitted to increase aerodynamic efficiency and reduce structural weight, a new bow was introduced with a

lower chine line to reduce spray height, more powerful engines were fitted, and crew accommodation was revised.

Ten P-5B Marlins were supplied to France's Aéronautique Navale, and the principal version currently serving with the U.S. Navy is the SP-5B equipped with Julie and Jezebel. The Marlin is expected to be phased out of service during the course of 1965.

P-5B MARLIN SPECIFICATION

Power Plants: *Two Wright R-3350-32W Turbo-Compound eighteen-cylinder two-row radial engines each rated at 3,450 h.p. for take-off and 3,700 h.p. with water injection.*
Armament: *Four 2,165-lb. torpedoes, four 2,000-lb. bombs, four 2,000-lb. Mk.55 mines, eight 1,000-lb. Mk.52 mines, sixteen 500-lb. bombs or sixteen 325-lb. depth charges internally, plus eight 1,000-lb. bombs or mines externally.*
Performance: *Max. speed, 251 m.p.h. at sea level; patrol speeds, 150–180 m.p.h. at 1,000–5,000 ft.; initial climb rate, 1,200 ft./min.; service ceiling, 24,000 ft.; normal range (ASW mission), 2,050 mls.; ferry range (with 670 Imp. gal. jettisonable tanks in weapons bays), 3,100 mls.*
Weights: *Empty, 50,485 lb.; loaded (ASW mission), 76,635 lb.; max. overload, 85,000 lb.*
Dimensions: *Span, 118 ft. 2¼ in.; length, 100 ft. 7¼ in.; height, 32 ft. 8½ in.; wing area, 1,406.33 sq. ft.*

McDONNELL F-101 VOODOO

Designed as a strategic penetration fighter for the U.S.A.F. Strategic Air Command, the Voodoo was destined never to serve in this rôle or with this Command, subsequently being developed as an all-weather interceptor for the Air Defence Command and for tactical rôles with the Tactical Air Command. As an interceptor, the Voodoo currently equips several U.S.A.F. Air Defence Command wings and three R.C.A.F. Air Defence Command squadrons; the fighter-bomber version equips one U.S.A.F. Tactical Air Command wing, and in tactical reconnaissance form it serves with several T.A.C. squadrons and with one squadron of the Chinese Nationalist Air Force.

The Voodoo's design history dates back to June 1946 when McDonnell began detail design of a strategic

penetration fighter intended to escort Strategic Air Command bombers, and two prototypes were ordered under the designation XF-88. Powered by 3,000 lb.s.t. Westinghouse J34-WE-13 turbojets, the first XF-88 (46-525) flew on October 20, 1948, the second aircraft, the XF-88A (46-526) with short afterburners boosting the thrust of its J34-WE-22 engines to 3,600 lb. each, following in 1950. However, changes in operational requirements led to the cancellation of the XF-88 contract in August 1950, although the design was revived in 1951 to meet new strategic fighter requirements under the designation F-101 (Weapon System 105), a pre-production series of twenty-nine aircraft being ordered in May 1953. The overall length of the fuselage was substantially

F-101A-30 VOODOO

increased, and J57 turbojets were substituted for the J34s. On September 29, 1954, the Strategic Air Command cancelled the requirement but, in the meantime, the Tactical Air Command had evinced interest in the aircraft, and development continued as a fighter-bomber.

The first pre-production F-101A (53-2418) flew initially on September 29, 1954, with J57-P-13 turbojets each rated at 11,700 lb.s.t. dry and 14,500 lb.s.t. with afterburning. All twenty-nine pre-production F-101A Voodoos were retained for the development programme, the first of fifty production F-101A fighter-bombers being delivered to T.A.C. in May 1957,

equipping the 81st Tactical Fighter Wing. In its initial form, the F-101A carried a built-in armament of four 20-mm. M-39 cannon, two retractable packs each housing six 2.75-in. spin-stabilised rockets, and three AIM-4A Falcon semi-active radar homing AAMs mounted on a rotary weapons bay door in the forward fuselage. APS-54 radar was installed, and there were five fuselage tanks with a total fuel capacity of 1,773 Imp. gal. Performance included a maximum speed of Mach 1.7 at 42,000 ft., maximum unrefuelled flight range being 1,700 mls. at Mach 0.9 at 36,000 ft.

Prior to delivery to the 81st Wing, one of the starboard 20-mm. cannon was removed to provide space

F-101C Voodoo (56-028) of the 78th Tactical Fighter Squadron, a unit of the 81st Tactical Fighter Wing.

An RF-101C-55 Voodoo of the 66th Tactical Reconnaissance Wing scheduled to re-equip with the RF-4C during 1965.

for the installation of TACAN equipment, the retractable rocket packs were deleted, and a fuselage centreline pylon and crutch were provided for a one-megaton tactical nuclear store or a pair of 375 Imp. gal. long-range tanks. Some structural strengthening introduced on the fifty-first production Voodoo (54-1486) to render it more suitable for low-level operations resulted in a change of designation to F-101C, forty-seven examples of which were built to bring total production of the Voodoo fighter-bomber (including pre-production aircraft) to 124 machines. These were also issued to the 81st Wing—the only Tactical Air Command unit to operate the Voodoo in the fighter-bomber rôle and scheduled to re-equip with the F-4C Phantom II during 1965—being operated alongside the earlier F-101As which possessed an essentially similar performance.

RF-101C VOODOO: To meet a Tactical Air Command requirement for a photographic reconnaissance aircraft with high supersonic speed capabilities, two examples of a modified version of the F-101A were ordered in June 1954 under the designation YRF-101A, the first of these (54-149) flying on May 10, 1956. Featuring an extended fuselage nose which increased overall length to 69 ft. 3 in., the YRF-101A had provision for from four to six electronically-controlled high-speed framing cameras with various accessories.

The first three production aircraft (54-1494 to -1496) were designated RF-101A-20, and had similar fuel tankage to the F-101A, but the fourth production aircraft (RF-101A-25) and all subsequent aircraft had the 1,773 Imp. gal. fuselage fuel tank capacity supplemented by a 75 Imp. gal. tank in each wing. Camera equipment normally comprised a long focal length Fairchild KA-1 framing camera, one vertical and two side oblique Fairchild KA-2 framing cameras, and one CAI KA-18 strip camera, and deliveries of the RF-101A to the Tactical Air Command began in May 1957, when the 63rd Tactical Reconnaissance Wing commenced conversion on the type.

A total of thirty-five RF-101A Voodoos was built, subsequent production contracts calling for the introduction of similar airframe strengthening as that applied to the F-101C fighter-bomber, resulting in the RF-101C, the principal single-seat production version of the Voodoo, 166 examples being delivered. The first RF-101C (56-040) flew on July 12, 1957, entering service in the following year, since which time the

aircraft has served as the workhorse of the Tactical Air Command's reconnaissance squadrons. During 1964, a modernization programme of the RF-101C's camera equipment was initiated, Hycon KS-72A cameras replacing the KA-2s and faster KA-45s which had been installed in some RF-101C Voodoos during 1963.

The RF-101C has normal and maximum loaded weights of 42,550 lb. and 48,720 lb. respectively, and performance is generally similar to that of the F-101C fighter-bomber. Twenty-five RF-101C Voodoos have been supplied to the Chinese Nationalist Air Force, and during 1965 the RF-4C Phantom II will begin to supplant this type in Tactical Air Command service.

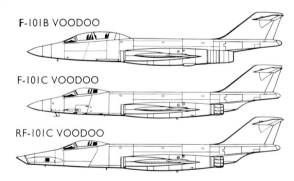

F-101B VOODOO

F-101C VOODOO

RF-101C VOODOO

F-101C VOODOO SPECIFICATION

Power Plants: *Two Pratt and Whitney J57-P-13 turbojets each rated at 10,100 lb.s.t. and 14,880 lb.s.t. with afterburning.*
Armament: *Three 20-mm. M-39 cannon and a one-megaton tactical nuclear store, or two 1,000-lb. or 2,000-lb. general-purpose bombs, or four 680-lb. mines.*
Performance: *Max. speed, 1,120 m.p.h. at 40,000 ft. (Mach 1.7), 716 m.p.h. at sea level (Mach 0.94); initial climb rate, 14,000 ft./min.; service ceiling, 52,000 ft.; max. range (internal fuel), 1,700 mls. at 595 m.p.h. at 36,000 ft. (Mach 0.9), (with two 375 Imp gal. drop tanks), 2,200 mls.; max. endurance (clean), 2 hr. 55 min.*
Weights: *Normal loaded, 39,680 lb.; max. overload, 46,960 lb.*
Dimensions: *Span, 39 ft. 8 in.; length, 67 ft. 4¾ in.; height, 18 ft. 0 in.; wing area, 368 sq. ft.*

CF-101B Voodoo all-weather interceptors of the R.C.A.F. Air Defence Command. Nos. 409, 416 and 425 Squadrons operate this type.

F-101B VOODOO: Although bearing an earlier suffix letter, the F-101B two-seat all-weather interceptor was, in fact, pre-dated by the single-seat F-101C fighter-bomber, the first F-101B (56-232) flying on March 27, 1957. Dimensionally similar to the single-seater, the F-101B embodied substantial fuselage redesign to adapt it for Air Defence Command use. An MG-13 fire control system was installed and a second cockpit introduced for the radar observer, necessitating some reduction in fuselage fuel capacity. More powerful J57-P-53 or -55 turbojets were installed, the cannon armament was deleted, and provision made for three semi-active radar homing or infra-red homing Falcon or Super Falcon AAMs on a rotary weapons bay door in the forward fuselage similar to that initially installed in the F-101A. In addition, external attachment points were provided for two unguided AIR-2A Genie AAMs with nuclear warheads.

The F-101B entered Air Defence Command service in 1959, together with the TF-101B with dual controls for pilot training but otherwise similar in operational capability, and nine A.D.C. squadrons received the Voodoo, production being completed in March 1961, a total of 478 aircraft being built. In June 1961 sixty-six ex-A.D.C. F-101Bs were transferred to the R.C.A.F.

after modifications, ten of these having provision for dual controls. The modified aircraft were re-designated F-101F and TF-101F by the U.S.A.F., being known in R.C.A.F. service as the CF-101B and CF-101F respectively. These are currently operated by Nos. 409, 416 and 425 Squadrons of the R.C.A.F. Air Defence Command, and although not originally equipped with nuclear missiles, the Canadian Voodoos were scheduled to receive AIR-2A Genie AAMs late in 1964.

F-101B VOODOO SPECIFICATION

Power Plants: Two Pratt and Whitney J57-P-53 or -55 turbojets each rated at 11,990 lb.s.t. and 14,990 lb.s.t. with afterburning.
Armament: *Two AIR-2A Genie nuclear-tipped AAMs and three AIM-4E semi-active radar homing or AIM-4F infra-red homing Super Falcon AAMs.*
Performance: *Max. speed, 1,220 m.p.h. at 40,000 ft. (Mach 1.85), 720 m.p.h. at sea level (Mach 0.95); initial climb rate, 17,000 ft./min.; service ceiling, 51,000 ft.; max. unrefuelled range, 1,550 mls. at 585 m.p.h. at 40,000 ft. (Mach 0.87).*
Weights: *Normal loaded, 39,900 lb.; max. overload, 46,673 lb.*
Dimensions: *Span, 39 ft. 8 in.; length, 67 ft. 4¾ in.; height, 18 ft. 0 in.; wing area, 368 sq. ft.*

An F-101B Voodoo all-weather fighter (58-0265) of the 29th Fighter-Interceptor Squadron of the Air Defence Command.

McDONNELL F-4 PHANTOM II

Undoubtedly one of the most versatile combat aircraft extant, the Phantom II two-seat multi-purpose fighter possesses the unique distinction of having begun life as a shipboard aircraft which, despite the acknowledged penalties associated with warplanes designed for operation from carriers, evinced a performance sufficiently striking to warrant its adoption as a standard land-based type also. Scheduled to equip the majority of the U.S. Navy's fleet fighter squadrons as well as those of the U.S. Marine Corps, the Phantom II will have re-equipped sixteen of the twenty-three U.S.A.F. Tactical Air Command fighter wings by the end of the 1965 Fiscal Year and, in modified form, has been selected to replace the British Navy's Sea Vixens.

The project that was to result in the current Phantom II began life on the McDonnell drawing-boards in 1953 as a single-seat twin-engined shipboard fighter attack aircraft for which a development contract was awarded in the following year under the designation AH-1. At that time it was proposed to install APQ-50 A.I. radar and a battery of four 20-mm. cannon, and engines were to be J65s in the test aircraft with J79s in production machines. Over the next eighteen months the U.S. Navy's mission requirement changed to that of long-range high-altitude interceptor relying solely on missile armament and accommodating the sophisticated Westinghouse APQ-72 A.I. and missile fire control radar, plus semi-automatic navigational devices. This fundamental revision of the basic concept demanded extensive redesign, and in July 1955, when the new design specifications had been established, the aircraft was redesignated F4H-1 (later changed to F-4A), and the decision was taken to install the J79 engine in all aircraft.

In its initial form, the new aircraft had an orthodox wing swept 45°, and the horizontal tail surfaces were similarly swept. However, the specification called for a maximum speed of the order of Mach 2.0, and many problems arose relating to both the transonic and Mach 2.0 plus speed regimes, the most serious proving to be pitch-up through wingtip stall at high angles of attack at both ends of the speed range, plus roll-coupling instability. To eliminate low-speed pitch-up through premature stalling of the tips of the swept wings, the outboard wing chord was extended by ten per cent and, at the same time, the outboard panels were given 12° dihedral to improve basic lateral

stability, this being simpler than applying 3° dihedral to the entire wing which, resulting in the same effect, would have necessitated extensive redesign of the mainplane and undercarriage. The vertical tail surfaces were enlarged, and to improve high speed pitch-up characteristics resulting from transonic downwash from the wing blanketing the slab-type tailplane, the tailplane halves were each given 15° of anhedral, carrying them clear of the downwash. The anhedral angle was later increased to 23°, although the second aircraft was tested with tailplane halves attached at the smaller angle. These changes bestowed a somewhat unorthodox appearance on the fighter.

A total of twenty-three pre-production F-4A* fighters was ordered under two contracts, these absorbing that for two AH-1 prototypes, and the first of these (BuA. No. 142259) was flown on May 27, 1958 with two General Electric J79-GE-3A engines rated at 9,600 lb.s.t. dry and 14,800 lb.s.t. with afterburning. These power plants were fed by variable-geometry intakes, each intake embodying a fixed forward ramp and a movable rear ramp. After forty-eight flights, they were replaced by YJ79-GE-2s of 10,350 lb.s.t. dry and 16,150 lb.s.t. with afterburning, and, later still, by improved J79-GE-2s and -2As. The third pre-production F-4A (BuA. No. 143388) was employed for a series of flight refuelling trials; the sixth (BuA. No. 143391) was the first to test the Phantom II's boundary layer control system in which compressor air was blown behind the forward and over the aft flap sections, and the seventh (BuA. No. 143392), the spin test aeroplane, was the first to be fitted with a mock-up of the large pointed nose radome for the scanner of the APQ-72, with an auxiliary bulge underneath for the infra-red or heat-seeking equipment. The 24-in. radar dish for the APQ-72 was replaced in the nineteenth and subsequent machines by a 32-in. dish, necessitating a still larger nose. The nineteenth aircraft also featured a revised canopy and stores stations for two Sidewinders or one additional Sparrow III under each wing, thus becoming the first aircraft of essentially production configuration.

* It should be noted that, when, in 1962, new designations were applied to most U.S. Navy aircraft, that of F-4A was allocated to the F4F-1F. This designation had originally been applied retrospectively to all early aircraft with J79-GE-2 or -2A engines, those becoming F-4As under the new system, and the first production aircraft fitted with the J79-GE-8 becoming the F-4B.

An F-4B Phantom II (Bu.No.150441) of VF-121, a training squadron of Carrier Air Wing 12 based at N.A.S. Miramar.

An F-4B Phantom II (Bu.No.150412) of VF-96, a component of Carrier Air Wing 9 from the U.S.S. Ranger.

The twenty-three pre-production and the sub-sequent twenty-four production Phantom IIs, which began to come off the production line in mid-1960, standardised on the J79-GE-2A engine, all being retrospectively designated F-4As. Initial carrier suitability trials with the sixth F-4A had taken place aboard the U.S.S. *Independence* during February 1960, and in February 1961, VF-121 began transitional training on the F-4A. In the following July, VF-101 also began conversion to the F-4A, the first U.S. Marine Corps Phantom II squadron being VMF-314, but by this time the F-4B had supplanted the -4A on the assembly line, this differing primarily in having J79-GE-8 engines which were first installed in the forty-eighth Phantom II. A pre-compressor cooling system of alcohol and water sprayed into the air ducts ahead of the compressor sections to reduce temperatures in the compressor above Mach 1.9 was tested on the second aircraft but not adopted for the production J79-GE-8 which was rated at 10,900 lb.s.t. dry and 17,000 lb.s.t. with afterburning.

F-4B PHANTOM II: The current production version of the Phantom II for the U.S. Navy, the F-4B, which was embarked aboard carriers of U.S. Navy's 6th Fleet in the Atlantic and 7th Fleet in the Western Pacific in 1961-62, is primarily a shipboard interceptor with secondary attack capability. The U.S. Marine Corps squadrons operating the F-4B also emphasize the air intercept mission, but as a result of its excellent low speed handling, the Phantom II can operate from short, unprepared strips as well as carriers, and the Marine units have undertaken a programme known as SATS (Short Airfield for Tactical Support) in which the F-4Bs operated from unimproved fields for close-support tasks, using portable arrester gear.

The F-4B crew layout is primarily for a pilot and radar intercept officer, and dual controls are not fitted as standard. The APQ-72 fire control system—also known as the Aero-1A Missile Control System—provides radar and infra-red target acquisition and tracking, attack phase steering information, CW target illumination and signals required for missile

An F-4B (Bu.No.150996) of U.S. Marine Corps Fighter-Attack Squadron VMFA-314 based at Atsugi, Japan.

guidance. It is equipped with anti-jamming devices and has a ground mapping mode. The subsidiary infra-red search and track set beneath the nose complements the main radar to facilitate detection and tracking of airborne targets. Armament normally comprises four or six AIM-7D or -7E Sparrow III semi-active radar-homing AAMs, or four Sparrow IIIs and four AIM-9 Sidewinder infra-red homing AAMs.

For a typical intercept mission carrying four Sparrow IIIs semi-buried beneath the fuselage, the F-4B has a gross weight at take-off of 46,000 lb., and is capable of Mach 2.2 if no other external stores are carried. For a mission carrying four Sidewinders plus external fuel tanks and at the same take-off gross weight, the tanks being dropped before the intercept, speed capability is Mach 2.4. Normal operational altitude with full fighter payload exceeds 60,000 ft., but pre-compressor cooling can boost this to 71,000 ft. In combat, the F-4B can accelerate from Mach 0.92 to Mach 2.05 in three-and-a-half minutes, and with internal fuel totalling 1,738 Imp. gal. supplemented by a 500 Imp. gal. drop tank on the fuselage centreline pylon and two 300 Imp. gal. drop tanks on underwing pylons, ferry range is 2,300 mls.

Pending the introduction of the F-111B in the late 'sixties, the F-4B Phantom II will equip all fleet fighter squadrons, except those operating from the *Essex*-class carriers which will operate the F-8E Crusader, and by August 1964 was serving with twelve U.S. Navy first line squadrons (VF-14, 21, 31, 41, 53, 74, 92, 96, 102, 114, 142, and 143), as well as the VF-101 and 121 training squadrons, and six U.S. Marine Corps squadrons (VMFA-115, 314, 323, 513, 531, and 542).

F-4C PHANTOM II: In 1961, the Director of Defence Research and Engineering instructed the U.S.A.F. to compare the Phantom II with contemporary land-based fighters, and in a programme known as "Project Highspeed" the shipboard fighter was compared with the Air Defence Command's F-106A Delta Dart. It was discovered that radar range for acquisition and tracking of targets exceeded that of the F-106A by twenty-five per cent, that payload and range capabilities were superior, and that maintenance manhours were only seventy per cent of the U.S.A.F. fighter. In a further test programme, the eleventh production F-4A was evaluated in the attack rôle, during which a maximum of twenty-two 500-lb. bombs was carried. This programme was primarily a U.S. Navy project, but the U.S.A.F. subsequently participated and, in March 1962, the Phantom II was ordered for service with the U.S.A.F. Tactical Air Command as the F-4C.

Whereas the U.S. Navy's F-4B is used primarily as an interceptor, the U.S.A.F.'s F-4C combines the air superiority rôle with broad interdiction and close support capabilities. For the intercept rôle similar loads of Sparrow III and Sidewinder missiles to those of the F-4B are carried, and the APQ-72 fire control system is retained, although a Litton inertial navigation system supplants the Eclipse-Pioneer dead-reckoning navigation computer of the U.S. Navy fighter, and dual controls are provided. Other changes in the F-4C include the installation of J79-GE-15 engines which are similar to the -8 engines of the F-4B but possess a self-contained cartridge starting system, a receptacle behind the second cockpit for the flying-

boom tanker system in place of the retractable installation for the probe-and-drogue system, a slightly lower instrument panel in the rear cockpit for improved visibility, and larger wheels.

During the summer of 1962, two U.S. Navy F-4Bs (BuA. Nos. 149405–6) were loaned to the U.S.A.F. Tactical Air Command for evaluation and familiarisation purposes, and subsequently additional F-4Bs were used at the MacDill Air Force Base, Florida, for the training of U.S.A.F. personnel prior to the delivery of F-4Cs, the first production example of which (63-7415) was flown on May 27, 1963.

RF-4C PHANTOM II: The intended successor to the RF-101C Voodoo, the RF-4C reconnaissance version of the Phantom II is to equip fourteen Tactical Air Command squadrons, being scheduled for operational deployment in 1965. The first production RF-4C (63-7740) was flown for the first time on May 18, 1964, being preceded by two YRF-4C prototypes, the first of which flew on August 20, 1963. The YRF-4C aircraft were converted on the assembly line from U.S. Navy F-4Bs and were intended for development and evaluation purposes, but the production RF-4C embodies all the changes introduced by the U.S.A.F.'s F-4C, and is modified to incorporate multiple-sensor reconnaissance systems, including cameras.

Intended for all-weather, high-low, day-night selective reconnaissance, the RF-4C carries a Hycon KS-72A forward oblique framing camera, and Fairchild KA-56 low- and high-altitude panoramic cameras in the nose bay which also houses the forward-looking radar, the dish scanner of which is enclosed by an upward-folding radome. This radar is appreciably smaller than that carried by the F-4C, resulting in a thirty-seven per cent weight reduction in the nose section. An alternative tri-camera array of two 6-in. side oblique cameras and one 3-in. vertical camera can be installed between the low- and high-altitude panoramic cameras. A SLAR (Side-Looking Aircraft Radar) antenna is mounted beneath the forward cockpit, the reference computer and recorder control being installed aft of the rear cockpit, and an infra-red line scanner in the lower fuselage, immediately ahead of the wing root. The forward-looking radar is primarily for terrain avoidance but is scope-monitored and has limited reconnaissance capability. The Litton ASN-48 inertial system differs from that of the F-4C in having a reconnaissance adapter unit stabilizing the various sensors in flight. A photo-flash cartridge ejector for night target illumination is provided in the aft fuselage. Powered by J79-GE-15 engines, the RF-4C has a generally similar performance to the F-4C, and apart from a thirty-three-inch increase in length to 61 ft., overall dimensions are the same.

An essentially similar reconnaissance model for the U.S. Marine Corps, the RF-4B, will be based on the F-4B airframe, and will enter operational service during 1965.

F-4J PHANTOM II: Early in 1964, it was decided to adopt the Phantom II for service with the Royal Navy as a successor to the Sea Vixen, and after the successful completion of trials at the U.S. Naval Air Test Centre, Patuxent River, with a modified F-4B featuring a drooped aileron installation and a slotted tail, two prototypes were ordered with Rolls-Royce RB168

F-4B PHANTOM II

Spey turbofans under the tentative designation F-4RN late in July 1964. The U.S. Department of Defence designation F-4J was subsequently assigned to this model.

The F-4B is not normally operated by the U.S. Navy from the 33,000-ton *Essex*-class carriers as safety margins are considered to be inadequate, but the Royal Navy plans to operate the F-4J from the 23,000-ton *Hermes*, among other carriers, necessitating an increase in lift coefficient for lower take-off and approach speeds. This is being obtained by means of the drooping ailerons. Provision is to be made for lengthening the nosewheel leg for the optimum angle of attack on Royal Navy catapults, and nose-folding is necessary in order to use the elevators of British carriers. The General Electric J79 turbojets are to be supplanted by Rolls-Royce RB.168-25R Spey turbofans which, apart from providing extra thrust from their basic rating of approximately 12,000 lb.s.t. dry boosted by seventy per cent with afterburning to some

An F-4C Phantom II (63-7465) of the U.S.A.F. Tactical Air Command which is to have sixteen F-4C fighter wings.

The eleventh production F-4A Phantom II (Bu.No.145310) was evaluated in the attack rôle with twenty-two 500-lb. bombs.

20,500 lb.s.t., offer markedly lower specific fuel consumption and increase the Phantom II's overall operating range by as much as thirty per cent. The installation of the Spey engines is unlikely to prove difficult as the existing intakes match the Rolls-Royce engine's required mass flow, and provision is already made for flap blowing.

In February 1962 McDonnell proposed a growth version of the Phantom II with RB.168 Spey turbofans to the U.S. Department of Defence as an appreciably cheaper alternative to the TXF. It was considered that the Spey-powered Phantom II could fulfil approximately eighty per cent of the TXF mission requirements at a fraction of the unit cost, but the proposal was not taken up. However, it provided a background of design detail for the selection of the aircraft for service with the Royal Navy.

No production contract for the F-4J had been negotiated at the time of closing for press, but it is known that the Royal Navy has an initial requirement for fifty and an ultimate requirement for 130 machines, with mid-1967 service introduction. The Phantom II is also favoured by the R.C.A.F. as a successor to the CF-104, and discussions have taken place concerning the feasibility of Spey-powered Phantom IIs being manufactured for both the Royal Navy and the R.C.A.F. by Canadair.

F-4B PHANTOM II SPECIFICATION

Power Plants: *Two General Electric J79-GE-8 turbojets each rated at 10,900 lb.s.t. and 17,000 lb.s.t. with after-burning.*

Armament: *(Intercept) Four or six AIM-7D or -7E Sparrow III semi-active radar-homing AAMs or four Sparrow IIIs and four AIM-9 Sidewinder infra-red homing AAMs, or (attack) eighteen 750-lb. or eleven 1,000-lb. bombs, fifteen 680-lb. mines, eleven 125 Imp. gal. napalm tanks, four AGM-12B or -12C Bullpup ASMs, or Snakeye Mk.81 or Mk.82 retarded bombs, Walleye homing glide weapons, Sadeye low-drag cluster-bombs, or any combination of these weapons up to a maximum of 13,320 lb.*

Performance: *Max. speed, 1,584 m.p.h. at 48,000 ft. (Mach 2.4), (with four Sparrow IIIs) 1,450 m.p.h. (Mach 2.2), 915 m.p.h. at sea level (Mach 1.2); initial climb rate, 28,000 ft./min.; operational ceiling, 62,000 ft.; sustained ceiling, 66,450 ft.; low-level tactical radius (with 6,000-lb. external weapons load), 400 mls. at 420 m.p.h.; ferry range (with max. external fuel), 2,300 mls. at 575 m.p.h. at 40,000 ft. (Mach 0.87).*

Weights: *Loaded (clean), 44,600 lb.; max. overload, 54,600 lb.*

Dimensions: *Span, 38 ft. 4¾ in.; length, 58 ft. 3¼ in.; height, 16 ft. 3 in.; wing area, 530 sq. ft.*

The first YRF-4C (illustrated below) was flown on August 20, 1963, and was a conversion of a U.S. Navy airframe with a mock-up of the photographic nose configuration. The first production RF-4C (63-7740) flew on May 18, 1964, and delivery to the U.S.A.F. Tactical Air Command began at Shaw A.F.B. in South Carolina in September 1964. Fourteen T.A.C. squadrons are to be equipped with the RF-4C.

NORTH AMERICAN A-5 VIGILANTE

The successful contestant in a design competition announced by the U.S. Navy in 1955, when the service outlined its requirements for an advanced shipboard attack aircraft combining extreme all-weather mission versatility and zero-speed over the deck with high Mach performance, the Vigilante displayed considerable ingenuity in coupling the low-speed handling characteristics necessary for carrier operation with higher run-in and escape speeds than possessed by any naval aeroplane at that time, and a higher gross weight than any aircraft previously developed for shipboard use.

The Vigilante embodied for the first time design features today accepted as conventional, and a remarkably similar layout was adopted very much later for the TSR-2 (see pages 84–85), although by comparison with the British strike aeroplane, the North American aircraft possesses substantially more wing area for maximum performance at extreme altitudes, this feature imposing structural limitations which restrict low-level speed. Changes in operational requirements since its conception have tended to circumscribe procurement of the Vigilante, and production has remained at a low rate by American standards, but in its definitive version, as a manned long-range reconnaissance system with attack capa-

bility, there can be little doubt that this aircraft is one of the most effective operational aircraft in the U.S. Navy's inventory.

North American Aviation received a U.S. Navy letter of intent covering production engineering, tooling and long lead-time equipment on June 29, 1956 for what was at that time known as the NAGPAW (North American General-Purpose Attack Weapon), followed two months later by an order for two YA-5A prototypes (then designated Y/A3J-1), the first of which (BuA.No.145157) flew on August 31, 1958 powered by two General Electric YJ79-GE-2 turbojets each rated at 10,350 lb.s.t. dry and 16,150 lb.s.t. with afterburning, the lateral intakes feeding these engines forming one of the many distinctive features of the aircraft. These were among the first variable-geometry intakes to be adopted for a production aircraft, and incorporated a sharp transverse lip at the upper edge, aft of which was a fixed ramp and forward and aft variable ramps controlling and directing the shock-wave.

The wing, matched to the maximum speed at maximum altitude case, was relatively large and had a thickness/chord ratio of the order of 3.5 per cent and was swept 37.5° at the leading edge. Hydraulically-operated variable-camber, three-section leading edges

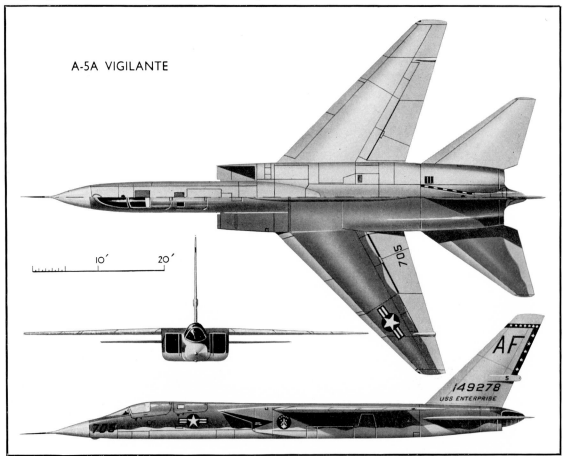

A-5A VIGILANTE

10'   20'

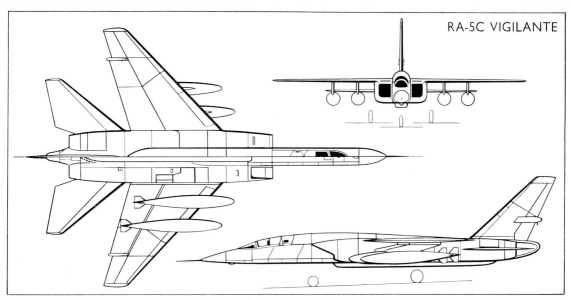

RA-5C VIGILANTE

and bleed-air blowing over the large, inboard flaps—the only movable trailing edge surfaces—provided the necessary low-speed control, and control about all three axes was furnished by a "taileron"—irreversible, fully powered slab tailplanes acting in the conventional manner for pitch and differentially for roll in conjunction with an unusual arrangement of hydraulically-actuated wing-mounted spoiler-deflectors—and a single slab vertical surface. Virtually the entire wing envelope was occupied by fuel, each wing having a single integral tank out to the fold-line, these being supplemented by a "saddle" tank above the engine and weapons bays, and flexible tanks across virtually the entire cross-section between the intakes.

The two crew members were seated in tandem North American HS-1 rocket ejection seats, and one of the unique features of the aircraft was its linear weapons bay—a tunnel running lengthwise in the aft fuselage, between the engines—from which stores were ejected rearwards. This bay, equipped with rails, a catapult, and four attachment stations, one behind the other, stored a free-falling nuclear weapon at its forward end, the launching system triggering a series of latches releasing the disposable tail cone. The bomb was attached to two 229 Imp. gal. tanks, the fuel from which was the first to be used during the mission, and the empty tanks were ejected with the bomb, re-

maining attached and acting as aerodynamic stabilizers for the fall to the target. Apart from the nuclear weapon, this bay could accommodate reconnaissance systems, auxiliary fuel, or other equipment.

A-5A VIGILANTE: The first production A-5A Vigilantes joined the test programme in 1960, the initial aircraft having J79-GE-2 engines, these being supplanted at an early stage by J79-GE-4s of similar thrust ratings but having steel stator cases and front frames as distinct from magnesium alloy. These, in turn, gave place to the definitive J79-GE-8 rated at 10,900 lb.s.t. dry and 17,000 lb.s.t. with afterburning.

An early production A-5A completed initial carrier trials aboard the U.S.S. *Saratoga* in July 1960, and four aircraft were delivered to VAH-7 at Sanford N.A.S. on June 16, 1961, this squadron deploying the

(Below) An RA-5C Vigilante (Bu.No.150837) of Heavy Reconnaissance-Attack Squadron RVAH-5, and (above, right) an A-5A Vigilante landing.

(*Above*) *A-5B* (*Bu.No.149034*) *and* (*below*) *RA-5C* (*Bu.No. 150824*).

A-5A operationally for the first time in August 1962 aboard the U.S.S. *Enterprise*. VAH-1 was the second U.S. Navy squadron to convert to the A-5A, VAH-3 being responsible for the training of Vigilante crews.

The A-5A's bombing-navigation system is the AN/ASB-12, or REINS (Radar Equipped Inertial Navigation System), which includes an inertial autonavigator and bombing computer, a mapping radar, and a closed-loop television. This offers a wide range of bomb modes and approach patterns, highly efficient target identification, and automatic navigation. The linear weapons bay is supplemented by two underwing pylons capable of carrying general- or special-purpose bombs, napalm tanks, AGM-12 Bullpup ASMs, or 330 Imp. gal. fuel tanks. The ejection system featured by the linear bay is intended to permit a wide variety of delivery manoeuvres, including loft bombing in which the aircraft climbs almost vertically to lob the bomb on a ballistic trajectory, then performing an Immelmann to escape in the opposite direction. High or medium altitude approaches can be made to the target, with the bomb being ejected during level, climbing or descending flight.

Some idea of the zoom climb capabilities of the A-5A was provided on December 13, 1960, when an

---

A-5A VIGILANTE SPECIFICATION

Power Plants: *Two General Electric J79-GE-8 turbojets each rated at 10,900 lb.s.t. and 17,000 lb.s.t. with after-burning.*

Armament: *Nuclear or conventional weapon in linear bay and two 1,000-lb. or 2,000-lb. general- or special-purpose bombs, napalm tanks or AGM-12B or -12C Bullpup ASMs on underwing pylons.*

Performance: *Max. speed, 1,385 m.p.h. at 40,000 ft. (Mach 2.1), 685 m.p.h. at sea level (Mach 0.95); max. stabilized speed, 1,254 m.p.h. (Mach 1.9); normal range, 2,300 mls. at 560 m.p.h. (Mach 0.85); tactical radius (including combat allowances), 1,000 mls.; service ceiling, 67,000 ft.; max. ceiling, 70,000 ft.*

Weights: *Normal loaded, 54,000–56,000 lb.; max., 62,000 lb.*

Dimensions: *Span, 53 ft. 0 in.; length, 73 ft. 2½ in.; height, 19 ft. 4¾ in.; wing area, 700 sq. ft.*

---

early production aircraft attained 91,446 ft. with a 2,200-lb. payload, and outstanding low-speed target area loiter capability is combined with exceptional high-altitude dash, maximum stabilized speed when carrying an internal combat load being Mach 1.9. However, the A-5A has suffered protracted teething troubles associated primarily with the revolutionary method of launching internally housed stores, and a growing belief in the U.S. Navy that strategic bombing should not be a part of the service's assignment has combined with these difficulties to curtail procurement of the Vigilante. Accent has now switched from the attack to the reconnaissance capabilities of the aircraft, and the fifty-five A-5A Vigilantes delivered to the U.S. Navy are being progressively modified to the later RA-5C configuration.

A-5B VIGILANTE: During 1961, means of extending the Vigilante's range and load-carrying capabilities were investigated, and two growth versions were proposed, introducing substantial airframe modifications and weight increases. The first of these, the A-5B, was, like its predecessor, intended primarily for the attack rôle, and the second, the RA-5C, was essentially a reconnaissance aircraft but retaining attack capability.

The first A-5B (BuA.No.149034) flew on April 29, 1962, and changes included the extension of the flap surfaces both spanwise and chordwise, and the modification of the boundary layer control system to blow bleed air over the top surfaces of the wing from front to rear instead of only over the rear portion as on the A-5A, these changes minimizing the adverse effect on take-off and landing performance resulting from a gross weight increase of some 10,000 lb. Internal fuel capacity was substantially increased by introducing larger capacity fuselage tanks, the dorsal contours of the fuselage being raised aft of the bombardier-navigator's cockpit to result in a pronounced humped-back effect, and changes to the inboard wing structure permitted the provision of four pylons each capable of lifting a 330 Imp. gal. drop tank or an equivalent load of offensive stores.

By the time the A-5B entered the flight-test phase, it had been decided to standardise on the RA-5C for which the A-5B prototypes subsequently served as development aircraft, and all examples of this interim model were converted to RA-5C standards on the line, no A-5Bs being delivered to U.S. Navy squadrons.

RA-5C VIGILANTE: The current production RA-5C, the prototype of which flew for the first time on June 30, 1962, embodies the same changes as those introduced by the A-5B, retains the REINS bombing-navigation system of the A-5A, and is similarly powered, but carries an extremely sophisticated reconnaissance system. SLAR (Side-Looking Aircraft Radar) is housed in a long ventral fairing, and photographic equipment includes vertical, oblique, and split-image cameras, and horizon-to-horizon scanning, non-photographic equipment, in addition to the SLAR, including sensors in radio and infra-red regions for electromagnetic intelligence and counter-measures tasks, and television capable of functioning in very low light levels. The associated electronic equipment is packaged in the linear weapons bay (devoted in the RA-5C version entirely to reconnaissance equipment and fuel), and two high-intensity strobe-type flasher pods are mounted on the underwing pylons, these illuminating the ground beneath the aircraft. The performance of the RA-5C is generally similar to that of the A-5A (which see specification) apart from the normal range which has been stretched to approximately 3,000 miles.

The first squadron to equip with the RA-5C was RVAH-5 (formerly VAH-5) whose aircraft were deployed aboard the U.S.S. *Ranger* in June 1964. RVAH-9 and RVAH-11 are also to equip with the RA-5C, and eventually the A-5A Vigilantes of RVAH-1 and RVAH-7 will be converted to RA-5C standards. In the spring of 1964, North American received a contract to convert an initial quantity of twenty-seven A-5As, the first of these being drawn from RVAH-1. Some fifty Vigilantes originally begun as A-5Bs have been converted on the line to RA-5Cs, and approximately a further forty were being built as RA-5Cs from the ground up. These will eventually be supplemented by the conversions of the original A-5As.

NORTH AMERICAN F-86 SABRE

Of post-war combat aircraft, that most assured of its place in aviation history among the truly great warplanes of all time is the North American Sabre. Although conceived nearly twenty years ago, the Sabre remains an important item in the active aircraft inventories of many nations, and a number of years are likely to elapse before this fighter makes its final landing to take up that niche in aviation's metaphorical hall of fame.

The Sabre-line was a prolific one, and the early development history of this outstanding North American fighter has been recorded on too many occasions to warrant repetition here. It suffices, therefore, to say that development was influenced by German wartime research into the effects of wing sweepback, and that the first XP-86 prototype of the Sabre (45-59597) was flown for the first time on October 1, 1947, with a Chevrolet-built General Electric J35-C-3 turbojet delivering 3,750 lb.s.t. From that point, the Sabre followed three distinct lines of development: day interceptor and fighter-bomber, shipboard interceptor and strike fighter, and all-weather interceptor. The shipboard derivatives of the Sabre have now been relegated to training rôles, and do not, therefore, come within the compass of this book, but examples of virtually every other production variant of the Sabre remain operational, and for ease of comparison, the day and all-weather versions are grouped separately.

The initial production model of the Sabre, the F-86A-1, had been ordered on December 20, 1946, while the prototypes were still under construction, and

powered by a J47-GE-1 turbojet, the first example (47-605) flew on May 20, 1948. Official performance tests undertaken with the J47-GE-7-powered sixth F-86A-1 (47-610) on September 23, 1948, revealed maximum speeds in clean condition of 677 m.p.h. at sea level, 642 m.p.h. at 16,000 ft., and 595 m.p.h. at 34,500 ft., maximum Mach numbers attained being 0.885 at sea level and 0.895 at 35,000 ft. Initial climb rate was 7,500 ft./min., and an altitude of 30,000 ft. was attained in 6.5 min.

The F-86A carried six 0.5-in. M-3 machine guns with 267 r.p.g. which were aimed by means of a Mk.18 sight, but this lead computing sight was supplanted in the last twenty-four production F-86As by the A-1CM sight which was coupled with AN/APG-30 radar installed in the upper lip of the nose intake. Most earlier F-86As were retrospectively fitted with the A-1CM sight and AN/APG-5C radar as F-86A-6s or, more commonly, with the AN/APG-30 radar as F-86A-7s.

The first U.S.A.F. combat unit to receive the F-86A was the 1st Fighter Group which, by the end of May 1949, was completely equipped. When the Korean War began on June 25, 1950, five Sabre Groups were active, and F-86A production was giving place to the F-86E, the 554th and last F-86A being completed early in December 1950. The F-86E was identical to the F-86A apart from the "all-flying" tailplane of the later model, and the first F-86E-1 (50-579) had flown on September 23, 1950. Many undesirable compressibility effects were eliminated by the introduction of the "all-flying" tail, and U.S.A.F.

F-86F Sabres of the Republic of Korea Air Force which received 112 F-86F-25s and -30s plus ten RF-86Fs.

(Above and below, left) F-86F Sabres of the Royal Thai Air Force which has received forty fighters of this type.

acceptances of the E-model began in February 1951, the 33rd Fighter-Interceptor Wing being the first unit to re-equip with this Sabre variant.

A total of 336 F-86E Sabres was eventually built, 225 of these originally being ordered as F-86F Sabres but completed as 'Es owing to shortages of the more powerful J47-GE-27 engine. In the meantime, licence manufacture of the F-86E had begun in Canada (see page 7), and sixty Canadian-built Sabres were supplied to the U.S.A.F. Some F-86A and F-86E Sabres remain in service with Air National Guard units, and a number of up-dated Canadian-built aircraft, designated F-86E(M), remain in service

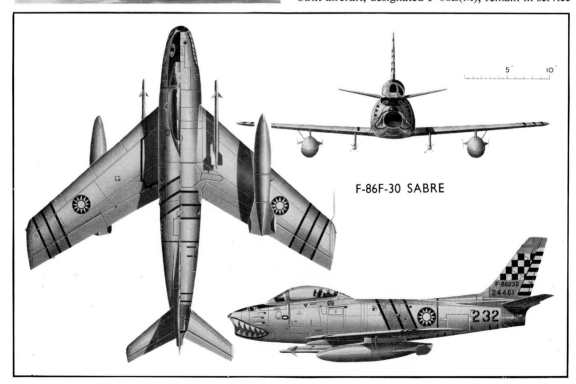

F-86F-30 SABRE

with the Greek, Italian, Turkish and Yugoslav air arms.

F-86F SABRE: Destined to be produced in larger numbers than any of the day fighter Sabre variants, the F-86F switched to the 5,910 lb.s.t. J47-GE-27 from the 5,200 lb.s.t. J47-GE-13 of earlier models, and the first F-86F-1 (51-2850) flew on March 19, 1952. Within three months, the new model was serving with the U.S.A.F.'s 51st Wing in Korea, and seventy-eight F-86F-1s were followed by sixteen F-86F-5s on which the underwing shackles were modified to take 166.5 Imp. gal. drop tanks in place of the 100 Imp. gal. tanks previously fitted, these boosting combat radius from 330 to 463 mls. The more powerful engine raised maximum speed to 688 m.p.h. at sea level and 604 m.p.h. at 35,000 ft., initial climb rate to 9,300 ft./min. and service ceiling to 48,000 ft.

The F-86F-10 switched to the simpler A-4 gun sight, the F-86F-20 adopted a revised cockpit arrangement, modified radio and armour protection for the tailplane control system, and the F-86F-30 introduced dual-store provision, a 100 Imp. gal. tank or a 1,000-lb. bomb being carried on each of the inboard pair of underwing shackles and 166.5 Imp. gal. tanks on the outboard pair. With four tanks ferry range became 1,600 mls. and combat radius was 568 mls. In the meantime, the so-called "6-3" wing leading edge—the automatic slats being deleted and the leading edge being extended six inches at the root and three inches at the tip—had been introduced and adopted as standard. This delayed the onset of buffet, providing the pilot with an increase in usable *g*'s at some penalty in low speed characteristics partly alleviated by the provision of small fences at approximately seventy per cent span.

The F-86F-35 Sabre, 264 examples of which were delivered between January and June 1954, was equipped with a LABS (Low Altitude Bombing System) computer, and provision was made for a 1,200-lb. tactical nuclear store to be carried under the port wing. More conventional loads comprised two 500-lb., 750-lb., or 1,000-lb. bombs, two 750-lb. Napalm tanks, or eight 5-in. HVARs, in addition to the standard sextette of 0.5-in. M-3 guns. It was anticipated that the "dash

thirty-five" would be the last F-model Sabre to be manufactured, but within a year of the delivery of the last aircraft of this type, events were to dictate the production reinstatement of the F-86F.

From 1954, the export of surplus U.S.A.F. F-86F Sabres began to Allied nations under the MDAP (Mutual Defence Assistance Programme), and within four years this variant of the North American fighter had become the world's most widely-used jet combat aircraft.

One of the first foreign recipients of the F-model Sabre was the Chinese Nationalist Air Force which received its first four F-86F-30s on November 29, 1954 and, by June 1958, had taken delivery of no fewer than 320 aircraft (including F-1s, F-5s, F-10s, and F-25s), plus seven RF-86F-30s, these each carrying one K-17 and two K-22 cameras in a special compartment beneath the cockpit. The Sabres equipped three Chinese Nationalist day interceptor wings and, from September 1958, were modified to carry a pair of AIM-9 Sidewinder infra-red homing AAMs. Two C.N.A.F. day fighter wings were still operating the F-86F at the end of 1964.

F-86F-40 SABRE SPECIFICATION

Power Plant: *One General Electric J47-GE-27 turbojet rated at 5,910 lb.s.t.*

Armament: *Six 0.5-in. Colt-Browning M-3 machine guns with 267 r.p.g. plus two AIM-9B Sidewinder infra-red homing AAMs, or two 500-lb., 750-lb., or 1,000-lb. bombs, two 750-lb. Napalm tanks, or eight 5-in. HVARs.*

Performance: *Max. speed (at 15,532 lb.), 678 m.p.h. at sea level (Mach 0.89), 599 m.p.h. at 35,000 ft. (Mach 0.9), (at 14,212 lb.), 687 m.p.h. at sea level (Mach 0.9), 604 m.p.h. at 35,000 ft. (Mach 0.902); initial climb rate (at 15,532 lb.), 8,100 ft./min., (at 14,212 lb.), 9,800 ft./min.; time to 30,000 ft. (at 14,212 lb.), 5.2 min.; service ceiling (at 15,532 lb.), 47,000 ft., (at 14,212 lb.), 49,600 ft.; combat radius (with two 166.5 Imp. gal. drop tanks), 463 mls. at 529 m.p.h.; ferry range (with two 100 and two 166.5 Imp. gal. drop tanks), 1,525 mls.*

Weights: *Empty, 11,125 lb.; loaded (clean), 15,198 lb.; max. overload, 20,611 lb.*

Dimensions: *Span, 39 ft. 1 in.; length, 37 ft. 6½ in.; height, 14 ft. 8¾ in.; wing area, 313.4 sq. ft.*

RF-86F Sabres which serve with the J.A.S.D.F.'s No. 501 Reconnaissance Squadron based at Iruma. Eighteen RF-86F conversions have been undertaken by Mitsubishi.

The Spanish Air Force, in exchange for American use of Spanish bases, received 244 F-86F-20s, -25s and -30s from April 1956, these equipping Nos. 1, 2, 3, 4, 5 and 6 day fighter wings of the Spanish Air Defence Command. Norway was provided with ninety F-86F-35s which currently equip the R.No.A.F.'s Nos. 332, 336 and 338 Squadrons; Peru acquired fourteen F-86F-25s which serve with one squadron of the Peruvian Air Force's Gruppo 12; twenty-two F-86F-30s were supplied for operation by two squadrons of the Venezuelan Air Force, and twenty-eight F-86F Sabres acquired by the Argentine Air Force are operated by that service's Fighter-Bomber Group I of Air Brigade IV.

The Philippines received forty F-86F-30s in 1957-58, these equipping the 5th Fighter Wing; Thailand received forty F-86Fs; the Portuguese Air Force took delivery of fifty F-86Fs which equip Nos. 20 and 21 Squadrons, and the Republic of Korea Air Force was provided with 112 F-86F-25s and -30s, and ten RF-86F Sabres.

Before the end of 1954, the U.S. government had realised that it could not fulfil its enormous MDAP Sabre commitments from surplus U.S.A.F. aircraft alone. Thus, on June 27, 1955, a contract for 215 additional F-86F Sabres was placed with North American, a further sixty-five being added on March 27, 1956. In the meantime, the resuscitated Japanese air arm, the Air Self-Defence Force, had selected the F-86F as its standard day fighter, and a licence and joint production agreement had been reached between the Japanese Mitsubishi concern and North American. The sub-variant covered by both the new U.S. and Japanese contracts was the F-86F-40, development of which had begun on October 28, 1954.

Before deliveries of the F-86F-40 to Japan began, the Japanese Air Self-Defence Force received eight F-86F-25s and twenty F-86F-30s for training operations, the first of these arriving in December 1955. Six years later, eighteen of these were converted by Mitsubishi to RF-86F configuration and now serve with the No. 501 Reconnaissance Squadron based at Iruma.

The F-86F-40, the first example of which (55-3816) was flown in October 1955, retained the J47-GE-27 turbojet of earlier F-models but reverted to leading-edge slats which were modified to combine their low-speed handling benefits with the high-speed advantages offered by the "6-3" wing leading edge. The improved handling qualities were such that this modification, together with the increased wing span and area from 37 ft. 1 in. to 39 ft. 1 in. and 302.3 to 313.4 sq. ft. introduced by the F-86F-40, was applied retrospectively to all F-86F-25 and -30 Sabres.

The first F-86F-40s manufactured by North American were shipped to Japan in 1956, and by mid-1957 the J.A.S.D.F. had received 180 aircraft from the U.S.A., although in the event the Japanese air arm did not possess that number of qualified fighter pilots, and forty-five of the North American-built F-86F-40s were not used and were held in storage until returned to the U.S.A.F. in February 1959. Mitsubishi assembled a total of 300 F-86F-40 Sabres from imported components, the first of these being flown on August 9, 1956, and the last being delivered on February 25, 1961. From November 1959, the J.A.S.D.F.'s F-86F-40 Sabres were adapted to carry two AIM-9 Sidewinders, and these aircraft currently equip

the 4th, 6th, and 7th Fighter Wings at Sendai, Komatsu and Iruma.

One hundred and twenty North American-built F-86F-40 Sabres were supplied to the Pakistan Air Force between 1956 and 1958, the last of the 280 "dash forty" aircraft built by the parent company (55-5047) and the 1,539th F-model Sabre having flown on December 28, 1956.

F-86H SABRE: Development of a variant of the Sabre specifically intended for the fighter-bomber rôle was initiated on March 16, 1951. From the outset it was intended to install the substantially more powerful General Electric J73 turbojet, and this demanded an increase in intake area. Therefore, the fuselage was split longitudinally and an additional 6-in. portion spliced in to increase its depth, this change being similar to that effected in the contemporary Australian version of the Sabre (see page 5). The deeper fuselage permitted a substantial increase in fuel capacity, from 362 to 468 Imp. gal., the area of the tailplane was increased, and provision was made for four underwing stores stations.

Designated F-86H, the first example of the new fighter-bomber (52-1975) was flown on April 30, 1953 with a J79-GE-3 engine rated at 8,920 lb.s.t. This and the second aircraft (52-1976) were used for test and development purposes, and the first true production F-86H-1 flew on September 4, 1953. In addition to the previously-mentioned modifications, the F-86H had a clamshell-type cockpit canopy, a heavier undercarriage, and improved suspension and release mechanism for the underwing loads, and although the first 113 production aircraft retained the standard Sabre armament of six M-3 machine guns, the 114th aircraft, the first F-86H-5, switched to a quartette of 20-mm. M-39 cannon with 150 r.p.g. Sixty F-86H-5s were followed by 300 F-86H-10s which differed only in having modified electrical systems, and the last of these was delivered to the U.S.A.F. on March 16, 1956.

Like the F-86F-35, the F-86H was equipped with a LABS computer, and provision was made for a 1,200-lb. tactical nuclear store. AN/APG-30 radar ranging was provided the A-4 gun and rocket sight, and a P-2 strike camera was standard. The appreciably more powerful turbojet resulted in only a marginal improvement in maximum speeds owing to the Mach limitations of the airframe, but take-off, climb rate and acceleration were appreciably better than the F-86F, and the F-86H was a very much better air-to-ground gunnery platform. The F-86H saw relatively limited service with the U.S.A.F., briefly equipping three wings before being supplanted by the F-100 Super Sabre, and was passed on to the Air National Guard with which it currently remains in service.

F-86D SABRE: The exploitation of a proven design for alternative rôles frequently results in an aircraft bearing little resemblance to its progenitor, and a case in point is provided by the F-86D, the first in the line of all-weather Sabres. The F-86D was virtually a new machine, retaining only the wing common to other members of the Sabre family, and its concept was unprecedented—an all-weather interceptor in which the second crew member standard in all aircraft of this category was supplanted by highly sophisticated electronic systems and the classic gun armament was relinquished in favour of rocket missiles.

An F-86H Sabre (52-5745) of the Maryland Air Guard. Four hundred and seventy-five F-86H fighter-bombers were built.

A contract for two YF-86D prototypes and 122 production F-86Ds was awarded on October 7, 1949, a further thirty-one F-86Ds being ordered on June 2, 1950. The first YF-86D (50-577) was flown on December 22, 1949 with a J47-GE-17 turbojet in which the 5,000 lb.s.t. was boosted to 6,650 lb.s.t. with afterburning. The most distinctive difference from other Sabres was the lowering of the engine air intake to provide space for a radome housing the scanner of the AN/APG-36 search radar. During the test programme, the first YF-86D was fitted with the retractable missile tray intended to provide the primary armament of the production model, this containing twenty-four 2.75-in. "Mighty Mouse" unguided rockets which were fired in the air for the first time in February 1951. By the following month, when the first F-86D (50-455) was accepted by the U.S.A.F., 341 D-model Sabres

F-86H-10 SABRE SPECIFICATION

Power Plant: *One General Electric J73-GE-3D or -3E turbojet rated at 8,920 lb.s.t.*

Armament: *Four 20-mm. M-39 cannon with 150 r.p.g. plus two 500-lb., 750-lb., or 1,000-lb. general-purpose bombs, or sixteen 5-in. HVARs.*

Performance: *Max. speed, 692 m.p.h. at sea level (Mach 0.91), 617 m.p.h. at 35,000 ft.; initial climb rate, 12,900 ft./min.; time to 30,000 ft., 5.7 min.; service ceiling, 50,800 ft.; tactical radius (clean), 519 mls. at 552 m.p.h., (with two 1,000-lb. bombs), 403 mls.; ferry range (two 100 and two 166.5 Imp gal. drop tanks), 1,810 mls.*

Weights: *Empty, 13,836 lb.; loaded (with two 166.5 Imp. gal. drop tanks), 21,852 lb., (plus two 1,000-lb. bombs), 24,296 lb.*

Dimensions: *Span, 39 ft. 1½ in.; length, 38 ft. 10 in.; height, 15 ft. 0 in.; wing area, 313.4 sq. ft.*

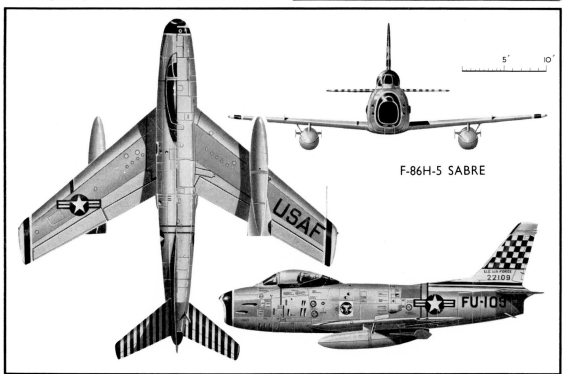

F-86H-5 SABRE

F-86D Sabres equipped with underwing racks for Sidewinder missiles in service with the Chinese Nationalist Air Force.

were on order, and within a further two months the total had been increased to 979 aircraft. The final production contracts placed two years later brought the final total of orders for the F-86D to 2,504 aircraft.

It was to be expected that so advanced an interceptor would suffer its share of teething troubles, and the first thirty-seven production aircraft, which were fitted with the 50-kw E-3 fire control system pending the availability of the appreciably more sophisticated 250-kw E-4, suffered almost continuous malfunction of one or more of the electronic control systems, and the thirty-seventh aircraft was not, in fact, delivered until October 1952. Even greater problems were presented by the E-4 system mounted in all subsequent aircraft, and at one time several hundred completed

F-86D-45 SABRE SPECIFICATION

Power Plant: *One General Electric J47-GE-33 turbojet rated at 5,550 lb.s.t. and 7,650 lb.s.t. with afterburning.*
Armament: *Twenty-four 2.75-in. folding-fin unguided missiles.*
Performance: *Max. speed, 693 m.p.h. at sea level (Mach 0.9), 616 m.p.h. at 40,000 ft. (Mach 0.934); initial climb rate, 12,000 ft./min.; time to 40,000 ft., 6.8 min.; service ceiling, 49,600 ft.; combat radius, 270 mls. at 550 m.p.h.; ferry range (with two 100 Imp. gal. drop tanks), 769 mls.*
Weights: *Empty, 13,498 lb.; loaded (point intercept), 18,160 lb., (area defence) 19,952 lb.*
Dimensions: *Span, 37 ft. 1½ in.; length, 40 ft. 3¼ in.; height 15 ft. 0 in.; wing area, 287.9 sq. ft.*

F-86D-45 SABRE

F-86K Sabre all-weather fighters of the Luftwaffe's Jagdgeschwader 74 based at Neubiberg.

airframes were in storage pending delivery of electronic control systems.

Various changes were introduced in each successive production block, and with the F-86D-40, the J47-GE-17 was replaced by the -17B offering 5,425 lb.s.t. and 7,500 lb.s.t. with afterburning, while the 239th F-86D-45 was the first D-model to receive the J47-GE-33 rated at 5,550 lb.s.t. and 7,650 lb.s.t. with afterburning, a total of 1,517 F-86Ds being delivered with -17 or -17B engines and the remaining 987 having the -33.

Three U.S.A.F. Air Defence Command Groups were formed with F-86D Sabres by June 1953, and by September 1955 there were twenty F-86D-equipped Wings. Although most of the teething troubles had been worked out of the F-86D's systems, it was admitted that this interceptor demanded more pilot training than any other single U.S.A.F. aircraft type. Nevertheless, the D-model Sabre was an effective interceptor offering radar target location, electronically computed aiming, and an extremely destructive armament. The AN/APG-37 radar located the target at distances of up to thirty miles, and after "locking-on", the AN/APA-84 computer determined a lead collision course and launched the missiles, the pilot electing whether to fire six, twelve or all twenty-four of the rockets.

The delivery of ex-U.S.A.F. F-86D Sabres to Allied air arms did not begin until 1958 when the security classification of the E-4 fire control system was modified, and thirty-eight aircraft were supplied to the R.Dan.A.F., these currently equipping Nos. 723, 726 and 728 Squadrons. One hundred and six were delivered to the Japanese Air Self-Defence Force and equip the 101st, 102nd, and 105th Squadrons of the 3rd Wing; sufficient aircraft were delivered to the Republic of Korea to equip two wings; others were delivered to the Chinese Nationalist Air Force, and eighteen were supplied to the Philippine Air Force. Fifty F-86D Sabres were delivered to the Royal Hellenic Air Force under the MDAP, a similar quantity was provided the Turkish Air Force, and no fewer than 130 were transferred to the Yugoslav Air Force.

F-86K SABRE: The F-86K all-weather interceptor was developed from the D-model for supply to NATO

F-86K SABRE SPECIFICATION
Power Plant: *One General Electric J47-GE-17B turbojet rated at 5,425 lb.s.t. and 7,500 lb.s.t. with afterburning.*
Armament: *Four 20-mm. M-24A-1 cannon with 132 r.p.g. and two AIM-9B Sidewinder infra-red homing AAMs.*
Performance: *Max. speed, 692 m.p.h. at sea level (Mach 0.9), 612 m.p.h. at 40,000 ft. (Mach 0.925); initial climb rate, 12,000 ft./min.; time to 40,000 ft., 7.3 min.; service ceiling, 49,600 ft.; combat radius, 272 mls. at 550 m.p.h.; ferry range (with two 100 Imp. gal. drop tanks), 744 mls.*
Weights: *Empty, 13,367 lb.; loaded (point intercept), 18,379 lb.; max., 20,171 lb.*
Dimensions: *Span, 39 ft. 1¼ in.; length, 40 ft. 11 in.; height, 15 ft. 0 in.; wing area, 313.37 sq. ft.*

forces under the MDAP and differed from its predecessor primarily in having a simpler fire control system and cannon armament. The AN/APG-37 radar was retained in the nose, but a North American-developed MG-4 fire control system supplanted the E-4, and four 20-mm. M-24A-1 cannon supplemented by two AIM-9B Sidewinder AAMs replaced the retractable missile tray of the F-86D.

Development of the F-86K began on May 14, 1953, and two government-furnished F-86D-40 Sabres were modified as YF-86K prototypes, the first of these (52-3630) flying on July 15, 1954. Powered by the J47-GE-17B, the YF-86K differed externally from the D-model in having a slightly longer fuselage nose and cannon ports in the walls of the nose intake. An agreement reached with the Italian Fiat company on May 18, 1953 provided for the assembly of the F-86K in Italy, and in order to accelerate deliveries, 120 F-86Ks were assembled by North American, all being completed by the end of 1955. The first of 221 Fiat-assembled F-86K Sabres was flown on May 23, 1955, and sixty-three aircraft, together with the two YF-86Ks that had been sent to Italy as pattern aircraft, were allocated to the Italian Air Force. These entered service with the 1° Aerobrigata which began re-equipment with the F-104G Starfighter during 1964. Sixty Fiat-assembled F-86Ks were delivered to the Armée de l'Air, equipping the 13e Escadre until replaced by the Mirage IIIC, and eighty-eight were supplied to the Federal German Luftwaffe, these currently equipping JG 74.

Of the 120 F-86K Sabres built by North American,

fifty-nine were delivered to the R.Neth.A.F., together with six Fiat-built aircraft, and these equipped Nos. 700 and 701 Squadrons until, after overhaul by Fiat in 1963–64, they were passed on to the Turkish Air Force with which they now serve.

F-86K interceptors were all modified during Dutch service with extended wingtips and leading edges similar to those of the last forty-five Fiat-assembled aircraft. Sixty F-86Ks produced by the parent company were also supplied to the R.No.A.F., together with four Fiat aircraft, and these equip Nos. 334, 337, and 339 Squadrons.

F-86L SABRE: During 1956 work began on a programme of reconditioning and modernising the F-86D, and adapting it for operation with the SAGE (Semi-Automatic Ground Environment) system. The modernisation of the electronics included the installation of an AN/ARR-39 Data Link receiver, the

replacement of the AN/ARC-27 command radio by -34, and the addition of a new glide slope receiver and an AN/APX-25 identification radar. Similar wing extensions to those introduced on late production F-86K Sabres were fitted, and empty weight rose to 13,822 lb., point and area intercept weights being increased to 18,484 lb. and 20,276 lb. respectively. Performance was generally similar to that of the normal D-model, and handling characteristics somewhat better with improved turning capability at altitude. The modified aircraft received the designation F-86L, and a total of 981 aircraft were converted.

The adaptation of the F-86 for the SAGE system extended the useful life of the interceptor until later types, such as the F-102A, became available, the F-86L Sabres then being handed on to the Air National Guard with which they still serve. A small number of F-86Ls have been delivered to the Royal Thai Air Force.

NORTH AMERICAN F-100 SUPER SABRE

The first fighter in the world capable of genuine supersonic performance and the first of the U.S.A.F.'s "Century-series" fighters, the F-100 Super Sabre was the first production machine designed to fly faster than sound as a matter of course, and for sustained periods, and its testing revealed aerodynamic phenomena that was to have a fundamental effect on the design of all

subsequent supersonic aircraft. Although now being supplanted in first-line U.S.A.F. service, the Super Sabre remains operational with the U.S. Air National Guard, the Armée de l'Air, the Chinese Nationalist Air Force, and the air arms of Denmark and Turkey, and is assured of an important place in the history of military aviation.

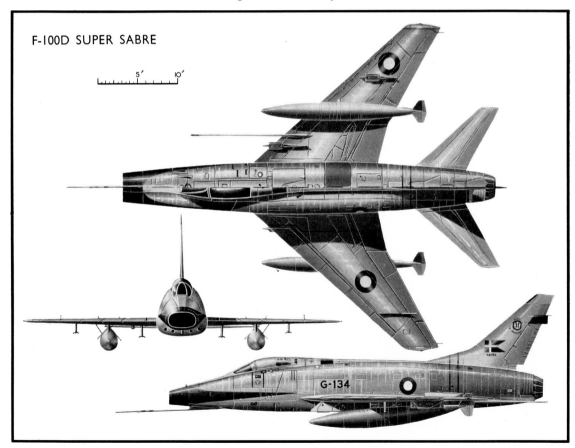

F-100D SUPER SABRE

G-134

An F-100D Super Sabre of the Royal Danish Air Force. Three R.Dan.A.F. Tactical Command squadrons are F-100D-equipped.

Development of the Super Sabre began on February 3, 1949, when work was initiated on the redesign of the Sabre with the aim of producing an aircraft capable of reaching and sustaining supersonic speeds in level flight. Originally dubbed "Sabre-45"—a reference to the fighter's forty-five degrees of wing sweepback—the project found favour with the U.S.A.F., and on November 1, 1951, an order was placed for two prototypes designated YF-100A and 110 F-100A production aircraft. The first YF-100A (52-5754) was flown on May 25, 1953, followed by the second (52-5755) on October 14, 1953, both aircraft being powered by the Pratt and Whitney XJ57-P-7 turbojet. The first production F-100A (52-5756) flew on October 29, 1953, this being essentially similar to the prototypes apart from having the production-type J57-P-7 engine rated at 9,700 lb.s.t. dry. The six per cent wing had full-span automatic leading-edge slats, the curiously flattened fuselage had a distinctive oval-section pitot air intake, and the slab-type tailplane was mounted at the base of the rear fuselage. Internal fuel capacity was 850 Imp. gal., the built-in armament comprised four Pontiac-built M-39E 20-mm. cannon, and an aerial mounted beneath the upper lip of the intake fed the AN/APX-6 radar gunsight.

Initially, flight testing progressed smoothly despite the radical advances embodied by the aircraft. One of the YF-100s attained Mach 1.38 at 35,000 ft., and the 479th Fighter Day Wing was designated the first unit to re-equip with the F-100A, but by September 29, 1954, when this unit was reactivated with its new equipment, there had been several inexplicable crashes which, on November 11, 1954, resulted in the grounding of all Super Sabres. For several months the cause of the accidents was investigated, and it was finally ascertained that, during a roll, the Super Sabre, with its weight distributed along a lengthy fuselage, pitched and yawed, and while the tail normally restrained these effects, under certain conditions the forces exceeded the power of the vertical surfaces to restore the aircraft. The vertical tail surfaces were subsequently redesigned and tested on the twenty-fifth production F-100A (53-1530). The area of the tail was increased by twenty-seven per cent and, simultaneously, wing span was increased by 2 ft. 2 in., these changes being made retrospective modifications on the

(Above) An F-100F-10-NA (56-4009) of the Armée de l'Air's 3e Escadre de Chasse.

seventy F-100As completed prior to their introduction on the assembly line.

The 104th production Super Sabre embodied a number of changes, including rearranged instrument panels and the improved AN/APX-6A radar gunsight, and from the 168th aircraft the early J57-P-7 was supplanted by the J57-P-39, and a total of 203 F-100A Super Sabres was built, deliveries being completed in March 1954. Six years later, in 1960, eighty ex-U.S.A.F. F-100A Super Sabres were brought up to the later F-100D standards and supplied to the Chinese Nationalist Air Force, these still equipping one fighter wing of that air arm.

In order to increase the versatility of the Super Sabre, some structural strengthening of the wing was undertaken, permitting heavier external stores loads, and provision was made for in-flight refuelling. Eight underwing pick-up points were provided for a maximum external stores load of 7,500 lb. as compared with six pick-up points on the F-100A, and designated F-100C, the first Super Sabre to embody these changes (53-1709) flew on January 17, 1955, the type entering service with the 322nd Fighter Day Group (at that time designated 450th Day Fighter Wing) on July 14, 1955. Initial F-100Cs retained the J57-P-39 engine, but the 101st production aircraft switched to the J57-P-21.

Like its predecessor, the C-model carried an armament of four M-39E cannon with 200 r.p.g., and an A-4 (APG-30) radar gunsight was installed. A total of 995 Imp. gal. of fuel was carried in the fuselage and wings, giving a combat radius of 550 mls. or a sortie time of 1.5 hr. Weighing 28,000 lb. in clean condition, the F-100C had a wing loading of the order of 73 lb./sq. ft., which, although not low by standards then appertaining in Europe, gave a relatively good altitude performance, service ceiling being 50,000 ft. An altitude of 35,000 ft. could be attained within four minutes of brakes off, and a supersonic performance was maintained down to 8,000 ft. at which altitude maximum speed was 810 m.p.h. (Mach 1.1). Production of the F-100C totalled 476 machines, and these were progressively phased out of U.S.A.F. service as supplanted by the F-100D, and passed to the Turkish Air Force which received 260 F-100C Super Sabres, these currently equipping four fighter-bomber wings each with three squadrons, and to the Air National Guard.

F-100D SUPER SABRE: The definitive single-seat production model of the Super Sabre was the F-100D, no fewer than 1,274 examples of which had been completed when production terminated in 1958. The F-100D differed from the C-model in having a Minneapolis-Honeywell autopilot, further revisions of the vertical tail surfaces, jettisonable cantilever under-wing stores pylons and, for the first time on any Super Sabre model, inboard landing flaps. The first F-100D (54-2121) flew on January 24, 1956, and within a few months Tactical Air Command squadrons had begun conversion, the D-model Super Sabre eventually equipping most tactical fighter squadrons. A substantial number of F-100D fighter-bombers were also delivered to NATO air arms under the U.S. Military Assistance Programme, recipients being the Armée de l'Air which currently operates two wings equipped with this type, the 3e and 11e Escadres de Chasse with the 1er CATac, and the R.Dan.A.F. in whose Tactical Command the F-100D is operated by Nos. 725, 727 and 730 Squadrons. Remaining U.S.A.F. F-100D units, which, late in 1964, included the 20th, 48th, 50th, and 53rd Tactical Fighter Wings in Europe and others in the Pacific and the U.S.A., should re-equip with the F-4C during the course of 1965.

The potency of the F-100D's armament in the intercept rôle was improved after its service introduction by the addition of AIM-9B Sidewinder 1A infra-red homing AAMs and, in the strike rôle, by AGM-12A Bullpup ASMs on the inboard pylons, the latter having first been test fired from an F-100D in 1959, and the modification of an initial batch of eighty T.A.C. aircraft for the missile being initiated late in that year. At the same time, ARN-21 navigation equipment was introduced. Several further single-seat

versions of the Super Sabre were proposed but failed to materialise, including the all-weather F-100J offered to Japan, the F-100L with a J57-P-55 in place of the -21A, and the F-100N which was a simplified D-model with reduced electronic equipment, and during 1964 proposals were made to re-engine NATO F-100Ds with the RB.168-25R Spey turbofan during IRAN (Inspect and Replace As Necessary) programmes.

F-100F SUPER SABRE: Derived from the single-seat F-100D tactical fighter-bomber, and combining this rôle with that of combat proficiency trainer, the tandem two-seat F-100F (56-3725) flew for the first time on March 7, 1957, being preceded on August 6, 1956, by a two-seat modification of the F-100C, the TF-100C (54-1966), which served as an aerodynamic prototype. The TF-100C had a 36-in. additional section inserted in the fuselage to provide accommodation for the second cockpit and was modified to carry similar landing flaps to those introduced by the F-100D, but it was essentially a conversion trainer and lacked all operational equipment.

The F-100F carried the complete range of operational equipment of the F-100D, but built-in armament was restricted to two 20-mm. M-39E cannon. A maximum external stores load of 6,000 lb. could be carried, a typical load being a tactical atomic store on the centreline pylon, a 229 Imp. gal. drop tank on two inboard pylons, and a 166.5 Imp. gal. tank on two outboard pylons. Performance included a maximum speed of 846 m.p.h. at 35,000 ft. (Mach 1.3), an altitude of 35,000 ft. was attained in 7.9 min., and empty weight was 22,300 lb., normal loaded and maximum overload weights being 30,700 lb. and 40,000 lb. respectively.

Three hundred and thirty-three examples of the F-100F were built, the last being delivered in October 1959, and the type currently serves primarily with the Air National Guard, the Armée de l'Air, and the Danish and Turkish air arms. A drone or missile director version is designated DF-100F, and in 1964 proposals were made for establishing a production line in France for some 200-250 two-seat Super Sabres designated F-100S by the parent company. Utilising the basic F-100F airframe, the F-100S proposal has a Rolls-Royce RB.168-25R Spey turbofan in place of the J57-P-21 or -21A offering an all-round improvement in performance.

(Below) An F-100D (55-2765) with flight refuelling probe attached beneath the starboard wing. This probe is normally carried only for long-distance ferry flights. The F-100D is widely used by the Air National Guard, and serves with the R.Dan.A.F. and the Armée de l'Air.

F-100D SUPER SABRE SPECIFICATION

Power Plant : *One Pratt and Whitney J57-P-21A turbojet rated at 11,700 lb.s.t. and 16,950 lb.s.t. with afterburning.* Armament : *Four Pontiac M-39E cannon with 200 r.p.g. plus (intercept) four AIM-9B Sidewinder 1A infra-red homing AAMs or (attack) six 1,000-lb. bombs, twenty-four HVARs, six 750-lb. incendiary bombs, six 500-lb. depth, demolition, fragmentation or incendiary bombs, or two AGM-12A Bullpup ASMs and two 500-lb., 750-lb., or 1,000-lb. bombs plus two 187 Imp. gal. drop tanks.* Performance : *Max. speed, 864 m.p.h. at 35,000 ft. (Mach 1.3), 810 m.p.h. at 8,000 ft. (Mach 1.1); normal range cruise, 565 m.p.h. at 36,000–45,000 ft. (Mach 0.86); initial climb rate, 16,000 ft./min.; time to 32,300 ft., 2.5 min.; combat radius (clean), 550 mls.; range (with two 375 Imp. gal. drop tanks), 1,500 mls.* Weights : *Empty, 21,000 lb.; normal loaded, 29,762 lb.; max. overload, 34,832 lb.* Dimensions : *Span, 38 ft. 9$\frac{1}{3}$ in.; length (over probe), 54 ft. 3 in.; height, 16 ft. 2$\frac{2}{3}$ in.; wing area, 385.2 sq. ft.*

NORTHROP F-5

The first U.S. post-war combat aircraft designed specifically to meet the needs of foreign air arms rather than a specialised U.S. military requirement, the Northrop F-5 multi-purpose fighter is being manufactured for supply to the smaller NATO and SEATO air forces, designated recipients under the Military Assistance Programme including Nationalist China, Greece, Iran, the Philippines, Norway, South Korea and Turkey. The training of pilots and ground personnel on the F-5 began under the direction of the U.S.A.F. Tactical Air Command at Williams Air Force Base, Arizona, in September 1964, this being the instructional centre for foreign personnel who will subsequently act as instructors on the Northrop fighter in their own countries.

Development of the F-5 began in 1954 when a Northrop team toured Europe and Asia to examine the defence needs of NATO and SEATO countries, its findings forming the basis of a project designated N-156F by the parent company—a relatively simple, economical and versatile aircraft, equally suitable for the intercept, strike or reconnaissance rôles, and making the minimum demands on logistics. Paralleling the N-156F project was one for an aerodynamically similar two-seat supersonic trainer, the N-156T. It was in the latter project that the U.S.A.F. evinced most interest, and on February 25, 1958, Northrop decided to proceed with the development of the N-156F as a private venture, a U.S. Department of Defence

contract for three prototypes and ground support equipment being awarded some nine months later.

The first N-156F (59-4987), initially powered by non-afterburning General Electric YJ85-GE-1 turbojets each rated at 2,100 lb.s.t., flew on July 30 the early turbojets soon being replaced by type J85-GE-5s each rated 3,850 lb.s.t. with full afterb (59-4988) was com programme, but shelved before co April 25, 1962, N-156F had bee fighter under the trials with the first two desirability of a strengthened wing structure to permit the introduction of an additional stores station under each wing, and the new wing, together with a sturdier undercarriage to take the greater loads, was built into the third prototype which became, in effect, the first production F-5A and flew in July 1963. Another change introduced in this aircraft was the provision of uprated J85-GE-13 turbojets offering 3,050 lb.s.t. dry and 4,080 lb.s.t. with afterburning.

The first and second prototypes were subsequently brought up to F-5A standards, and the first two genuine production F-5As (63-8367 and -8368) had joined the test programme by the end of 1963, the first example of the tandem two-seat version, the F-5B

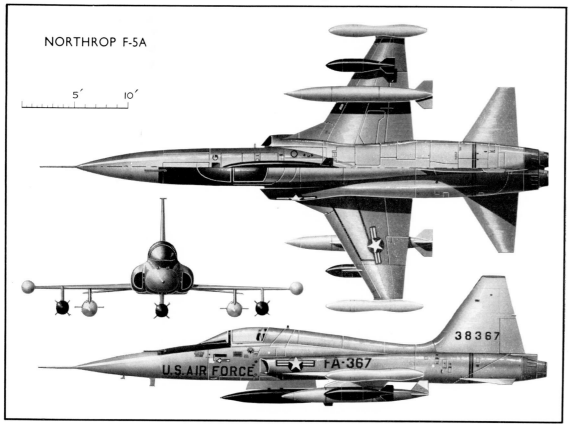

NORTHROP F-5A

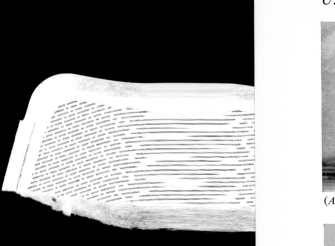

(*Above*) *The second production two-seat F-5B (63-8439), and (below) the first and third prototypes and the first two production F-5A in formation.*

(63-8438), flying on February 24, 1964. The initial production contract for the F-5 was awarded on October 22, 1962 and a further contract was placed on August 27, 1963, these initial orders calling for approximately 170 machines of which the ratio of single-seat F-5As to two-seat F-5Bs is about 9 : 1, and a production rate of twelve aircraft per month was programmed for the end of 1964, the first deliveries of the fighter to nations militarily aligned with the U.S.A. being scheduled to begin early in 1965. One of the first recipients of the F-5 will be the Royal Hellenic Air

Force, this service anticipating receiving forty aircraft to re-equip two squadrons. The Royal Norwegian Air Force has placed orders for sixty-four F-5s to re-equip three squadrons, and deliveries to Norway will begin early in 1966.

The F-5 combines second-generation supersonic aerodynamics with the highest possible degree of functionability; maintenance demands lower than those of the subsonic fighters of the last decade; the ability to lift more payload per pound of airframe weight than any supersonic fighter extant, and suitability for grass strip operation. The wing plan-form is a compromise between supersonic drag requirements and the characteristics necessary for good low-speed handling, and apart from the replace-ment of the twin 20-mm. Colt-Browning M-39 cannon and their ammunition, which forms the standard built-in armament of the single-seat F-5A, by a second cockpit, there are few differences between the two-seat F-5B and the single-seater. The F-5B adds training capability to its full range of operational rôles. The individual manually-operated canopies of this version are separated by a fixed windscreen for protection of the rear cockpit during ejection, and the rear seat is elevated ten inches above the front seat to increase the forward visibility of the instructor or observer. The take-off gross weights of both configurations vary from 12,000 lb. for "reduced-fuel" close support missions to a maximum of some 19,800 lb., and there is only a marginal difference in performance, the F-5A attaining a maximum speed of Mach 1.4 in clean configuration, that of the F-5B being Mach 1.34.

Apart from the cannon, the two F-5 versions possess similar ordnance lifting capabilities, seven stores stations being provided externally, the centreline station taking a 2,000-lb. class store, the two inboard wing stations each taking a 1,000-lb. class store, and the two outboard wing stations each taking a 750-lb. class store, while an AIM-9B Sidewinder infra-red homing AAM or a 41.6 Imp. gal. fuel tank may be attached to each wingtip. Total usable internal fuel capacity is 485 Imp. gal., and the auxiliary supply system comprises three 125 Imp. gal. drop tanks and two removable 41.6 Imp. gal. tip tanks. The extreme versatility of the F-5 enables it to fulfil a wide variety of aerial combat rôles. For the subsonic area intercept mission, the F-5A has a combat radius of 288 mls. without external fuel and 645 mls. with external fuel, while combat radius for the supersonic area intercept mission is 173 mls. For the point intercept mission,

---

F-5A SPECIFICATION

Power Plants: *Two General Electric J85-GE-13 turbojets each rated at 3,050 lb.s.t. and 4,080 lb.s.t. with after-burning.*

Armament: *Two 20-mm. Colt-Browning M-39 cannon with 285 r.p.g. and up to 6,200 lb. of ordnance on seven external stations. Typical loads include two AIM-9B Sidewinder AAMs and one 2,000-lb. MK.84 bomb plus two 1,000-lb. MK.83 bombs and two 750-lb. M 117 bombs, or nine 250-lb. bombs and two AGM-12B Bullpup ASMs.*

Performance: *Max. speed (at 10,000 lb.), 945 m.p.h. at 36,860 ft. (Mach 1.43), 760 m.p.h. at 5,000 ft. (Mach 1.02); max. range cruise (clean), 560 m.p.h. (Mach 0.85); combat radius (clean) (subsonic area intercept mission), 288 mls.; ferry range, 1,865 mls.; initial climb rate (at 11,100 lb.), 28,600 ft./min.; time to 40,000 ft., 4.3 min.; service ceiling, 50,000 ft.*

Weights: *Empty, 7,733 lb.; loaded (basic mission), 13,337 lb.; max. loaded, 19,756 lb.*

Dimensions: *Span, 25 ft. 3 in.; length, 47 ft. 2⅓ in.; height, 13 ft. 2 in.; wing area, 173.82 sq. ft.*

the F-5 will attain an altitude of 40,000 ft. from "brakes off" in 4.3 min., and for the Hi-Lo-Hi attack mission offers a tactical radius of 627 mls. For the Lo-Lo-Hi attack mission cruising at 5,000 ft. the tactical radius is 507 mls., while for the Lo-Lo-Lo mission with maximum fuel the tactical radius is 403 mls., and 184 mls. with maximum weapons load.

In mid-1964, consideration was being given to the installation of air-to-air and air-to-surface radar and a lead-computing gunsight in the F-5A, and first flight trials of an F-5A fitted with this equipment are scheduled to commence in January 1966. The additional electronic equipment is expected to be installed retrospectively in all production aircraft.

REPUBLIC F-84F THUNDERSTREAK

Serving with the U.S. Air National Guard, the French, Belgian, Netherlands, Federal German, Italian, Greek and Turkish air arms, the F-84F Thunderstreak was largely a new aircraft despite its designation as the sixth in the basic F-84 series of fighter-bombers. Its existence is due solely to the Korean War for, until the invasion of South Korea by North Korean forces, the U.S.A.F. had evinced little interest in the aircraft. However, the outbreak of hostilities radically changed the fortunes of the Thunderstreak, no fewer than 2,711 examples of this single-seat tactical fighter-bomber having been built when production finally terminated in August 1957, 1,301 of these being manufactured for NATO forces.

The Thunderstreak was evolved during a period of drastically restricted governmental expenditure on new combat aircraft development, and the original project was the essence of simplicity and economy— swept wing and tail surfaces married to the fuselage of the existing F-84E Thunderjet to increase its limiting Mach number, a 5,800 lb.s.t. Allison J35-A-29 turbojet being expected to put this increase to some practical use. It was anticipated that almost sixty per cent of the tooling used for the earlier fighter could be utilised and a sole prototype was ordered as the YF-84F (49-2430), this flying for the first time on June 3, 1950 with a 5,200 lb.s.t. Allison YJ35-A-25 engine.

The YF-84F employed a standard F-84E fuselage, and the wing was swept 38.5° at quarter-chord and had a twelve per cent constant section with maximum thickness at forty-five per cent chord, although chord-wise thickness ratio was only nine per cent. Carrying 1,253 Imp. gal. of fuel internally and externally, the YF-84F had a maximum loaded weight of 23,350 lb., empty weight being 12,150 lb., and performance included a maximum speed (clean) of 693 m.p.h. at sea level (Mach 0.96), and an economical cruise of 514 m.p.h. (Mach 0.778). Altitude performance fell off badly however, service ceiling was only 38,300 ft., and 14.8 minutes were required to climb to 35,000 ft. With the outbreak of the Korean War it was decided that the marginal performance gain over the F-84E was inadequate and, with additional funds available, the design was reworked to take the very much more powerful Wright J65 with which the first of two additional YF-84Fs (51-1344) flew on February 14, 1951.

To cater for the increased airflow demanded by the

(Below) F-84F Thunderstreak fighter-bombers of the Luftwaffe's Jabo.G.34, and (above right) F-84Fs of the R.Neth.A.F.

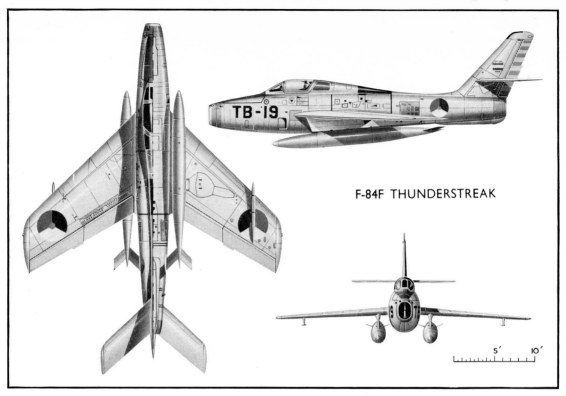

F-84F THUNDERSTREAK

more powerful engine, an additional seven-inch section was spliced into the fuselage along the horizontal plane, resulting in an elliptical nose air intake. An upward-hinging cockpit canopy was adopted, and a high proportion of press forgings replaced the built-up components in the wing. The third YF-84 (51-1345) was fitted with wing root intakes for comparison with the pitot-type intake of its predecessor, but the thrust losses resulting from these intakes were considered to nullify the advantages of increased internal capacity that they offered, and the simpler nose intake was retained for the production model, the first example of which (51-1346) flew on November 22, 1952, powered, like the second and third prototypes, by a YJ65-W-1 engine.

F-84F THUNDERSTREAK: The first production F-84F-1-RE was officially accepted by the U.S.A.F. in December 1952, and the remainder of the initial batch received the 7,220 lb.s.t. J65-W-1, this being supplanted by the improved J65-W-3 or (Buick-built) J65-B-3 in the F-84F-5-RE and all subsequent production batches. Deliveries to the Tactical and Strategic Air Commands began in 1954, and the pilots of these Commands found it to be a formidable aircraft, its weight and touch-down speed of 155-156 m.p.h. demanding respect from pilots accustomed to lighter, slower-landing machines. Later batches of aircraft, commencing with the F-84F-25-RE, introduced an all-moving, slab-type tailplane, and with maximum external stores load the permissible overload take-off weight rose to no less than 28,000 lb.

The total internal fuel capacity of the F-84F is 475 Imp. gal., but two 191.5 Imp. gal. drop tanks are normally carried underwing, while for ferry purposes, two 375 Imp. gal. and four 191.5 Imp. gal. tanks may be carried to provide a range of 2,140 mls. A radar-ranging A.4 gunsight is provided for use with the battery of six 0.5-in. M-3 machine guns, four of which are mounted in the fuselage with two in the wing roots, and twenty-two different combinations of offensive stores and drop tanks may be carried, a typical load comprising two 1,000-lb. bombs, eight 5-in. HVARs and two 191.5 Imp. gal. drop tanks to provide a loaded weight of 26,030 lb.

During the mid 'fifties, the delivery of the F-84F Thunderstreak to NATO air arms began, and this aircraft equipped the bulk of the tactical fighter-bomber elements until re-equipment with the F-104G Starfighter started in 1963. The principal European recipient of the F-84F was Federal Germany, the first Luftwaffe Jagdbombergeschwader equipped with this type, Jabo G.31, becoming operational on June 20, 1958. Four Geschwader, Jabo G.32, 34, 35, and 36, are currently operating the F-84F or are in process of re-equipment with the F-104G, and the type is expected to be phased out of the Luftwaffe's first-line inventory by the end of 1965, some ex-Luftwaffe F-84Fs being passed to Greece and Turkey. The 1er, 4e and 9e Escadres of the Armée de l'Air operate the F-84F as a part of the 1er CATac but will begin to re-equip with the Mirage IIIE early in 1965. The 2ème and 10ème Wings of the Belgian Air Force are F-84F equipped, the former being scheduled to retain its Thunderstreaks until 1970; four squadrons of the R.Neth.A.F. operate the F-84F, two, Nos. 311 and 312, being scheduled to re-equip with the F-104G during 1965, and two, Nos. 314 and 315, being destined to retain the older type; the Italian Va and VIa

(Above) An RF-84F Thunderflash of the Luftwaffe's Aufkl.G.52, and (below, right) an RF-84F of Waffenschule 50.

Aerobrigati Caccia-bombardieri with NATO's 5th ATAF have F-84Fs, and six F-84F-equipped squadrons of the Royal Hellenic Air Force together with a similar number of Turkish Air Force F-84F squadrons form the bulk of the 6th ATAF.

RF-84F THUNDERFLASH: Developed in parallel with the F-84F, the RF-84F Thunderflash possesses an essentially similar airframe, apart from the wing root air intake duct location adopted to permit the installation of a camera bay in the nose. The prototype Thunderflash, the YRF-84F (51-1828), was flown in February 1952, this being, in fact, the first pre-production machine, trials with the wing root air intake location having been conducted with the third YF-84F (51-1345), and deliveries to the reconnaissance units of the Strategic Air Command and Tactical Air Command began in March 1954, 715 machines of this

type being manufactured, 386 of these being for supply to foreign air forces under the MDAP.

The first production RF-84Fs employed the 7,200

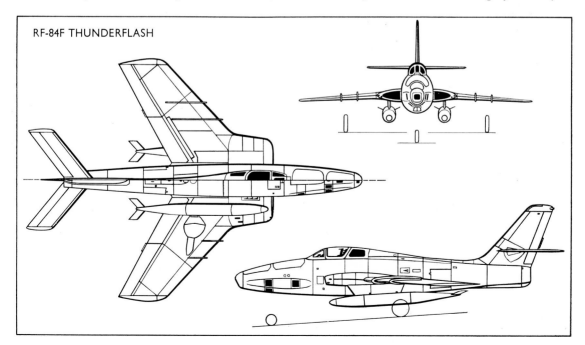

RF-84F THUNDERFLASH

lb.s.t. Wright J65-W-3 turbojet, but among modifications introduced in later batches of aircraft was the installation of the 7,800 lb.s.t. Wright J65-W-7. The camera bay in the nose may accommodate up to six cameras in forward-facing, trimetrogen and individual oblique and vertical installations. The vertical camera bay has hydraulically-operated retractable doors, and behind these there is an aperture for a vertical viewfinder with periscopic presentation on the cockpit panel. The wing root intakes are slightly less efficient than the nose intake of the F-84F, but the performance handicap is marginal, the RF-84F being redlined at Mach 1.175 as compared with Mach 1.18 for the fighter-bomber.

The Thunderflash carries a fuel load of nearly 1,250 Imp. gal., including two 375 Imp. gal. drop tanks, with which it attains a maximum range of 2,200 mls. Initial climb rate exceeds 10,000 ft./min. in clean condition, and maximum speed at sea level is 720 m.p.h. (Mach 0.94). Armament comprises four 0.5-in. M-3 machine guns mounted in the outer intake walls, and normal and maximum loaded weights are 26,800 lb. and 28,000 lb. respectively.

In addition to service with the Air National Guard, the RF-84F is currently operated by one squadron of the Chinese Nationalist Air Force; by two Auf-

klärungsgeschwader of the Luftwaffe (Aufkl.G 51 and 52); by Escadron 1/33 of the Armée de l'Air; by No. 729 Squadron of the R.Dan.A.F.; by the 42ème Escadrille of the Belgian Air Force; by the Italian 3ª Aerobrigata; by No. 717 Squadron of the R.Nor.A.F., and by one squadron each of the Greek and Turkish air arms.

F-84F THUNDERSTREAK SPECIFICATION

Power Plant: One Wright J65-W-3 turbojet rated at 7,220 lb.s.t.
Armament: Six 0.5-in. Colt-Browning M-3 machine guns plus a maximum of 6,000 lb. of external ordnance, a typical load comprising two 2,000-lb. bombs and eight 5-in. HVARs, or four 1,000-lb. bombs and twenty-four 3-in. rockets.
Performance: Max. speed (clean), 695 m.p.h. at sea level (Mach 0.91), 658 m.p.h. at 20,000 ft. (Mach 0.94); combat radius (clean), 450 mls., (with two 191.5 Imp. gal. drop tanks), 810 mls.; ferry range (max. external fuel), 2,140 mls.; initial climb rate (clean), 8,200 ft./min., (at 25,380 lb.), 3,620 ft./min.; service ceiling, 46,000 ft.
Weights: Loaded (clean), 19,340 lb.; max. overload, 28,000 lb.
Dimensions: Span, 33 ft. 7¼ in.; length, 43 ft. 4¾ in.; height, 14 ft. 4¾ in.; wing area, 325 sq. ft.

REPUBLIC F-105 THUNDERCHIEF

A strike and air superiority fighter capable of global deployment, the Thunderchief has been justifiably described as "the most powerful one-man airplane in the world". The first operational tactical fighter-bomber incorporating electronic systems integrated to provide automatic navigation, flight control and weapons delivery, the Thunderchief can, in its final production form, fly the complete spectrum of tactical missions with no less than four thousand different combinations of offensive stores, both conventional and nuclear, and currently equips the 4th, 8th, 18th, 36th, 49th, 355th, and 388th Tactical Fighter Wings and the 4520th Combat Crew Training Wing of the U.S.A.F. Tactical Air Command, serving in the U.S.A., Europe and the Pacific.

Operational since January 1, 1959, the Thunderchief was first conceived as a private-venture Mach 1.5 successor to the F-84F Thunderstreak before that aircraft had entered U.S.A.F. service. No less than 108 configurations were investigated by the Republic team under the generic designation AP-63 before the basic concept was finalised as a single-seat, single-engined aircraft primarily for the nuclear strike rôle with a secondary air-to-air capability. The airframe was thus matched to the extremely exacting requirements of high-speed, low-level operation, and by 1954 the design had crystallized sufficiently for a development contract to be placed under the WS-306A weapon system designation.

From the outset it was intended that the aircraft would be powered by the new Pratt and Whitney J75 engine, but the non-availability of this power plant necessitated the installation of the less powerful Pratt and Whitney J57-P-25 in the two YF-105A-1-RE prototypes (54-0098 and -0099), the first of which flew on October 22, 1955. Prior to this event, however, the availability of new aerodynamic data on supersonic

aircraft design had led to the realization that, with some design modifications, drag could be reduced to such an extent that speeds far higher than originally envisaged would be achieved. Thus, the third aircraft, the F-105B-1-RE (54-0100) which flew on May 26, 1956, was, although superficially similar to its predecessors, largely redesigned in detail. It was also the first Thunderchief to employ the new Pratt and Whitney engine, the J75-P-3. This aircraft was the first of a batch of twelve pre-production machines for development purposes, three of which, started as RF-105Bs, were completed as JF-105B systems test machines.

Deliveries of the F-105B to the 335th Tactical Fighter Squadron of the 4th Tactical Fighter Wing began on May 27, 1958, and the 334th and 336th Squadrons were similarly equipped, but these were destined to be the only units to receive the F-105B as, on June 9, 1959, an appreciably more advanced model, the F-105D (58-1146) with much improved mission electronics and instrumentation to permit all kinds of offensive strike and reconnaissance operations in all weathers, had flown for the first time, this equipping the 4th Wing's remaining squadron, the 333rd, and supplanting the B-model on the assembly line with the seventy-ninth Thunderchief.

F-105D THUNDERCHIEF: The principal feature of the F-105D is its highly sophisticated integrated electronics. The AN/APN-131 Doppler airborne navigation system automatically and independently of ground installations supplies the pilot with continual present-position co-ordinates, ground speed, track, heading and distance to target, wind direction and velocity, and alternative destination selection. The NASARR R-14A all-purpose monopulse radar is optimized in both air-to-ground and air-to-air modes and for both low-level and high-level missions—air

F-105D Thunderchief strike fighters of the 4520th Combat Crew Training Group at Nellis A.F.B., Nevada, responsible for the training of pilots for the seven Thunderchief-equipped Tactical Fighter Wings.

search, automatic tracking, ground and contour mapping and terrain avoidance—irrespective of visibility, ceiling or target-area condition, and this, the Doppler and the General Electric FC-5 flight control system and autopilot, are tied together to form an automatic navigation system. The AN/ASG-19 Thunderstick fire control system, which includes the NASARR, provides automatic or manual and blind or visual weapons delivery, with automatic or manually-controlled weapons release in all the various modes, from over-the-shoulder toss to retarded lay-down.

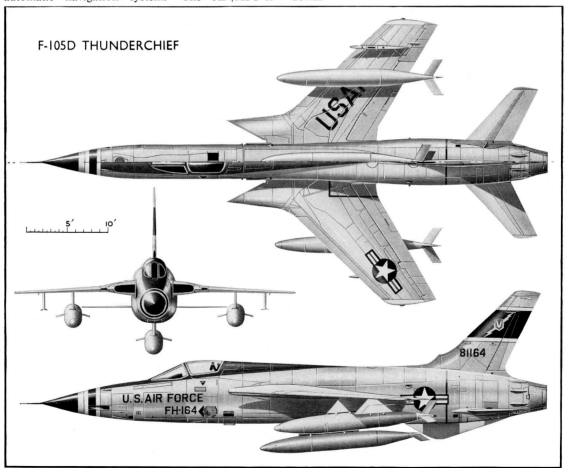

F-105D THUNDERCHIEF

5′　　10′

(Above) The first tandem two-seat F-105F Thunderchief (62-4412), production of which was completed in 1964.

Whereas the J75-P-5 engine of the interim F-105B offered a maximum afterburning thrust of 23,500 lb., the J75-P-19W standardised for the F-105D affords 17,200 lb.s.t. dry and a maximum of 26,500 lb.s.t. with afterburning and water injection. Built-in armament is similar to that of the earlier model, comprising a six-barrel 20-mm. M-61 Vulcan gun with 1,029 rounds of ammunition, and with a nuclear store in the internal weapons bay, the Thunderchief can bomb in the clean configuration for maximum speed delivery. However, with the F-105D-25-RE and subsequent production batches of the Thunderchief, increased emphasis has been placed on conventional capability, and an exceptionally wide range of external store combinations can be lifted up to the maximum of 12,000 lb. provided by sixteen 750-lb. bombs on the five external stations. Four AGM-12 Bullpup ASMs may be carried on the wing pylons and, for the intercept rôle in which the search and lock-on capabilities of the NASARR are employed in the classic interceptor fashion, four AIM-9 Sidewinder AAMs supplement the M-61 cannon.

The internal weapons bay can accommodate a 325 Imp. gal. auxiliary fuel tank, this supplementing the normal internal fuel load of 966 Imp. gal. which may be further augmented by a 541 Imp. gal. auxiliary tank on a centreline pylon and a 375 Imp. gal. tank on each inboard stores pylon to provide an unrefuelled range of 2,390 miles at 584 m.p.h. The flight envelope of the F-105D covers maximum speeds ranging from Mach 1.11 at sea level to Mach 2.1 at the tropopause. The optional water injection which boosts thrust by 2,000 lb. for one minute enables the F-105D to operate from

any NATO runway in Europe at maximum gross weight, and in a test at Edwards A.F.B., a Thunderchief using water injection attained Mach 1.0 and 8,000 ft. altitude from a standing start on the runway in fifty-five seconds. Other tests have included a symmetrical pull-out of 7.5 *g* at Mach 1.41 at 8,700 ft., and a 5.8 *g* pull-out at Mach 1.97 at 41,400 ft.

F-105F THUNDERCHIEF: During the Thunderchief's production life several tandem two-seat versions were proposed, the first of these being the F-105C trainer which was cancelled before the completion of the prototype. This was followed by the F-105E all-weather fighter-bomber which was also cancelled before completion, the few examples of this version under construction being converted to F-105D configuration on the production line. The F-105F dual-purpose mission trainer and tactical fighter did attain production status, however, a small number of aircraft of this type being ordered in the autumn of 1962 in lieu of a similar number of single-seat F-105Ds, the first F-105F (62-4412) flying on June 11, 1963.

The F-105F differs from the D-model primarily in having an additional section inserted in the forward fuselage to provide space for the second cockpit, increasing overall length to 69 ft. 7¼ in., and slightly taller vertical tail surfaces to compensate for the increased forward side area, overall height being 20 ft. 2 in. Normal loaded weight (clean) is increased to 40,073 lb., maximum overload weight being 54,027 lb. The second cockpit duplicates the front position, with the exception of the gunsight, and the powerplant, systems and armament are identical to those of the single-seat model, performance being within three per cent.

During 1964, in which year the first Air National Guard squadron received the Thunderchief, the F-105 was finally phased out of production after the completion of between eight and nine hundred aircraft.

F-105D THUNDERCHIEF SPECIFICATION

Power Plant: *One Pratt and Whitney J75-P-19W turbojet rated at 17,200 lb.s.t. and 24,500 lb.s.t. with afterburning which may be boosted for take-off to 26,500 lb.s.t. for one minute with water injection.*
Armament: *One 20-mm. M-61 Vulcan rotary cannon with 1,029 rounds and (intercept) four AIM-9 Sidewinder AAMs or (strike) up to 12,000 lb. of external ordnance. Typical conventional external loads include sixteen 750-lb. M-43 general-purpose bombs, nine 750-lb. incendiary bombs, nine 1,000-lb. general-purpose, armour-piercing or fragmentation bombs, sixteen 250-lb. or 500-lb. depth, demolition, fragmentation, or incendiary bombs, two 2,000-lb. bombs, or four AGM-12 Bullpup ASMs.*
Performance: *Max. speed (clean), 855 m.p.h. at sea level (Mach 1.11), 1,390 m.p.h. at 36,000 ft. (Mach 2.1), 1,122 m.p.h. at 50,000 ft. (Mach 1.7); initial climb (clean), 34,400 ft./min.; tactical radius (with two AGM-12 ASMs and one 541 and two 375 Imp. gal. drop tanks), 920 mls. (plus 30 min. loiter at 5,000 ft), (with sixteen 750-lb. bombs), 230 mls. (plus 10 min. loiter); ferry range (max. external fuel), 2,390 mls. at 584 m.p.h. (average) at 39,400 ft., or (tanks retained), 2,075 mls.*
Weights: *Empty, 28,000 lb.; normal loaded (clean), 38,034 lb.; max. overload, 52,546 lb.*
Dimensions: *Span, 34 ft. 11¼ in.; length, 67 ft. 0⅓ in.; height, 19 ft. 8⅓ in.; wing area, 385 sq. ft.*
